LOW-ENERGY COOLING

A GUIDE TO THE PRACTICAL APPLICATION OF PASSIVE COOLING AND COOLING ENERGY CONSERVATION MEASURES

DONALD W. ABRAMS
D. W. ABRAMS, P.E. & ASSOCIATES
ATLANTA, GEORGIA

 VAN NOSTRAND REINHOLD COMPANY
———————————————————————— New York

Copyright © 1986 by Van Nostrand Reinhold Company Inc.

Library of Congress Catalog Card Number 85-20170

ISBN 0-442-20951-7

Printed in United States of America

Van Nostrand Reinhold Company Inc.
115 Fifth Avenue
New York, New York 10003

Van Nostrand Reinhold Company Limited
Molly Millars Lane
Wokingham, Berkshire RG11 2PY, England

Van Nostrand Reinhold
480 La Trobe Street
Melbourne, Victoria 3000, Australia

Macmillan of Canada
Division of Canada Publishing Corporation
164 Commander Boulevard
Agincourt, Ontario M1S 3C7, Canada

16 15 14 13 12 11 10 9 8 7 6 5 4 3 2 1

Library of Congress Cataloging-in-Publication Data

Abrams, D. W.
   Low energy cooling.

   Includes index.
   1. Air conditioning. 2. Buildings—Energy conservation. I. Title. II. Title: Passive cooling.
TH7687.5.A37 1986   697.9′3   85-20170
ISBN 0-442-20951-7

Let us cross over the river and rest under the shade of the trees.
General T. J. "Stonewall" Jackson

For my Dad, William F. Abrams, Jr.

PREFACE

Most of us are inevitably more concerned with heating our homes and the small commercial buildings we operate than with cooling them. Heating represents the greater energy load in most buildings, and certainly on a national scale it is a more significant economic concern than cooling. More basically, cold weather poses a very real threat to human survival; we simply could not live without heated shelters. We can survive quite easily, however, if not comfortably, without mechanical cooling. Needless to say, simple survival is not the issue; the concern here is on a higher level in the hierarchy of needs. Modern comfort standards, social practices, and design practices have made mechanical cooling an essential requirement in all but a few buildings.

The cooling problem that confronts us encompasses both a human comfort component and an energy consumption/economics component. High temperature and humidity combine to make the problem most severe in the sunbelt states, but other areas of the country are not exempt. Modern large commercial buildings simply cannot operate without air conditioning, regardless of location. High summer temperatures strike almost all of the country each summer. For instance, the extreme design dry-bulb temperatures for Philadelphia, Newark, Kansas City, New York City (Central Park), and Bismarck, North Dakota are equal to or higher than the design temperature for New Orleans. As a result, about three-fourths of the new homes built in the United States this year will incorporate central air-conditioning systems.

Humidity adds another element to the comfort issue—and to the possibility of passive or natural solutions. Evaporative and radiative cooling have real potential only in the arid Southwest and parts of the Rockies. In the balance of the country—again, not just in the South—humidity levels preclude the use of these and other natural cooling alternatives. For all practical purposes, there simply are no passive means for providing positive control of comfort conditions to hold them to present standards. Conventional air conditioning systems are required. Only in the extreme North, arid areas, and at higher elevations can air conditioning be altogether avoided. Even there a comfort problem will still exist to a lesser degree. Of course, natural cooling methods can be relied upon in any location so long as a compromise in comfort standards is understood.

Low-Energy Cooling looks for practical solutions to the problem of providing comfort in residences and small commercial buildings. It deals in realistic methods for making people comfortable in the nonarid regions—that is, most of the United States. It does not indulge in the wishful notion that some magic passive or natural solution will provide an endless supply of cooling in violation of common sense and thermodynamics. Instead, the book examines the problems and opportunities that arise in each aspect of the cooling and comfort problem and the building design and operation process. A comprehensive approach is suggested:

- Understand cooling loads and comfort so as to be able to provide comfort by means other than strict temperature control.
- Reduce heat gain to the building in question to improve comfort and reduce air-conditioning loads.
- Use ventilation as a substitute for, as well as a supplement to, air conditioning.
- Provide an efficient cooling system and operate it efficiently.

Specific chapters address each of these concerns. In addition, other chapters explore alternative cooling methods, including evaporative cooling, radiative cooling, earth cooling, and various innovative concepts. In an effort to respond to the level of interest shown in such interesting, but largely unworkable, alternatives as solar chimneys and earth cooling tubes, detailed discussions of these devices are included.

The fundamental intent of *Low-Energy Cooling* is to provide readers with the means for selecting the best solution to their individual situation and needs. Comfort and minimum construction and operating costs are the objective. Three general strategies are recognized: (1) comfort at any cost, (2) minimum cost with necessary comfort compromises, and (3) reasonable comfort and reasonable cost. The third strategy is encouraged. Specific measures and alternatives are dealt with realistically, with both their opportunities and limitations identified. This treatment allows the users of the book to make informed judgments and compose a specific solution to their own cooling problem.

Donald W. Abrams, P.E.

CONTENTS

1

INTRODUCTION

One of the finest examples of a naturally, or passively, cooled residence is the Hay House in Macon, Georgia (Fig. 1.1). Designed by Thomas and Griffith Thomas, the grand, 23,000-ft^2 house was completed in 1859. Like other Thomas designs, it was an example of 19th-century "high tech," incorporating many quite innovative features. A spring routed through the property drove a ram pump to provide hot and cold running water and operate hydraulic elevators and flush toilets. A voice tube intercom system was included to communicate with the staff of 12.

The heating and cooling systems were also state-of-the art and rather luxurious by standards prevailing then. The design emphasized cooling to provide comfort in the hot, humid central-Georgia climate. Of necessity, the cooling system relied solely on natural, or, as we call them today, passive, measures. Ventilation was the key. The design provided for both horizontal and vertical air flow through the house, using wind-induced ventilation and stack-effect ventilation.

Large windows, as tall as 15 ft were used liberally. Numerous smaller windows high above the gallery floor in a "lantern" were opened and closed by the staff as required. Another of the first-floor rooms incorporated vertical air flow through openings cleverly concealed in the decorative ceiling. The central stair in the house provided another vertical flow path. The house's 21 fireplaces could be used as ventilation shafts during the summer, in conjunction with a network of ventilation chases opening onto each of the several levels of the house (Fig. 1.2).

The design also included earth cooling features in the form of extensive underground chambers beneath the house. Ventilation air could be drawn through these chambers and through the wine cellar to cool it before it entered the living areas. Air inlets around the perimeter of the first level allowed air to be drawn in from above ground at the coolest locations. Movable solid panels and grilles in doors allowed air circulation while still providing security and privacy.

The design incorporated other common sense measures to reduce undesirable heat gain during the hot summers. The summer kitchen was housed in a separate

Figure 1.1. Hay House, front elevation.

building adjacent to the main house. Shutters and heavy drapes helped block solar gains. The massive exterior walls were finished with white stucco to reflect solar heat. High ceilings, typically 17 ft but rising as high as 40 ft, kept hot interior air far away from the occupants below.

Economics and imagination were certainly no limitations in the design of the house. The original owner, William Butler Johnson, was quite wealthy and something of a technological innovator. He owned the local ice house and the first gas works in the city. The architects were some of the most knowledgeable of the time. Every effort was made to create a comfortable interior environment in a severe summer climate. Compared with other houses of the time, the Hay house was a great success. Even in modern times, the house has never had a mechanical cooling system. The members of the group who now care for the house report that it is remarkably comfortable in summer. Interior temperatures remain reasonable even when the outdoor temperature climbs to 100°F. High humidity is a problem, however.

In the 125 years since the Hay house was completed, we have added few additional passive techniques to our repertoire for coping with hot, humid climates. The most significant advantages we have today are greatly improved insulating materials and a variety of specialized glazing materials to block and reflect the sun. Should a similar project be undertaken today without the aid of

Figure 1.2. Hay House, rear elevation.

mechanical cooling, little more could be done. Although much of the discomfort associated with summer heat could be ameliorated, humidity would remain a problem. In all but the more arid and cool areas of the country, natural, or passive, cooling simply cannot provide the controlled interior conditions offered by air conditioning. If we demand temperatures no higher than 78°F and protection from high humidity, passive cooling does not work.

We have often misused mechanical cooling systems. Building designers and occupants frequently ignore thermal design considerations and sensible operations and simply overpower their mistakes with air conditioners. While we were blessed with low energy costs we became spoiled; we developed expensive tastes for rigidly controlled conditions. Today most of us are unwilling to compromise those standards; many of us consider air conditioning a necessity. We have grown accustomed to buildings and lifestyles that leave no alternative but to rely on air conditioning.

What then can natural, or passive, cooling do for us? If we are willing to accept reduced levels of comfort, natural cooling can allow us to eliminate air conditioning systems from many buildings. Perhaps more importantly natural cooling can work effectively in conjunction with modern construction and design practices and mechanical systems to reduce the cost of meeting more rigid comfort requirements. We can use rational design and natural cooling to reduce the load on air conditioners. We can supplant the use of energy-consuming systems during the milder portions of the cooling season. We can provide comfort by alternative methods that reduce energy consumption.

This book does not suggest that natural, or passive, measures can provide a one-for-one replacement for air conditioning. To idealistically pretend that they can is foolish. Instead, a more pragmatic and realistic approach is taken. This book seeks to describe methods for designing, building, and operating residential buildings to reduce the adverse thermal load during the cooling season and to improve comfort conditions. The central objective is to reduce the cost of staying cool in our homes. Regardless of your individual orientation—avoiding air conditioning or avoiding discomfort—the principles discussed here are valuable.

COOLING—A THERMAL SYSTEM VIEWPOINT

Cooling involves manipulating thermal systems—networks of interrelated heat flows and heat storage. As designers, builders, operators, and occupants of buildings, we commonly deal with four major thermal systems:

1. the building site
2. the building
3. the mechanical system and
4. the human body

Each of these thermal systems exchanges heat with its environment, generates heat internally, and stores heat. Each demands specific internal temperatures for efficient operation and proper function. It is the job of building and mechanical system designers to use the first three systems as tools to reduce the stress on the human thermal system and provide comfort.

All thermal systems obey basic laws that describe the relationship between heat and energy flows. The first law of thermodynamics states that the sum of all the energy flows in a system must be zero. The heat gained is equal to the heat lost plus the heat stored. Every British thermal unit (Btu) of heat must be accounted for; energy is neither created nor destroyed. The second law dictates that heat will always flow from high-temperature to low-temperature regions, unless additional energy is added to the process. These principles are frequently overlooked in examining natural cooling systems, resulting in hopeful designs

HEAT GAIN = HEAT LOSS + HEAT STORAGE

Figure 1.3. First Law of Thermodynamics—heat balance.

that do little but remind the owners of the inviolate nature of the laws of thermodynamics (Fig. 1.3).

A convenient parallel can be drawn between the two thermal systems of most interest—the human body and the building. Both behave similarly as thermal systems, generating, storing, gaining, and losing heat. A building exchanges heat with the surrounding air by conduction through the walls, roof, and floor; the body does the same. Whenever the surrounding air is warmer than the building surface or the body's skin surface, heat flows into the building or the body. The difference in temperature between the air and the surface provides the potential, or driving force, for the flow of heat. The greater the temperature difference, the greater the rate of heat transfer. Similarly, heat loss—cooling—occurs when the temperature of the surrounding air falls below the temperature of the building or body surface.

Air motion may also be responsible for heat flow in both systems. Air leakage or ventilation through a building and the body's respiration process have similar effects. Both the building and the human body are also subject to radiant heat gains and losses, solar heat gain, for example.

Internal heat generation also occurs in both the body and buildings. In a building, lights, machinery and equipment, and people are sources of interior heat; in the human body the metabolic process provides a parallel. Thermal storage can be particularly significant in buildings where mass has been added for passive solar systems. However, because the human body demands a relatively stable interior temperature, heat storage in the body is less significant.

In searching for cooling strategies and techniques to reduce energy consumption and costs, each of the four major thermal systems should be examined. The site, the building, the mechanical system, and the human body all present opportunities. The challenge is to use those mechanisms to produce human comfort with minimum use of purchased energy. Energy-consuming, mechanical cooling systems are usually a requirement for buildings, but they should be operated only when other alternatives have been exhausted. And when they are used, they must be used efficiently.

Human-Scale Cooling

The ultimate objective of space-cooling systems for homes and most commercial buildings is to provide comfortable conditions for the human occupants. Prior to the advent of mechanical cooling systems, the focus was on actually cooling the *people* in the buildings. Open windows permitted breezes to reach the occupants. High ceilings allowed heat to rise away from occupied zones.

Fans provided cooling in localized areas. Even with window air conditioning units, rooms were closed off and only the occupied areas were conditioned. Of course, not all the ideas suggested were widely adopted, as Fig. 1.4 illustrates. There is a major shortcoming of such natural cooling methods—the inability to cope with extremes of temperature and humidity. Except in a few locations in the United States, consistently comfortable conditions in buildings can be produced only with mechanical systems. People can survive without air conditioning, but they will be uncomfortable at times.

The power and convenience of mechanical cooling systems have brought on an unfortunate change in our building design and operation practices. The emphasis has shifted from the human system to the building system. The objective has become providing uniform, comfortable temperature and humidity throughout the *entire building*, losing sight of the basic issue of making people com-

ARM AND LEG MOVEMENT
OPERATE SERIES OF FINS

Figure 1.4. Cooling suit. Reproduced by Permission from *Principles of Air Conditioning*, Delmar Publishing, Inc., 1972.

fortable. Other means of providing comfort, such as air motion, are overlooked, and areas that require little or no conditioning, such as storage areas and entry vestibules, are wastefully heated and cooled with the occupied portions of the building. Recently interest has surged in "natural" home designs, often despite the facts that conventional comfort standards may not be met and the first costs are not justified by savings. People with six-digit incomes will spend hours cutting wood to save $300 in heating costs. Is something missing from the typical surburban house? A friend once described a visit from his grandfather, who still lived in a drafty rural house heated only by a woodstove. The old gentleman stalked around his grandson's house (heated by a heat pump) for half a day and then grumbled, "I'm not exactly cold, but I'll be damned if I can find a place to warm my hands."

Certainly fireplaces and ceiling fans are not the answer to our heating and cooling needs; they are inconvenient and often leave us uncomfortable. But they can provide a point of focus in a building, places that *feel* different, where the heating or cooling is concentrated. This contrast to "thermal boredom" may partially explain the popularity of fireplaces, woodstoves, and ceiling fans.

Mechanical systems are necessary for our current lifestyle, providing pleasant indoor conditions in any kind of weather. But they should be designed and used judiciously, conditioning only the appropriate occupied portions of a building. The central objective of making people comfortable should be kept in mind, and alternative measures for "people cooling" rather than building cooling should be considered.

There are no simple natural, or passive, methods to consistently cool a building to the comfort conditions that most Americans demand. Although there are methods that work quite well during portions of the cooling season, most of us are not willing to do without air conditioning. Consequently, this book is directed at methods of achieving comfort with the minimum expenditure of energy, making only reasonable compromises, using natural concepts and mechanical systems in sensible combination. It deals with the building, the human occupants, mechanical equipment, and the building site. Rather than focusing exclusively on removing heat from the building, it examines methods of cooling by reducing or even avoiding heat gains.

2

THE COOLING PROBLEM

There is virtually no location on earth that is too hot for man to survive. In the long, slow course of evolution man's physiology has been tailored to his environment, meeting the challenges of mild and severe climates alike. Even Death Valley, California, and Tasmania, Australia, with their 130°F temperatures support human life. For centuries, Indians and aborigines have lived in these inhospitable areas without mechanical cooling systems. These locations represent the hot extreme of the earth's climate. The areas of the world in which the majority of the population is concentrated are much milder, seldom experiencing temperatures above 100°F. Except in cases of individual illness or infirmity, our environment poses no high-temperature threat to man's survival. As a species, man has evolved to match his environment and has done so with remarkable success.

In a well-developed society, such as that of the United States, however, most people spend the majority of their lives in another environment—the building interior. A primary function of man's shelter has always been to ameliorate the daily and seasonal fluctuations in climate conditions. Examples of the clever and effective development of architectural styles to meet the requirements of local environmental conditions are numerous. With the advent of oil, gas, and electric heating and cooling, the degree to which interior conditions can be controlled has increased dramatically. Over the past three decades it has become possible to completely disregard the effects of climate forces in the design and construction of buildings and to overcome these forces with mechanical space-conditioning equipment. We commonly create interior environments that provide remarkable comfort conditions, but depend entirely upon the use of large quantities of energy. The common glass office building without operable glazing must have air conditioning. During power outages, such buildings often must be evacuated. In many cases, it is not possible for man to exist in his new environment without the use of energy-intensive mechanical systems.

As the building interior environment has changed, we have made distinct changes in our lifestyles, dress, customs, and preferences. These modifications have then added to our climate-related cooling problem to further increase the need for mechanical cooling. Our clothing styles are a good example. Most people have largely abandoned traditional, practical clothing in favor of dress considered fashionable. Business suits are a standard uniform for male office workers in the United States, regardless of location or season. Long sleeves, vests, coats, and closed collars insulate the body and prevent the dissipation of heat. Consequently, lower air temperatures are required to maintain comfort conditions. Cats, dogs, and horses have the good sense to shed their winter coats in the summer. Don't we?

Standards of hygiene and appearance have also risen significantly over the past few decades, and with them the demands we place on cooling systems. Body odors and perspiration-dampened clothing are no longer acceptable. Popular magazines from the 1940s ran advertisements for absorbant pads to be placed to prevent underarm perspiration from moistening ladies' dresses. Such solutions are generally unheard of today.

On a larger scale, man's actions have changed the environment itself. Trees, shrubs, and grasses shade the ground and either reflect solar radiation or allow winds to dissipate it into the atmosphere. As cities form, buildings and man-made surfaces displace vegetation. Buildings and paved surfaces typically have high absorptance values and retain heat far into the night.

In photosynthesis, vegetation releases huge amounts of water. As liquid turns to vapor and leaves the plant, heat is absorbed. The trees on a residential building site can provide site cooling measured in millions of Btus per day. In contrast, buildings consume energy for lighting, cooling, and equipment and release the waste heat to the air. Essentially all of the energy consumed in a residence or office building leaves the building as heat.

The result of these effects is a significant increase in the air temperatures in cities, commonly 2 to 4°F above the surrounding rural areas. Differences of up to 10° occur frequently. In residences, an increase of only 3° corresponds to an increase of more than 10% in cooling loads.

A portion of our present cooling problem is an inevitable consequence of the climate and the nature of our modern society. However, a large portion of the total problem arises as a result of our indifference to the implications of our habits, lifestyles, and building practices. This indifference was a luxury permitted by the low-priced energy sources of the past. With the reality of present energy costs and the specter of future increases, the need to reassess lifestyles and design practices is clear. Fortunately, a combination of traditional common sense methods, modern materials and mechanical systems, and new knowledge are available to ease the burden. It is possible to maintain comfortable homes and workplaces without excessive energy expenditures. We have a great deal of room for improvement.

COOLING LOADS IN PERSPECTIVE

In attempting to design and operate a building for minimum energy costs, it is important to maintain a broad overall orientation toward the problem. The primary objective is to save energy and reduce costs with the least expenditure of effort and capital and the least inconvenience and compromise of comfort. The first priority should be those alternatives that match this objective best, regardless of whether they are associated with cooling, heating, lighting, equipment, water heating, or some other energy use. When the designer or operator of a building focuses solely on a single aspect of energy use, higher costs and a less than optimum solution are inevitable. Cooling must be considered within the overall perspective of energy consumption and comfort in buildings as only one of several aspects of the energy conservation program. Neither cooling nor any other part of the problem should receive disproportionate attention.

Only in relatively few locations in the United States is cooling the major energy use in residential and small commercial buildings. In the majority of the country and even in the majority of the South, heating is the dominant concern. For well-insulated and weatherized houses in locations where combined heating and cooling degree-days are less than about 4500 per year, water heating can even be the major single energy use. In commercial buildings, lighting is frequently the major load.

Too often, people form a perception of their energy-use patterns based only on the highest month's utility bill, often a summer electric bill that includes air conditioning, water heating, lighting, and miscellaneous electric consumption. While the monthly heating season bills might be lower, they occur over a greater number of months.

Before starting a design or an energy conservation program, an energy budget for the building or the proposed design should be established. At the least, the balance between annual heating and cooling loads and costs should be understood. The distinction between loads and costs must be kept in mind; electricity costs often vary from summer to winter, different energy sources are used for heating and cooling, and the efficiency of the heating and cooling equipment is usually different. Setting altruistic energy conservation goals aside, cost is the fundamental governing force.

An indication of the cooling/heating balance in typical residences is provided by the following information, which was originally developed by Andy Lau and Ted Hyatt at the Southern Solar Energy Center in Atlanta (Ref. 2.1). For 30 locations throughout the country, annual cooling and heating energy loads and costs are calculated for a 1536-ft^2 single-story house representative of the average new house being built. Three different design and insulation conditions are assumed, representing a standard house, an energy-conserving house, and a sun-tempered house that incorporates energy conservation features and basic, passive solar direct gain measures. These loads and costs for electric air conditioning and heating with gas, electric resistance, and heat pump are plotted on maps in Figs. 2.4 through 2.6. The basic house and the features of the three alternative conditions are described in the following text and in Figs. 2.1 through 2.3.

Common Features

Construction: single-story, wood frame, slab-on-grade, ventilated attic, dark roof, 32 × 48 ft = 1536 ft^2
Window Area: 184 ft^2, 12% of the floor area
Ceiling Height: 8 ft
Internal Gains: 80,000 Btu/day sensible (summer and winter)
             20,000 Btu/day latent (considered in summer only)
Indoor Design Conditions: 70°F and 50% relative humidity (RH) winter, 75°F
             and 50% RH summer
Outdoor Design Conditions: ASHRAE $97\frac{1}{2}$% winter, $2\frac{1}{2}$% summer
Window Treatment: Results represent the average of calculations for full shading by awnings and no shading.

The glazing was distributed as shown in the figures. For the sun-tempered house, a code-required minimum amount of glazing was left on the north side of the house, and glazing on the east and west walls was eliminated; glazing was added to the south wall to maintain the 184-ft^2 total area.

Design cooling and heating loads were calculated using the standard ASHRAE residential methods from the *Fundamentals Handbook* (Ref. 2.2). Cooling energy consumption was estimated using the equivalent full load hours of operation method; annual heating energy consumption figures were developed using the degree-day method. Cooling energy consumption calculations are explained in Chapter 5. The standard design and the energy-conserving design were analyzed with both a north-south orientation and an east-west orientation; the maps represent the average of the two. The sun-tempered design was assumed to face south.

Figures 2.4 through 2.6 present the results of the calculations. The numerator of the fraction at each location is the annual cooling load, the amount of energy that must be removed from the building during the cooling season. The denominator is the annual heating load. The ratio of the cooling load to the heating load is also given. These figures consider only building loads, i.e., the energy flow to or from the building; they do not acount for the efficiency of the cooling and heating systems.

The amount of energy that must be purchased is estimated by dividing the building load values from the figures by the COP or efficiency of the cooling or heating systems. The cooling/heating ratio for purchased energy is estimated from the building loads in the figures modified as described below. The modi-

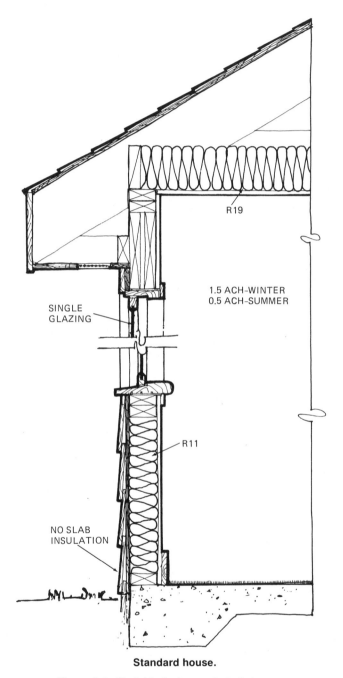

R19

1.5 ACH–WINTER
0.5 ACH–SUMMER

SINGLE
GLAZING

R11

NO SLAB
INSULATION

Standard house.

Figure 2.1. Variable features of study house.

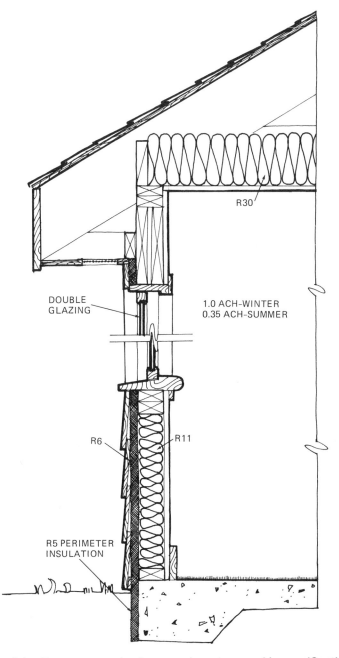

Figure 2.1.   Energy conserving house and sun-tempered house. (*Continued*)

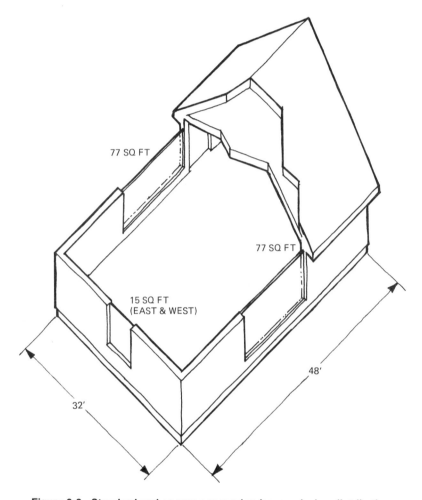

77 SQ FT

77 SQ FT

15 SQ FT
(EAST & WEST)

48′

32′

Figure 2.2. Standard and energy conserving house glazing distribution.

fications account for the efficiencies of the various mechanical systems. The efficiency values used in the calculations are provided in parentheses.

Electric resistance heat and air conditioning: Divide ratio by the COP of the air conditioner (2.5).

Gas or oil heat and electric air conditioning: Multiply ratio by (gas or oil furnace efficiency/COP of air conditioner), (0.70/2.5 = 0.28).

Heat pump: Multiply ratio by (seasonal heating COP/seasonal cooling COP), (about 1.0).

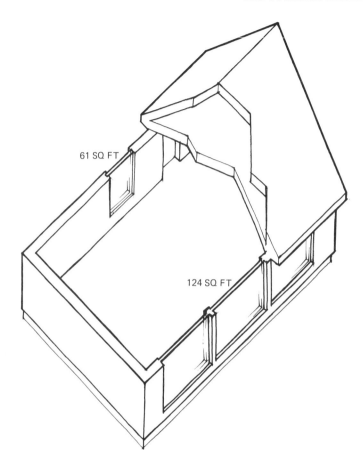

61 SQ FT

124 SQ FT

Figure 2.3. Sun-tempered house glazing distribution.

Notice that the areas where cooling is the major load are restricted to the deep South. The line where cooling loads are roughly equal to heating loads runs through the lower portion of the Gulf States. Also, the ratio of cooling load to heating load increases for the better insulated houses, reflecting the fact that most conservation efforts are more effective in reducing heating loads than cooling loads. Insulation does nothing to reduce solar heat gains through windows, humidity loads, and internal heat generation. Finally, notice that the purchased energy cooling/heating ratio changes dramatically with the type of equipment used. The energy usage and cost patterns for a building with electric heat and air conditioning may be quite different from those for a building with a heat pump.

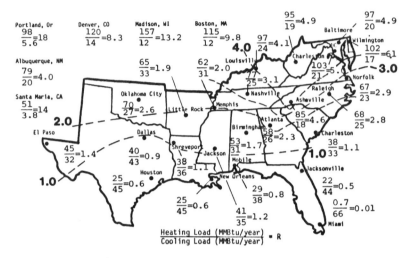

Figure 2.4. Standard house building heating and cooling loads.

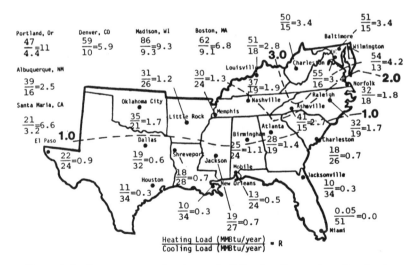

Figure 2.5. Energy-conserving house building heating and cooling loads.

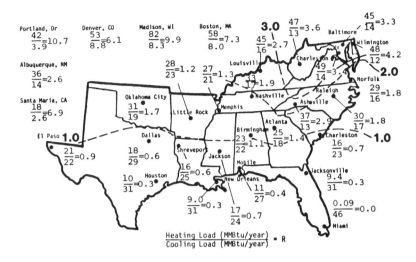

Figure 2.6. Sun-tempered house building heating and cooling loads.

But once again, loads are only a part of the issue; costs are the primary concern. The ratio of cooling to heating costs for a particular location may be calculated as

$$C/H = (Qc/Qh) \times (Efc/Efh) \times (Ccf/Chf)$$

where

C/H = ratio of annual cooling costs to annual heating costs

Q_C/Q_H = ratio of annual cooling load to annual heating load

E_{FH}/E_{FC} = ratio of seasonal heating system efficiency to seasonal cooling system efficiency

C_{FC}/C_{HF} = ratio of metered cooling fuel cost to heating fuel cost. Where electricity costs vary from summer to winter, the appropriate rate should be used for each case.

If specific efficiency information on the cooling and heating systems is not available, the following values are suggested.

Natural gas heating: 70% efficient
Electric heat: 100% efficient
Heat pumps: COP = 2.5
Air conditioners: COP = 2.5.

Example: Consider a house in Atlanta and the following energy costs

> Electricity: $0.055/kWh winter, $0.075/kWh summer
> Natural gas: $0.55/therm

The gross energy costs (COP and efficiency are not considered) per million Btus are

Electricity
  Winter:
    (1,000,000 Btu/3413 Btu/kWh) × $0.055/kWh = $16.16/mBtu
  Summer:
    (1,000,000 Btu/3413 Btu/kWh) × $0.075/kWh = $21.96/mBtu
Natural Gas
    (1,000,000 Btu/100,000 Btu/therm) × $0.55/therm = $5.50/mBtu

From the figures, the building loads and cooling/heating ratios are

	Cooling load (mBtu)	Heating load (mBtu)	Ratio Clg/Htg
Standard house	26	58	0.45
Energy-conserving house	19	28	0.68
Sun-tempered house	18	25	0.72

Purchased energy loads for various system types with the assumed efficiencies are shown in Table 2.1.

Notice that the ratio of energy consumption for cooling and heating and the cost ratio can be substantially different. Changes in the rates for gas and electricity will result in changes in the ratios and the emphasis for the project. It is necessary to consider the probable future costs of energy in arriving at a best course of action. In all cases, the relative importance of cooling, as indicated

Table 2.1. Cooling/Heating Cost Ratios, Atlanta.

	Standard	Energy-Conserving	Sun-Tempered
Heat pump COP = 2.5	0.63	0.96	1.02
Electric resistance electric AC, COP = 2.5	0.24	0.37	0.39
Gas heat, 70% efficient electric AC, COP = 2.5	0.50	0.76	1.12

by the ratio of heating and cooling, increases for the energy-conserving and sun-tempered cases.

UNDERSTANDING ENERGY COSTS IN EXISTING BUILDINGS

In an existing building, monthly utility bills provide a wealth of information that can be used to interpret the building's thermal performance and to guide retrofit efforts. Although precise interpretation is often hindered by changes in weather, occupancy, and mechanical system and building modifications, the fundamental information is quite useful. Many of the uncertainties involved in attempting to project performance for a new design are eliminated.

The procedure outlined here provides a means to use energy bills for a particular building to estimate the individual energy costs for heating, cooling, and all other functions. Any method that relies solely on monthly energy data cannot provide a precise ratio of heating and cooling costs. There are some months in which both the heating and cooling systems may operate, and it is not always clear whether a particular month is part of the heating season or the cooling season. Year-to-year weather variations also create uncertainties. But even a simple analytical method is useful in understanding the relative balance between cooling and heating costs and setting conservation strategies.

1. Collect energy bills, including electricity, gas, and oil, for at least one year. For greater accuracy, use several years of billing information, and average the figures to obtain a monthly profile for each energy source.

2. Convert the monthly profiles for each energy source into present costs using the current utility rates. Add the individual fuel costs for each energy source in each month to obtain a total energy cost profile. This profile is also useful as an energy cost budget for the building; actual monthly costs can be compared with it to help track the effects of conservation efforts or to highlight changes in energy-use patterns or potential problems.

3. Select the month in the spring or fall with the lowest cost, normally May or October. In these months, most houses and small commercial buildings do not use a significant amount of heating or cooling, so the cost represents the base monthly cost of energy for lights, appliances, equipment, fans, water heating, and other year-round loads.

4. Subtract the base monthly cost from the cost for each month in the profile to find the costs of energy used for heating and cooling. Total the figures for the summer months to get the cooling season costs and those for the winter months to get the heating season costs. Multiply the base monthly cost by 12 to find the annual cost of lights, appliances, water heating, and other uses.

5. Find the ratio of cooling costs to heating costs by dividing the total cooling cost by the total heating cost for the year. The following table will assist in deciding where the best energy savings may be achieved in the building.

Selecting an Energy Cost Reduction Strategy

Ratio of Cooling Cost to Heating Cost	Action	Examples
Less than 0.75	Look for heating energy conservation or comfort improvement alternatives	High-efficiency furnace, simple passive solar, movable window insulation
0.75 to 1.25	Look for alternatives that provide both heating and cooling benefits or balance heating and cooling efforts	Insulation and weatherization measures
More than 1.25	Look for cooling energy conservation alternatives	Sun control, whole-house fan, high-efficiency air conditioning

In some cases, costs other than heating and cooling may dominate the energy consumption and cost patterns for a building. An example is a convenience store where lighting and refrigeration loads are the major energy consumers.

Example: The natural gas and electric consumption histories for an energy-conserving 1700-ft^2 residence in Atlanta are listed below. The house incorporates R30 ceilings, R15 walls, double-glazing, and good infiltration control measures. It is heated by a gas furnace and cooled with electric central air conditioning. Water is heated with natural gas.

The monthly consumption figures are the average of two years' of data. The costs are calculated by multiplying the energy consumption for each month by the current costs of natural gas and electricity (different summer and winter rate).

	Natural Gas		Electricity	
Month	Consumption (Therms)	Cost ($)	Consumption (kWh)	Cost ($)
January	120.40	56.59	553	38.60
February	90.60	47.11	452	31.55
March	82.00	45.10	459	32.04
April	36.00	19.80	393	27.43
May	34.80	19.14	568	46.58
June	31.80	17.49	722	59.20
July	23.60	12.98	1230	100.86
August	20.50	11.28	1247	102.25
September	27.60	15.18	973	79.79
October	26.60	14.63	267	18.64
November	32.80	17.06	436	30.44
December	77.10	36.24	767	53.50

The total monthly energy cost is simply the sum of the heating and cooling energy costs.

Monthly Total Energy Costs.

Month	Total Cost ($)
January	95.19
February	78.66
March	77.14
April	47.23
May	65.72
June	76.69
July	113.84
August	113.53
September	94.97
October	33.27
November	47.50
December	89.74
Total annual energy cost	933.48

The lowest total energy cost for the year—$33.27—occurs during October, when heating and cooling loads for the building are negligible. Assume that this represents the base consumption for year-round loads, and find the net monthly costs for heating and cooling by subtracting the October cost from the cost for each month.

The total annual cost of heating is found by adding the monthly costs for the months in the heating season. Total annual cooling costs are found similarly.

Month	Total Heating and Cooling Costs ($)	Heating Cost ($)	Cooling Cost ($)
January	61.92	61.92	
February	45.39	45.39	
March	43.87	43.87	
April	13.96	13.96	
May	32.45		32.45
June	43.42		43.42
July	80.57		80.57
August	80.26		80.26
September	61.70		61.70
October	0.00		
November	14.23	14.23	
December	56.47	56.47	
Annual totals	534.24	235.84	298.40

The annual cost of energy for lighting, appliances, water heating, and other year-round loads is 12 × $33.27, or $399. Annual cooling costs are $298, and annual heating costs are $236. The ratio of cooling to heating costs is $298/ $236, or 1.26, indicating that cooling is slightly more important than heating in a cost-reduction program. However, note that the cost of other loads in the house is greater than either the cooling costs or the heating costs. A balanced conservation effort would address all the energy loads in the house, directing slightly more effort toward cooling than heating.

An analysis might also be based on energy consumption, rather than cost. Such an analysis is useful if utility rates are likely to change significantly or to evaluate alternative mechanical systems and energy sources. A procedure similar to the one just described could be used, with costs replaced by energy consumption calculated with the conversion factors listed below.

1 gal of oil = 140,000 Btu
1 therm = 100,000 Btu
1 CCF of natural gas = approximately 103,000 Btu
1 kWh = 3413 Btu

LOW-ENERGY COOLING STRATEGIES AND OBJECTIVES

The objective of low-energy cooling is to make the occupants of a building comfortable at the lowest possible total cost. The relative balance between comfort and minimum cost is a highly individual factor. Some building owners are willing to tolerate reduced comfort standards to avoid the cost of air conditioning. However, for many residences and almost all commercial buildings, there are minimum comfort requirements set by the owners that dictate that air conditioning be installed. The methods described in this book are consistent with both sets of conditions. For the non-air-conditioned building, they provide ways to improve comfort conditions. For the air conditioned building, they provide ways to maintain comfort conditions and reduce energy consumption and cost.

Subsequent chapters will deal with a diverse set of low-energy cooling strategies to reduce costs and improve comfort. By combining all the measures it is possible to significantly reduce the need for purchased energy and to maintain or improve interior comfort conditions. These strategies include

reducing the cooling requirements of building occupants
building design
people cooling rather than building cooling
HVAC system design
efficient mechanical equipment
reducing the length of the cooling season
efficient building operation
broader standards of comfort
humidity control
alternative methods of heat removal

Methods of Cooling

Using a building as an example, let's consider the cooling process from an overall perspective. Two factors are important: the amount of energy—in this case heat—and the temperatures involved. Heat naturally flows from high-temperature areas to low-temperature areas; additional energy input is required to make heat flow from areas with low temperatures to those with high temperatures. Obviously, it is desirable to use natural heat flows whenever possible and to avoid the expense of adding energy to the system.

The simplest method of cooling is to reduce heat gains. These heat gains take place from a variety of sources, all at temperatures above the temperature of the building interior. The thermal system can be cooled by eliminating the source of heat gain (turning off the lights or adding insulation to the building skin) or by shunting the heat gain to another low-temperature region (reflecting solar gains to the surroundings. Either the heat source is eliminated or another high-temperature-to-low-temperature heat flow path is established to divert the flow of heat (Fig. 2.7).

When interior temperatures are outside the comfort zone, simply avoiding excess heat gains is not enough. Heat removal is essential, requiring a lower temperature region in which to discharge the heat, a heat sink. Two situations can occur: (1) the ambient air temperature is in the comfort range and the build-

Figure 2.7. Cooling by avoiding heat gain.

ing interior is warmer than the ambient as a result of various heat gains, or (2) the ambient temperature is above the comfort range.

In the first condition, the ambient air provides a readily available heat sink, and the building can be inexpensively cooled by ventilation (Fig. 2.8). Using the outdoor air as a heat sink, we can reject huge amounts of energy, but only if the interior building temperature remains above the outdoor air temperature. Interior temperatures cannot be lowered below that of the outside air (the outdoor air temperature is the limit of the cooling process).

When the outdoor air temperature is above the comfort range, the air is not usable as a natural heat sink. Under such conditions it is necessary to provide an artificial heat sink at a temperature below that of the building interior (Fig. 2.9). The evaporator coils of a typical air conditioning unit run at a temperature of approximately 55°F, allowing heat transfer from the inside air to the coil surface. It is then necessary to remove heat from the evaporator and reject it to the outside air through the condenser. This can be done only with the addition of energy to the process—energy to drive the fans and the compressor. The convenience and assured availability of the mechanical system are available only at a cost. Obviously, it is desirable to use simpler methods first and rely on air conditioning only when less costly means have been exhausted.

Evaporative and radiative passive cooling systems provide an alternative method for creating a low-temperature heat sink, but climate restrictions limit

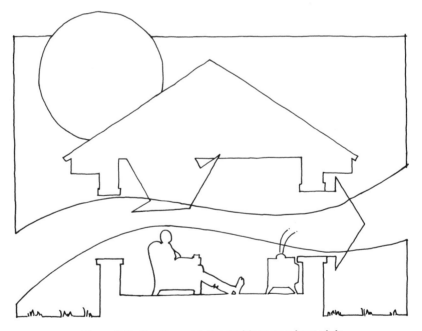

Figure 2.8. Cooling with the ambient as a heat sink.

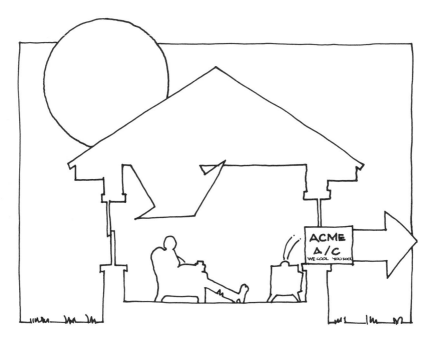

Figure 2.9. Cooling with a mechanical heat sink.

their applicability. In most areas, night air temperatures are high, and humidity and haze reduce the ability to transfer heat to natural heat sinks by evaporation and radiation. However, a variety of measures can be taken to reduce cooling loads and increase the efficiency of conventional mechanical cooling systems. Even in the harshest, hot, humid areas there are long periods during the early and late portions of the cooling season when natural cooling alternatives are usable. The total effect of a balanced, low-energy cooling effort can be good comfort conditions with a substantial reduction of cooling costs and good comfort conditions maintained.

Understanding the Effects of Climate

The climate at a site influences not only the heating and cooling loads on a building, but also the passive means available for meeting those loads. Climate governs the availability of passive cooling heat sinks: the air for evaporation cooling, the night sky for radiation cooling, cool night air for stored cooling, and the earth for a variety of earth-contact alternatives.

Heating and cooling degree-days are often used to describe the climate and the space-conditioning loads at a site. Degree-days are calculated from the difference between the average outdoor temperature for each day and an interior reference temperature of 65°F. The base temperature may be different to account for the particular building's gains and insulation level. A day with a high temperature of 96°F and low temperature of 70°F has an average temperature of 83°F and 18 cooling degree-days.

$$(83 - 65)°F \times 1 \text{ day} = 18 \text{ cooling degree-days}$$

Degree-days are not as effective for describing cooling loads, for they consider only temperatures and ignore solar gains and humidity. Still, they provide a good general indication of the severity of the local climate. Maps of heating and cooling degree-days are provided in Figs. 2.10 and 2.11.

Passive Heating and Cooling Resources

The distribution of passive heating and cooling resources around the country does not necessarily coincide with the need for heating and cooling. For passive heating, the key is access to the heat of the sun during winter. For cooling, the key is the availability of heat sinks for heat rejection during summer. Humidity is the governing climatic factor. Clouds and humidity block solar gains and access to the deep sky for radiative cooling and limit day-to-night temperature variations to ranges too small for simple stored cooling systems. High humidity

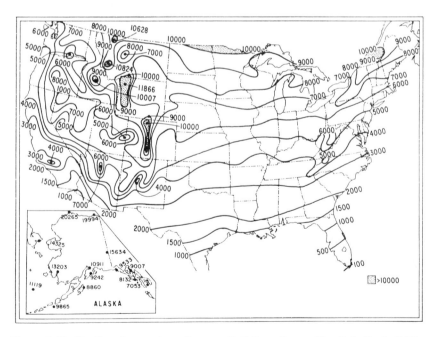

Figure 2.10. Heating degree days. Source. *Buildings Energy Use Data Book, Edition 2*, December, 1979, Oak Ridge National Laboratory.

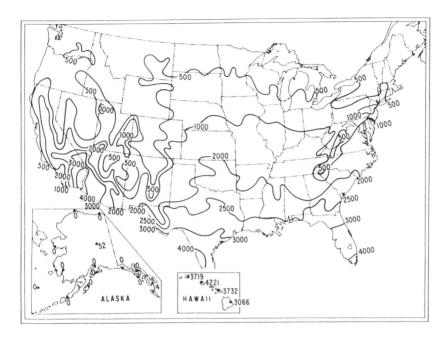

Figure 2.11. Cooling degree days. Source: *Buildings Energy Use Data Book, Edition* **2, December, 1979, Oak Ridge National Laboratory.**

limits evaporative cooling to temperatures too high for useful cooling. In addition to limiting passive cooling measures, humidity is itself a comfort problem. Dehumidification by passive means is very difficult.

Figure 2.12 illustrates the average relative humidity for August around the country. In general, areas with lower humidity are more favorable for both passive heating and cooling. Climate conditions in the Southwest and the Rockies are ideal; passive cooling and passive heating in those areas are relatively straightforward. In other areas of the country, passive measures are much less effective.

Humidity levels and the potential for evaporative cooling are reflected in the wet-bulb temperature at a location. An examination of the design wet-bulb temperatures in Fig. 2.13 points out the limitations of evaporative cooling in areas like the Southeast and the opportunities it presents in New Mexico and Arizona.

Radiative cooling is also hampered by humidity. High humidity blocks useful heat rejection to night skies from man-made systems and also prevents the earth from cooling itself. In arid areas, the earth's surface cools off more quickly at night by radiating heat to the sky, making it possible to use the night air as a heat sink. A large day-to-night, or diurnal, temperature swing can be used very effectively for cooling both directly at night and during the following days by storing ''coolth'' inside a building. Throughout the Southeast and the East, the

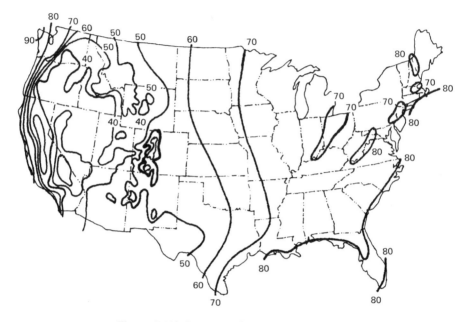

Figure 2.12. Average relative humidity, August.

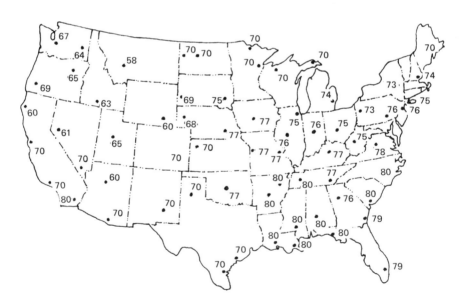

Figure 2.13. Design wet-bulb temperature.

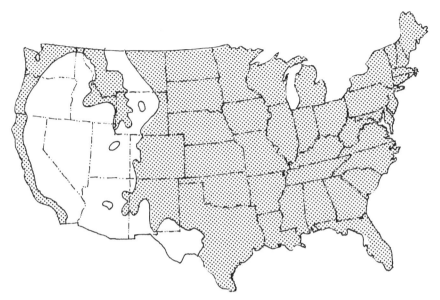

Figure 2.14. Locations with mean annual relative humidity greater than 50%.

average diurnal temperature swing during summer is only 18–25°F, though in the Rockies it exceeds 40°F.

Cooling can be accomplished by passive means in the arid zones of the United States, but it has much more limited application in humid areas. In humid areas, more limited passive measures must be supplemented by mechanical cooling to provide comfort. This book is concerned primarily with low-energy cooling alternatives in the humid majority of the country (Fig. 2.14).

Developing Climate Information for a Particular Site

Climate data analysis sometimes seems to be done to excess; technical papers at past technical conferences even suggested the use of a consulting meteorologist in each design project. However, without going overboard, the designer can certainly profit by a fundamental understanding of the climate and the problems and opportunities it presents. At the very minimum, anyone seriously interested in building energy performance should obtain a set of monthly and annual *Local Climatological Data* publications. From these a basic set of interpretative information should be developed for each area in which the designer works. Suggested items for inclusion are

- Plot of the distribution of outdoor temperature during the cooling season, hours above various base temperatures (Fig. 2.15). Purpose: To visualize

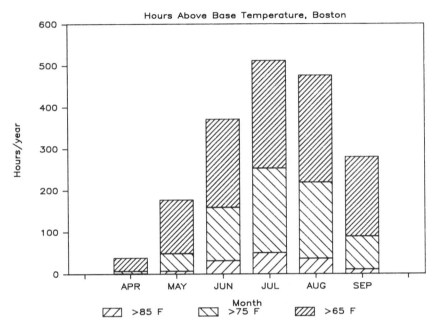

Figure 2.15. Outdoor temperature distribution, cooling season, Boston.

the length and severity of the cooling season and assess the opportunity for ventilative cooling.

• Plot of average hourly climatic conditions on an Olgyay bioclimatic chart, shown in Fig. 2.16 for Memphis, Tennessee. Ref. 2.4. Purpose: To visualize the effects of ambient temperature and humidity on comfort and to identify those periods in which natural cooling methods can be viable and those periods in which mechanical cooling is required.

Recommended sources of information include:
Facility Design and Planning Engineering Weather Data AFM 88-29. (Ref. 2.5.) This publication provides an excellent collection of temperature data for 213 sites in the United States as well as many foreign locations. The majority of the sites listed are military bases and facilities. The most interesting material is the extensive set of temperature BIN tables, which provide tabulations of the number of hours of temperature occurrences in 5° temperature "bins" for the entire year. The data are broken down into three periods during the day, 0100 to 0800, 0900 to 1600, and 1700 to 2400 hours. Also included are tables of design data for the sites, including design temperature and humidity conditions, prevailing winds, and heating and cooling degree-days.

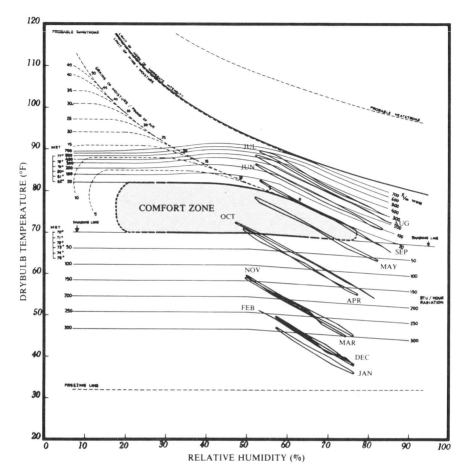

Figure 2.16. Climate conditions and comfort, Olgyay Bioclimate chart, Memphis, TN. (*Source: Climatic Data Base*, Tennessee Valley Authority Solar Outreach and Technology Group.)

Insulation Manual, Homes and Apartments Ref. 2.6. Design temperatures and equivalent full load hours of operation for 370 U.S. sites.

ASHRAE Handbook, Fundamentals, 1985, Ref. 2.2. The definitive source of weather conditions for design purposes.

Climatic Atlas of the United States, 1931–1960. Ref. 2.3. A summary of temperature, humidity, precipitation, cloud cover, and wind rose data for larger cities in the United States. Includes useful interpretative data, such as the mean annual number of days above 90°F. Very useful for observing regional patterns and differences in conditions. Solar radiation data should not be relied upon for design purposes, due to inaccuracies in the data collection

Normals, Means, And Extremes

Month	Temperatures °F							Normal Degree days Base 65 °F		Precipitation in inches										
	Normal			Extremes						Water equivalent							Snow, Ice pellets			
	Daily maximum	Daily minimum	Monthly	Record highest	Year	Record lowest	Year	Heating	Cooling	Normal	Maximum monthly	Year	Minimum monthly	Year	Maximum in 24 hrs.	Year	Maximum monthly	Year	Maximum in 24 hrs.	Year
(a)			53		53						45		45		45		45		45	
J	47.4	27.6	37.5	80	1950	-12	1940	853	0	2.86	7.97	1978	0.64	1981	3.31	1962	28.5	1940	21.6	1940
F	49.9	28.8	39.4	83	1932	-10	1936	717	0	3.01	5.97	1979	0.48	1978	2.67	1979	19.5	1979	10.9	1979
M	58.2	35.5	46.9	93	1938	11	1960	569	0	3.38	8.04	1975	0.94	1966	2.04	1942	19.7	1960	12.1	1962
A	70.3	45.2	57.8	96	1976	25	1977	226	13	2.77	5.32	1952	0.64	1963	2.60	1978	2.0	1940	2.0	1940
M	78.4	54.5	66.5	100	1941	31	1956	64	99	3.42	8.87	1972	0.87	1965	3.08	1981	0.0		0.0	
J	85.4	62.9	74.2	104	1952	40	1967	0	258	3.52	9.24	1938	0.38	1980	4.61	1963	0.0		0.0	
J	88.2	67.5	77.9	105	1977	51	1965	0	397	5.63	18.87	1945	0.52	1963	5.73	1969	0.0		0.0	
A	86.6	65.9	76.3	102	1953	46	1934	0	366	5.06	14.10	1955	0.52	1943	8.79	1955	0.0		0.0	
S	80.9	59.0	70.0	103	1954	35	1974	21	180	3.58	10.98	1975	0.26	1978	3.82	1955	0.0		0.0	
O	71.2	47.4	59.3	99	1941	21	1962	203	23	2.94	9.39	1971	0.30	1963	6.50	1961	T	1979	T	1979
N	60.6	37.3	49.0	86	1974	10	1933	480	0	3.20	7.64	1959	0.36	1965	4.07	1956	7.3	1953	7.3	1953
D	49.1	28.8	39.0	80	1971	-1	1942	806	0	3.22	7.07	1973	0.40	1980	3.16	1958	12.5	1958	7.5	1966
YR	68.8	46.7	57.8	JUL 105	1977	JAN -12	1940	3939	1336	42.59	18.87	JUL 1945	0.26	SEP 1978	8.79	AUG 1955	28.5	JAN 1940	21.6	JAN 1940

Means and extremes above are from existing and comparable exposures. Annual extremes have been exceeded at other sites in the locality as follows: Highest temperature 107 in August 1918; minimum monthly precipitation 0.11 in November 1890 and earlier.

(a) Length of record, years, through the current year unless otherwise noted, based on January data.
(b) 70° and above at Alaskan stations.
* Less than one half.
T Trace.

NORMALS - Based on record for the 1941-1970 period.
DATE OF AN EXTREME - The most recent in cases of multiple occurrence.
PREVAILING WIND DIRECTION - Record through 1963.
WIND DIRECTION - Numerals indicate tens of degrees clockwise from true north. 00 indicates calm.
FASTEST MILE WIND - Speed is fastest observed 1-minute value when the direction is in tens of degrees.

Figure 2.17. Sample LCD, annual for Richmond, VA.

program. Includes large (16 × 22-in.) maps of the country with plotted climatic data.

Local Climatological Data, Annual Summary with Comparative Data. Ref. 2.7. Available for individual years at approximately 280 sites in the United States. Includes specific year and normal, mean, and extreme data, including temperature, degree-days, precipitation, RH, wind direction and speed, and cloud cover by month. Previous years' data are summarized for average temperature, heating degree-days, precipitation, and snowfall. Includes a useful narrative description of the local climate, particularly valuable when working with unfamiliar sites. $0.65 per year per site; $65.00 per year for all 280 sites. A bargain (Fig. 2.17).

Local Climatological Data, Monthly Summary. (Ref. 2.7.) Same basic information as in the annual summary, presented for individual days at 3-hour

Relative humidity pct. Hour 01	07	13	19 (Local time)	Wind Mean speed m.p.h.	Prevailing direction	Fastest mile Speed m.p.h.	Direction	Year	Pct. of possible sunshine	Mean sky cover, tenths, sunrise to sunset	Mean number of days Sunrise to sunset Clear	Partly cloudy	Cloudy	Precipitation .01 inch or more	Snow, Ice pellets 1.0 inch or more	Thunderstorms	Heavy fog, visibility ¼ mile or less	Temperatures °F Max. 90° and above	32° and below	Min. 32° and below	0° and below	Average station pressure mb. Elev. 177 feet m.s.l.
48	48	48	48	34		15			31	31	32	37	37	37	37	45	45	53	53	53	53	10
77	81	57	69	8.0	S	43	NW	1971	52	6.4	8	7	16	10	1	*	3	0	3	21	*	1012.3
74	79	52	63	8.5	NNE	45	SW	1951	57	6.1	9	6	13	9	1	*	2	0	2	19	*	1012.7
73	78	49	59	8.9	W	42	SE	1952	60	6.2	8	8	15	11	1	1	2	*	*	10	0	1010.6
74	75	45	55	8.8	S	40	NW	1972	64	6.1	8	9	13	9	*	2	2	1	0	2	0	1010.1
84	80	51	65	7.6	SSW	45	N	1962	64	6.3	7	10	14	11	0	6	2	3	0	*	0	1008.8
87	82	54	68	7.2	S	52	NW	1952	67	6.1	7	12	11	10	0	7	2	9	0	0	0	1009.7
89	86	57	71	6.6	SSW	56	NW	1955	66	6.1	7	12	12	11	0	9	2	13	0	0	0	1010.1
90	89	58	76	6.3	S	54	W	1964	65	6.0	7	12	12	10	0	7	3	11	0	0	0	1011.5
90	90	57	79	6.5	S	45	SE	1952	64	5.8	9	9	12	8	0	3	3	4	0	0	0	1011.6
87	89	53	77	6.9	NNE	68	SE	1954	61	5.3	12	7	12	7	0	1	3	*	0	2	0	1012.8
80	84	51	70	7.4	S	38	NW	1977	57	5.7	10	7	13	8	*	1	2	0	*	10	0	1013.3
78	81	55	70	7.6	SW	40	SW	1968	52	6.2	10	6	15	9	1	*	3	0	2	20	*	1013.0
82	83	53	68	7.5	S	68	SE	OCT 1954	62	6.0	102	105	158	113	4	37	28	42	7	86	1	1011.4

Figure 2.17. (*Continued*)

intervals and as averages. Excellent source for analyzing weather patterns. $0.65 per month; annual subscriptions are available for $8.45.

Less detailed climatological data summaries are available for entire states at $1.50 for either a monthly report or the annual summary. Annual subscriptions of 12 monthly reports and the annual summary are available for $19.50. Several excellent references are available as guides for interpreting weather data. One recommended publication is *Design With Climate*, Victor Olgyay, Princeton University Press.

Average Temperature

Year	Jan	Feb	Mar	Apr	May	June	July	Aug	Sept	Oct	Nov	Dec	Annual
1946	40.0	41.5	47.0	53.9	69.0	79.2	78.5	78.4	68.4	57.3	47.5	38.6	58.3
1947	38.6	40.4	45.2	56.2	71.6	76.4	77.7	75.4	71.2	57.0	48.2	36.1	57.9
1948	34.2	40.8	58.6	61.4	63.9	76.2	76.2	75.2	73.6	57.8	49.6	33.4	58.4
1946	38.0	41.7	53.8	57.2	65.8	72.8	75.4	72.6	70.0	60.9	52.9	43.4	58.8
1947	44.6	33.5	40.0	57.5	67.0	72.2	74.8	78.5	70.1	63.7	46.4	38.4	57.2
1948	31.1	39.6	50.8	57.7	66.3	74.4	78.2	75.7	68.6	56.2	52.9	42.0	57.8
1949	45.2	46.5	48.4	55.7	66.0	75.2	80.1	76.6	67.4	62.5	49.0	42.4	59.6
1950	49.7	40.7	48.6	54.7	65.0	76.8	76.8	75.5	68.2	61.2	47.3	36.1	57.8
1951	40.8	41.3	46.8	56.6	64.6	74.3	78.6	76.0	70.0	61.6	44.7	42.0	58.1
1952	42.4	42.2	47.0	58.1	67.0	77.6	80.9	76.4	69.2	55.7	39.2	37.6	59.0
1953	42.9	44.3	48.3	58.0	71.5	75.2	77.0	77.8	69.4	60.7	48.1	40.5	59.9
1954	38.0	40.1	48.3	61.2	67.5	75.8	78.6	76.8	74.8	60.3	48.5	38.2	59.8
1955	35.8	40.9	50.2	60.8	67.2	70.1	81.3	78.7	70.6	59.5	46.1	34.8	58.0
1956	36.0	43.0	46.3	55.5	65.0	74.7	77.8	76.5	67.9	60.9	47.6	46.9	58.3
1957	36.6	33.8	42.3	61.5	66.7	74.8	78.1	74.6	71.9	60.5	50.3	43.0	58.4
1958	37.6	33.6	42.3	57.9	65.7	71.3	80.2	79.0	69.1	59.4	51.2	33.4	59.0
1959	37.5	40.9	50.4	59.3	65.5	75.8	76.1	75.8	70.8	61.4	46.9	41.6	59.0
1960	38.8	39.3	35.9	60.8	67.2	70.1	76.3	77.5	69.3	57.1	50.1	34.6	56.6
1961	33.5	42.2	52.2	53.0	63.6	72.8	78.5	77.1	73.5	58.1	50.1	37.1	57.5
1962	36.6	45.0	45.0	57.5	70.6	74.6	76.1	74.6	66.2	60.5	50.4	36.1	58.5
1963	33.9	33.3	47.6	55.4	64.4	73.0	76.1	75.7	65.5	53.4	50.4	32.4	56.1
1964	38.1	37.2	50.6	61.1	69.6	73.1	75.8	73.1	67.1	56.4	46.2	42.9	56.8
1965	35.6	38.8	43.0	53.9	69.6	70.7	74.9	75.9	70.7	56.1	48.2	41.3	56.6
1966	31.1	37.7	47.5	52.8	63.1	71.4	76.4	74.6	67.2	55.5	49.5	38.0	55.4
1967	40.6	34.2	52.0	58.8	64.7	74.0	76.5	75.5	65.7	57.2	49.9	41.9	56.2
1968	33.9	34.9	52.0	58.8	64.7	75.7	78.9	78.9	70.9	61.9	51.3	37.0	58.2
1969	36.8	36.8	42.3	57.6	65.5	75.7	78.0	75.1	68.1	58.5	49.6	35.5	58.2
1970	30.1	37.1	42.9	58.2	69.1	75.7	78.3	78.0	74.8	62.9	49.9	40.4	58.1
1971	33.8	39.5	44.5	55.0	63.3	74.1	76.6	76.1	71.4	64.4	48.5	48.0	57.9
1972	40.7	37.6	47.2	57.9	64.6	70.1	77.1	77.5	70.1	58.0	47.5	40.8	57.4
1973	37.6	38.5	58.5	57.9	65.1	77.6	76.0	80.1	70.3	62.5	51.1	41.7	59.2
1974	45.8	40.5	50.4	59.2	65.8	74.6	76.0	77.8	67.3	56.9	48.1	40.0	58.5
1975	40.7	41.4	45.3	52.9	67.7	73.6	76.7	78.8	68.3	62.5	53.6	40.0	58.5
1976	35.1	48.5	52.6	60.5	65.2	74.6	77.3	75.7	68.7	54.4	52.3	36.7	57.7
1977	26.3	40.5	55.7	61.1	68.2	73.0	81.4	79.8	74.2	57.3	52.5	39.5	58.9
1978	33.4	30.3	45.3	57.3	68.3	73.0	80.1	80.1	71.0	58.3	42.3	42.3	58.3
1979	36.4	28.6	51.1	55.4	67.1	72.8	76.0	77.8	71.0	56.9	53.3	42.3	57.5
1980	38.8	36.0	48.0	61.1	68.3	72.8	80.0	80.7	74.7	56.0	53.0	38.6	57.5
1981	31.2	34.2	44.6	60.6	64.1	77.9	79.6	75.1	69.4	56.4	49.1	38.0	57.3
1982	31.6	41.7	49.1	55.9	70.4	73.4	78.6	75.0	69.8	59.2	51.9	46.1	58.6
RECORD MEAN	37.3	39.2	47.1	57.2	66.3	77.8	77.8	76.3	70.1	56.4	48.8	39.8	57.7
MAX	47.2	49.9	58.6	69.7	85.1	85.1	88.1	86.5	80.9	70.6	49.9	49.9	57.7
MIN	27.4	28.5	35.6	44.6	54.4	62.8	67.4	65.1	59.3	46.7	37.2	29.6	46.6

Heating Degree Days

RICHMOND, VA

Season	July	Aug	Sept	Oct	Nov	Dec	Jan	Feb	Mar	Apr	May	June	Total
1962–63	0	0	73	175	526	891	897	882	434	218	102	1	4199
1963–64	0	0	71	197	439	1004	826	801	537	306	74	12	4267
1964–65	0	0	32	352	402	676	909	726	674	339	17	34	4161
1965–66	6	0	25	275	498	726	1043	759	538	371	133	27	4401
1966–67	0	0	47	293	466	833	738	841	560	230	171	17	4196
1967–68	0	0	64	256	623	708	956	887	416	191	86	0	4187
1968–69	0	0	0	161	403	664	957	783	677	231	66	0	4166
1969–70	0	0	45	221	541	907	1076	778	677	231	51	0	4527
1970–71	0	0	12	124	445	756	960	709	627	295	104	3	4035
1971–72	0	0	11	69	513	524	843	788	554	286	58	21	3573
1972–73	0	1	17	285	513	588	843	735	394	247	79	0	3701
1973–74	0	0	28	163	589	744	876	691	455	204	75	5	3345
1974–75	0	0	62	310	513	715	746	654	604	368	44	1	4017
1975–76	0	0	27	121	356	770	917	480	386	227	78	11	3773
1976–77	0	1	32	332	660	1227	1227	660	554	176	42	7	4335
1977–78	0	0	17	259	401	784	979	964	627	235	88	9	4341
1978–79	0	0	16	254	366	784	876	1011	455	218	75	4	3862
1979–80	0	1	8	242	353	698	806	935	541	135	47	2	3667
1980–81	0	0	14	267	557	813	1042	633	626	171	107	1	4230
1981–82	0	1	29	273	473	834	1029	645	486	280	6	0	4057
1982–83	6	0	10	213	399	585							

Cooling Degree Days

Year	Jan	Feb	Mar	Apr	May	June	July	Aug	Sept	Oct	Nov	Dec	Total
1969	0	0	0	21	90	328	321	721	147	26	0	0	1350
1970	0	0	0	35	185	328	418	410	313	57	0	0	1756
1971	0	0	0	0	56	297	367	381	209	62	22	5	1345
1972	0	0	7	30	52	178	381	726	178	32	8	2	1171
1973	0	0	13	42	91	338	391	795	231	21	6	0	1544
1974	0	0	0	58	102	182	377	410	141	41	26	0	1259
1975	0	0	0	16	135	267	348	433	165	51	18	0	1433
1976	0	0	8	90	91	307	389	737	133	12	0	0	1385
1977	0	0	0	66	148	258	513	467	289	27	0	0	1814
1978	0	0	9	12	112	302	393	475	263	15	0	0	1573
1979	0	0	0	30	30	188	374	409	195	42	0	1	1373
1980	0	0	0	25	157	243	472	494	313	23	0	0	1729
1981	0	0	0	45	89	395	458	719	169	16	0	0	1492
1982	0	0	0	13	181	259	428	323	157	43	13	7	1424

Figure 2.17 (Continued)

Precipitation

Year	Jan	Feb	Mar	Apr	May	June	July	Aug	Sept	Oct	Nov	Dec	Annual
1943	2.87	2.27	3.01	2.11	4.04	3.15	3.87	0.52	5.13	2.90	1.44	1.98	33.29
1944	2.83	5.17	5.85	3.50	5.09	1.42	3.76	6.44	5.50	1.79	3.94	2.26	48.40
1945	2.25	3.57	1.33	3.50	5.92	1.71	18.87	2.92	8.49	0.91	3.09	5.28	57.01
#1946	2.16	2.69	2.23	2.59	7.73	6.01	6.64	3.87	4.39	2.36	1.90	2.71	45.28
1947	4.31	1.43	2.22	4.69	4.48	2.53	3.13	6.38	3.05	2.37	7.03	4.16	45.20
1948	4.11	2.66	5.54	4.59	6.42	2.73	4.05	7.75	3.05	3.21	5.74	4.18	55.99
1949	3.26	2.55	5.12	2.22	5.11	3.53	6.14	8.99	2.64	3.87	1.94	1.99	44.45
#1950	2.17	1.71	3.20	0.74	4.27	0.99	6.69	3.32	4.04	1.77	1.74	2.73	33.37
1951	1.08	1.90	2.85	2.26	2.51	5.85	2.63	5.23	0.98	2.71	4.52	3.63	36.15
1952	5.71	2.76	5.05	5.32	3.72	4.50	2.71	6.41	2.04	2.04	6.42	3.37	50.36
1953	4.47	3.36	3.95	3.16	2.36	3.09	2.04	0.99	6.84	2.16	1.85	2.94	37.17
1954	3.70	1.56	2.44	3.08	4.36	1.00	1.30	3.95	0.69	4.99	1.86	2.43	31.45
1955	1.09	3.18	2.66	3.14	1.79	3.06	7.93	14.10	5.79	2.57	1.76	0.86	47.93
1956	1.65	3.57	3.06	2.25	4.35	3.28	10.32	2.28	2.96	4.92	6.11	1.98	49.23
1957	3.36	5.29	2.82	2.75	2.75	3.92	3.43	7.46	3.43	5.35	6.73	6.88	50.61
1958	2.96	4.38	3.81	4.35	5.79	6.09	3.27	9.77	1.90	5.35	1.43	4.43	53.53
1959	1.31	1.87	2.92	4.32	2.39	3.45	12.85	5.75	3.30	3.25	1.64	2.24	51.34
1960	2.13	4.56	3.29	3.57	3.59	0.91	7.34	7.20	6.21	3.31	0.85	3.04	46.00
1961	2.57	5.39	4.02	1.87	4.83	6.49	2.85	3.90	1.64	8.78	1.81	5.05	49.06
1962	5.95	3.00	4.87	3.47	4.08	5.57	5.65	3.46	0.95	0.50	6.73	2.64	48.62
1963	1.55	2.98	5.62	2.39	4.57	5.05	6.56	6.50	1.78	0.30	6.00	2.80	37.46
1964	4.16	4.46	2.61	2.71	1.14	7.40	6.46	9.88	2.56	3.50	0.98	3.05	45.03
1965	2.51	2.77	3.68	1.41	0.87	3.39	6.33	4.81	4.81	1.38	0.36	0.72	29.76
1966	4.58	3.80	0.94	2.18	2.58	2.54	4.07	1.31	5.06	4.81	1.31	3.07	36.25
1967	1.50	3.35	2.34	1.92	3.71	3.58	5.00	6.65	0.95	1.00	1.76	6.28	37.64
1968	2.53	0.98	4.00	2.93	3.11	3.50	3.41	0.99	1.59	1.59	2.60	4.28	33.10
1969	2.04	3.95	3.95	2.60	1.32	2.39	13.90	1.49	3.89	1.88	1.87	5.26	56.33
1970	1.32	2.37	3.70	4.51	1.84	1.12	4.74	1.69	1.02	1.55	3.10	5.00	28.29
1971	1.84	4.37	2.68	1.76	6.82	4.10	4.40	3.73	2.35	9.89	2.76	0.75	44.95
1972	1.43	5.15	2.11	3.35	8.87	8.82	5.80	4.34	3.35	7.89	5.82	2.91	59.34
1973	2.66	5.14	3.44	6.60	3.56	5.55	3.64	4.83	1.82	2.56	5.07	7.07	50.50
1974	3.21	2.54	1.79	1.58	3.02	1.80	2.25	6.84	4.83	0.39	1.23	6.00	35.70
1975	5.71	2.96	8.04	4.29	2.59	4.00	12.29	14.03	10.98	3.10	2.04	4.51	61.13
1976	3.39	1.35	2.14	1.08	3.76	2.85	2.63	1.35	4.78	6.99	1.88	2.56	34.76
1977	2.22	1.34	2.67	2.33	3.99	1.25	4.20	5.93	2.16	7.88	4.32	5.57	44.08
1978	7.97	0.48	5.67	3.44	4.13	5.26	4.24	0.26	1.21	1.21	4.57	1.64	41.62
1979	6.16	5.97	2.59	3.97	3.80	2.42	4.36	7.08	9.76	3.87	5.50	5.12	57.12
1980	6.05	1.01	5.49	4.28	4.68	0.38	12.22	2.15	2.37	6.96	2.18	1.13	41.13
1981	0.64	2.76	1.52	2.96	6.62	3.69	4.01	2.89	2.70	2.36	0.68	5.04	35.87
1982	2.76	4.44	3.74	2.97	3.48	3.97	9.21	4.39	2.55	2.90	2.70	3.37	46.48
RECORD MEAN	3.13	2.99	3.48	2.88	3.74	3.67	5.62	4.92	3.63	3.39	3.12	3.21	43.78

Snowfall

Season	July	Aug	Sept	Oct	Nov	Dec	Jan	Feb	Mar	Apr	May	June	Total
1943-44	0.0	0.0	0.0	0.0	0.5	1.4	2.5	1.6	0.0	0.0	0.0	0.0	6.0
1944-45	0.0	0.0	0.0	0.0	0.0	0.2	0.5	0.0	0.0	0.0	0.0	0.0	0.5
#1945-46	0.0	0.0	0.0	0.0	0.0	8.3	6.0	0.0	0.0	0.0	0.0	0.0	14.2
1946-47	0.0	0.0	0.0	0.0	0.0	0.2	6.0	0.1	10.5	0.0	0.0	0.0	23.1
1947-48	0.0	0.0	0.0	T	1.0	16.1	16.1	7.1	1.5	0.2	0.0	0.0	26.2
1948-49	0.0	0.0	0.0	0.0	0.0	0.6	0.6	0.0	0.0	T	0.0	0.0	2.1
#1949-50	0.0	0.0	0.0	0.0	0.0	2.6	2.9	2.9	5.9	0.0	0.0	0.0	8.8
1950-51	0.0	0.0	0.0	0.0	0.0	0.7	T	0.0	T	0.0	0.0	0.0	0.7
1951-52	0.0	0.0	0.0	0.0	1.0	T	2.4	11.0	5.6	0.2	0.0	0.0	13.4
1952-53	0.0	0.0	0.0	0.0	7.3	T	7.5	1.4	0.0	T	0.0	0.0	6.8
1953-54	0.0	0.0	T	0.0	0.0	2.2	9.3	1.4	0.0	0.0	0.0	0.0	14.8
1954-55	0.0	0.0	0.0	0.0	0.0	2.2	0.0	0.0	0.0	0.0	0.0	0.0	12.9
1955-56	0.0	0.0	0.0	0.0	T	T	1.1	T	T	T	0.0	0.0	1.1
1956-57	0.0	0.0	0.0	0.0	0.0	2.9	3.7	7.7	6.3	1.2	0.0	0.0	7.7
1957-58	0.0	0.0	0.0	0.0	12.5	2.4	2.4	T	0.7	T	0.0	0.0	20.6
1958-59	0.0	0.0	0.0	0.0	1.2	1.2	2.5	0.9	19.7	0.0	0.0	0.0	14.9
#1959-60	0.0	0.0	0.0	T	0.0	1.7	7.2	5.0	16.2	T	0.0	0.0	32.3
1960-61	0.0	0.0	0.0	0.0	0.7	8.1	20.6	1.2	3.9	0.6	0.0	0.0	13.9
1961-62	0.0	0.0	0.0	0.0	0.9	4.0	6.5	6.7	7.0	1.4	0.0	0.0	38.9
1962-63	0.0	0.0	0.0	0.0	T	0.2	5.7	4.2	7.0	0.0	0.0	0.0	16.0
1963-64	0.0	0.0	0.0	0.0	0.4	3.0	12.4	4.6	0.4	0.0	0.0	0.0	22.5
1964-65	0.0	0.0	0.0	0.0	0.0	0.0	4.4	4.6	0.0	0.0	0.0	0.0	20.4
1965-66	0.0	0.0	0.0	0.0	0.2	0.2	26.2	3.0	0.0	0.0	0.0	0.0	29.2
1966-67	0.0	0.0	0.0	0.0	0.2	2.6	2.3	2.4	2.8	0.0	0.0	0.0	35.1
1967-68	0.0	0.0	0.0	0.0	0.0	1.6	3.7	1.4	1.0	0.0	0.0	0.0	17.9
1968-69	0.0	0.0	0.0	0.0	1.0	1.3	5.4	0.0	0.0	0.0	0.0	0.0	7.6
1969-70	0.0	0.0	0.0	0.0	0.0	T	4.3	0.0	0.0	0.0	0.0	0.0	7.6
1970-71	0.0	0.0	0.0	T	0.0	0.2	3.3	3.7	8.4	0.6	0.0	0.0	15.2
1971-72	0.0	0.0	0.0	0.0	0.6	0.9	4.3	4.0	1.4	1.4	0.0	0.0	26.7
1972-73	0.0	0.0	0.0	0.0	0.6	0.9	2.7	2.9	0.4	0.0	0.0	0.0	16.7
1973-74	0.0	0.0	0.0	0.0	0.4	T	0.0	0.0	0.0	0.0	0.0	0.0	14.9
1974-75	0.0	0.0	0.0	0.0	0.0	0.0	0.2	T	1.0	0.0	0.0	0.0	6.0
1975-76	0.0	0.0	0.0	0.0	T	1.7	11.1	5.1	5.0	0.0	0.0	0.0	1.2
1976-77	0.0	0.0	0.0	0.0	1.0	T	1.3	5.1	0.0	0.0	0.0	0.0	13.4
1977-78	0.0	0.0	0.0	0.0	0.0	T	11.3	9.5	5.0	0.0	0.0	0.0	11.4
1978-79	0.0	0.0	0.0	0.0	T	T	16.6	7.0	15.0	0.0	0.0	0.0	20.2
1979-80	0.0	0.0	0.0	0.0	0.0	T	0.0	0.0	0.0	0.0	0.0	0.0	36.6
1980-81	0.0	0.0	0.0	0.0	T	0.9	0.6	T	0.2	0.0	0.0	0.0	1.0
1981-82	0.0	0.0	0.0	0.0	T	7.0	8.3	10.8	T	0.2	0.0	0.0	21.2
1982-83	0.0	0.0	0.0	0.0									
RECORD MEAN	0.0	0.0	0.0	T	0.4	2.1	5.2	3.9	2.9	0.1	0.0	0.0	14.6

# Indicates a station move or relocation of instruments. See Station Location table.

Record mean values above are means through the current year for the period beginning in 1930 for temperature, 1938 for precipitation and snowfall. Data are from airport locations.

Figure 2.17. (Continued)

3

COOLING PROCESSES

COOLING PROCESSES AND PSYCHROMETRICS

Understanding and applying cooling measures of any kind requires a working knowledge of psychrometrics, the science that deals with moist air. The air we live in is a mixture of dry air and water vapor called *moist air*. Although the amount of water in the air is small, its effects are great. In cooling air from 85°F and 60% RH to 75°F and 50% RH, the energy required to remove the moisture from the air is 2.7 times that required just to reduce the temperature of the air. The amount of moisture in the air affects mechanical cooling systems, passive cooling systems, and the human cooling system. The rate at which our bodies can use evaporation for cooling is determined directly by the relative humidity of the air around us.

Fundamentals

Cooling processes involve both sensible cooling, or the simple reduction of the temperature of moist air, and latent cooling, or the removal of moisture from the air. In an air conditioner, sensible cooling is evidenced by the flow of cool air from the unit, and the dripping of condensed moisture from the evaporator coils indicates that latent cooling is taking place.

Controlling air temperature in buildings—sensible heating and cooling—is usually the primary concern, but humidity control— latent heating and cooling—is also important. Removing moisture from the air requires a significant amount of energy, 20 to 40% of the total cooling energy required in most buildings. Moisture is particularly significant in processes where it changes phases, between a liquid and a solid or between a liquid and a vapor. As with most materials, great amounts of heat are involved in these phase changes, far more than in simply changing the temperature within a given state. Cooling 1 lb of water from 70 to 69°F requires the removal of 1 Btu of heat. But changing 1 lb of water vapor at 212°F to 1 lb of water at 212°F requires the removal of about 1050 Btu of heat. In buildings, any process that involves adding or removing moisture from the air holds the potential for enormous energy effects.

Before proceeding, it is necessary to define some terms. Summary definitions are provided here for convenience; more thorough definitions and examples follow.

Dry-bulb temperature: The temperature of the air as measured with a normal thermometer. Abbreviated dbt with units of degrees F.

Wet-bulb temperature: The temperature of air as measured by a thermometer with a moist sleeve around the sensing element; provides an indication of the amount of moisture in the air. The greater the difference between the dry-bulb and wet-bulb temperatures, the drier the air. Abbreviated wbt with units of degrees F.

Relative humidity: A measure of the *concentration* of water vapor in a moist air sample, expressed as a percentage of the maximum amount of water vapor the air can hold at the particular temperature. Abbreviated RH.

Humidity ratio: A measure of the *absolute amount* of water vapor in a moist air sample. The humidity ratio, W, is defined as

$$W = \frac{\text{Mass of water vapor}}{\text{Mass of dry air}}$$

expressed in units of pounds of water vapor per pound of dry air. Or, grains of water per pound of dry air may be used; 1 lb = 7000 grains.

Sensible heat: Sensible heat is heat associated with a change in temperature; the heat quantity calculated in the equation

$$Q = m \times Cp \times \Delta T$$

The key element is the temperature change. Expressed in Btu.

Latent heat: Latent heat is heat associated with a change in the moisture content of an air sample. The evaporation of 1 lb of water provides a cooling effect of about 1050 Btu at the surface where the evaporation occurred and adds an equal quantity of latent heat to the air. Usually expressed in Btu, but may be equated to a quantity of water.

Enthalpy: A measure of the *total heat* contained in moist air considering both sensible heat and latent heat. Abbreviated H with units of Btu/lb.

Specific volume: The volume occupied by 1 lb of air; the inverse of density, measured in ft^3/lb.

Dewpoint temperature: The temperature at which water vapor begins to condense from moist air. As the air temperature is reduced, its relative humidity increases and finally reaches 100%; that temperature is the dewpoint temperature. Expressed in degrees F.

Psychrometric Chart

In applying psychrometrics, a graphic representation of the properties of moist air, called the psychrometric chart, is frequently used (Fig. 3.1). Developed by Dr. Willis Carrier, it is simpler to understand than equations and far more convenient to use. It is simply a plot of the properties of moist air at various temperatures and humidity levels, including dry-bulb temperature, wet-bulb temperature, relative humidity, dewpoint temperature, specific volume, and humidity ratio. The chart is useful both in determining moist air properties at specific conditions and in examining cooling processes. Although it initally appears complex, the psychrometric chart is actually quite simple to understand and use.

The psychrometric chart is fundamentally a plot of the moisture-holding capacity of air against the dry-bulb temperature. Dry-bulb temperature increases from left to right on the chart, and moisture content increases from bottom to top. A scale for dry-bulb temperature forms the lower edge of the chart. A scale for absolute moisture content, or humidity ratio, forms the right edge (Figs. 3.2 and 3.3). Lines describing constant humidity ratio run horizontally. The humidity ratio is a direct measure of the actual amount of water in the air. It is defined as the mass of water per pound of dry air. On the Carrier chart, humidity ratio is presented in both grains of water per pound of dry air and pounds of water per pound of dry air. One pound is equal to 7000 grains.

Other lines represent relative humidity, enthalpy, wet-bulb temperature, specific volume, and dewpoint temperature. Each of these lines on the chart for a particular property represent points where that property is the same. For example, any point along the vertical line labeled 70°F represents air with a dry-bulb temperature of 70°F.

Air conditions are commonly described by the dry-bulb temperature and the relative humidity. If the dry-bulb temperature and the relative humidity (or any other pair of properties) are known, the point on the chart representing the air conditions is completely defined, and all other properties may be found. Dry-bulb temperature is simply the temperature of the air as measured with a conventional thermometer—the temperature that the weather service reports and that thermostats respond to. It is the primary determinant of human comfort.

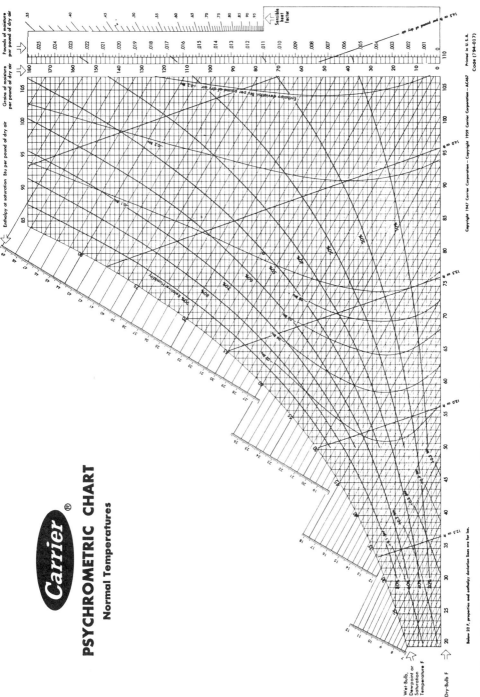

PSYCHROMETRIC CHART
Normal Temperatures

Carrier®

Figure 3.1. Carrier psychrometric chart. (Reproduced Courtesy of Carrier Corporation. Copyright 1959 Carrier Corporation.)

Copyright 1947 Carrier Corporation — Copyright 1959 Carrier Corporation — ACA67   Printed in U.S.A.
Code (794-017)

39

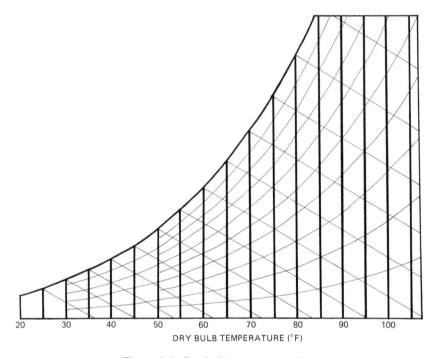

Figure 3.2. Dry bulb temperature lines.

Relative humidity, or RH, is a measure of how completely the air is saturated with water vapor. It does not indicate the absolute amount of water in the air, but only the fraction of the air's capacity to hold moisture that has been utilized. When air is completely saturated with moisture, the humidity is 100%—the ability of the air to hold moisture is 100% utilized. A relative humidity of 60% indicates that the air holds only 60% as much moisture as it might at its present temperature.

On the psychrometric chart, the curved line forming the upper edge of the chart represents 100% relative humidity, or saturation. This line is essentially a plot of the maximum amount of moisture that the air can hold at the temperatures indicated along the bottom of the chart. Notice that the moisture capacity of the air increases as the temperature increases (to the right on the chart). The ability of air to hold dissolved water vapor is a function of its temperature. Just as it is easier to dissolve sugar in hot tea than in iced tea, warm air can hold more moisture than cool air. If the air inside a building is cooled without removing moisture, its relative humidity will increase, while the absolute amount of water vapor contained in it will remain constant. RH does not describe the actual amount of water vapor in moist air, but only the fraction of the maximum possible amount at a specific temperature.

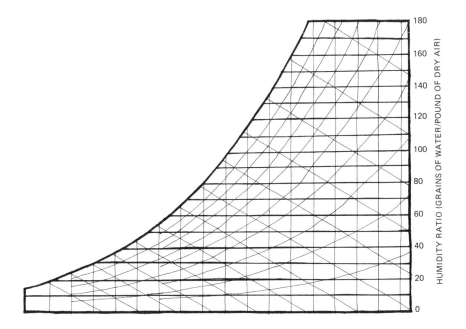

Figure 3.3. Humidity ratio lines.

For example, consider the change in relative humidity that occurs as air at 80°F and 70% RH is heated or cooled. At 90°F, the air can hold more moisture, and the relative humidity has decreased to almost 50%. As the air is cooled, its ability to hold moisture decreases, and the relative humidity increases, reaching 100% at about 69°F. At that point the air is fully saturated with moisture.

The 0% RH line, representing completely dry air, is the horizontal line forming the bottom boundary of the chart. The other relative humidity lines resemble the 100% RH line and simply represent the fraction of the distance from the 0% RH line upward to the 100% RH line. As an example, consider air at 67°F and a humidity ratio of 30 grains/lb of dry air. If 100% saturated at 67°F, air could hold 100 grains of moisture/lb of dry air. With only 30 grains of moisture, our example air is only 30/100 or 30% saturated. Thus the 30% relative humidity line runs through this point (Fig. 3.4).

The saturation line is also used to find the dewpoint temperature of any moist air sample. The dewpoint is the temperature to which air must be cooled for condensation to begin. From any point on the chart read left along a constant moisture line to the saturation curve to find the dewpoint temperature. The dewpoint temperature alone is adequate to indicate the amount of water vapor in moist air.

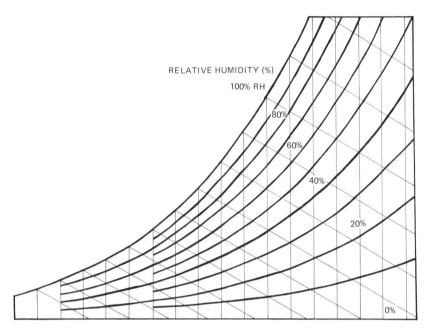

Figure 3.4. Relative humidity lines.

Wet-bulb temperature (wbt) is plotted in °F as a set of roughly parallel lines that slope downward from left to right across the chart. Wet-bulb temperature is the temperature that would be measured by a thermometer wrapped in a moist cloth. It indicates the lowest temperature that could be achieved by direct evaporation. As the moisture content of air decreases, the wet-bulb temperature also decreases, indicating that more evaporation could take place.

Wet-bulb and dewpoint temperature should not be confused; they represent entirely different quantities. The wet-bulb temperature is the lowest temperature that can be produced by the direct evaporation of water. The dewpoint temperature is the temperature to which air must be cooled to reach 100% RH and cause condensation to take place.

From a particular set of moist air conditions on the chart, 71°F and 70% RH for example, wet-bulb temperature is found by reading up and to the left along the sloped lines to the saturation curve and reading 64°F on the scale. Dewpoint temperature is found by reading to the left along the horizontal lines of constant moisture to the 100% RH line; for the example the dewpoint is 61°F.

Dewpoint temperature and wet-bulb temperature are equal only when the relative humidity of an air sample is 100%. No further evaporation is possible, and any further reduction in temperature will cause condensation.

The remaining information on the psychrometric chart includes humidity ratio, enthalpy, and specific volume. *Enthalpy* is a term used to describe the total amount of energy in a sample of air, both sensible and latent. The enthalpy of air at any combination of moisture content and dry-bulb temperature reflects the sum of the sensible heat and latent heat content of the air. Enthalpy increases as the temperature of moist air increases and as the moisture content increases. Moisture content is the more significant of the two factors, so that the enthalpy lines follow the wet-bulb temperature lines on the chart very closely. The enthalpy scale lies along the extreme left side of the chart and has sloping lines for 7 through 49 Btu/lb of dry air extending across the chart to the right. The enthalpy lines are exactly parallel to one another and should not be confused with the wet-bulb temperature lines, which are not parallel.

Another set of lines on the psychrometric chart represents the specific volume of the air in ft³/lb of dry air. The specific volume is simply the volume occupied by 1 lb of dry air. It is the inverse of the density. Specific volume lines are curved lines that run roughly vertically on the chart

$$\text{Specific volume} = 1/\text{density}$$

Any two of these properties are enough to fix the location of a point on the chart and fully describe all the other properties of a moist air sample. For example, plot the point representing air at 75°F and 70% RH. The point could also be located by the wet-bulb temperature, 68°F, and the dewpoint temperature, approximately 65°F, or the enthalpy, 32.4 Btu/lb, and the specific volume, approximately 13.75 ft³/lb, or any other combination of two points.

Using the Psychrometric Chart to Find the Properties of Moist Air

The use of the psychrometric chart to determine the properties of moist air is best illustrated by examples. Consider the air inside a building at a dry-bulb temperature of 80°F and a relative humidity of 60%. Locate the point on the chart describing that condition by finding the 80°F line on the scale at the bottom of the chart and following it upward to the 60% RH line. See Fig. 3.5. Values for other properties are then estimated from the charts; for comparison, more exact calculated values are included in parentheses (*ASHRAE Fundamentals*, p. 6.3). (A) The wet-bulb temperature line representing 70°F passes almost directly through the point plotted, so that the wet-bulb temperature is approximately 70°F. (B) The specific volume of the air must be interpolated, because the point lies between the lines for 13.5 ft³/lb of dry air and 14.0 ft³/lb. An approximate value of 13.9 ft³/lb of dry air (13.894) is obtained. (C) The humidity ratio, also interpolated, is 0.0132 (0.01340) lb of water/lb of dry air. (D) Finally, the enthalpy is estimated by moving from the plotted point parallel to a constant enthalpy line to the enthalpy scale. A value of 33.9 Btu/lb of dry air (33.91) is obtained.

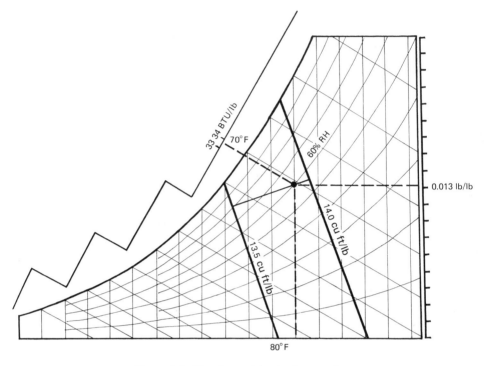

Figure 3.5. Psychrometric chart example.

Note that the humidity ratio estimated from the chart seems to differ notice-ably from the calculated values taken from the ASHRAE tables. There is a slight deviation in the values of humidity ratio and enthalpy plotted on the chart. The error is small and is usually safely ignored.

The mass of air and water vapor in a space can be easily estimated with information from the psychrometric chart.

Example: A 40- × 65-ft building with 8-ft ceilings contains air at 80°F and 60% RH. Find the mass of dry air and the mass of water vapor in the building.

$$\text{Mass of dry air} = \text{volume/specific volume}$$

$$= (40 \times 65 \times 8) \text{ ft}^3/13.9 \text{ ft}^3/\text{lb of dry air}$$

$$= 1496 \text{ lb}$$

$$\text{Mass of water vapor} = \text{humidity ratio} \times \text{mass of dry air}$$

$$= (0.0134 \text{ lb water/lb dry air}) \times 1496 \text{ lb dry air}$$

$$= 20.1 \text{ lb water}$$

Note that the sensible heat content is described completely by the dry-bulb temperature, and that latent heat is described completely by the dewpoint temperature. Sensible heat content changes only if the dry-bulb temperature changes, and latent heat content changes only if the dewpoint temperature changes.

Cooling Processes and the Use of the Psychrometric Chart

Any cooling process can be represented by lines on the psychrometric chart. The beginning and ending conditions are plotted on the chart, a line or set of lines is then drawn to describe the process, and a variety of information may be derived from the representation of the process on the chart. For example, the energy required to complete the process is easily estimated by considering the enthalpy change during the process.

Each of the most significant cooling processes will be discussed with an example process plotted on the psychrometric chart. Of course, every cooling process has a reciprocal heating process that is represented by the same line, but with the process moving in the opposite direction. These examples show perfect processes; in reality the losses and inefficiencies associated with real equipment will usually cause the results to be less desirable than shown here. In some cases, processes may overshoot the end point and return. The actual amount of energy consumed may be greater than indicated by the difference in enthalpy between the beginning and end points. A good example is the use of terminal reheat in commercial buildings. Air is cooled to a low temperature to remove humidity in a central unit and then heated back to a comfortable temperature as it is delivered to individual spaces. Precise control of conditions is possible, but energy costs are high.

Sensible Cooling

Sensible cooling involves only a reduction in the temperature of the moist air. The absolute amount of moisture is not changed, but relative humidity increases.

Example: Consider the process of cooling the air inside a 2000-ft^2 home with 8-ft flat ceilings from 90°F and 50% RH to 75°F without removing any moisture. The amount of heat that must be removed could be estimated individually for both the dry air and the moisture by the following equation

$$Q = m \times C_p \times T$$

where

Q = heat removed, Btu
m = mass of air, lb

C_p = specific heat of air, Btu/lb°F
(C_p = 0.24 Btu/lb°F for air)
(C_p = 1.00 Btu/lb°F for water)
T = change in temperature, °F

Two separate calculations would be required, one for the air and another for the water contained in the air.

Alternatively, the psychrometric chart may be used to represent the process and the energy requirement estimated by a single calculation using the change in enthalpy. The initial and final air conditions are plotted on the chart, and the enthalpy at each point is estimated. The process is represented as a straight line between the initial and final points. As there is no dehumidification, the humidity ratio is constant at about 0.0153 lb/lb of dry air (107 grains), and the process is a horizontal line.

The total heat removed is

$$Q = (h_i - h_f) \times m$$

where

Q = heat removed, Btu
h_i = initial enthalpy of moist air, Btu/lb dry air
h_f = final enthalpy of moist air, Btu/lb dry air
m = mass of air, lb dry air

The initial and final enthalpy values are read directly from the chart as 38.6 and 34.8 Btu/lb dry air, respectively (Fig. 3.6). The mass of dry air in the house is equal to the volume of the house divided by the initial specific volume of the air, or

$$(2000 \text{ ft}^2 \times 8 \text{ ft})/14.2 \text{ ft}^3/\text{lb} = 1130 \text{ lb}$$

The heat removed is

$$Q = (38.6 - 34.8) \text{ Btu/lb dry air} \times 1130 \text{ lb dry air}$$
$$= 4290 \text{ Btu}$$

Though no moisture is added or removed in a sensible cooling process, the relative humidity changes. In this example the cooling process leaves air at 75°F and 83% relative humidity.

Dehumidification, or Latent Cooling

A latent cooling, or dehumidification, process involves only a reduction in the amount of water vapor dissolved in the air. Real dehumidification processes also involve sensible cooling or heating. But a theoretically perfect latent cool-

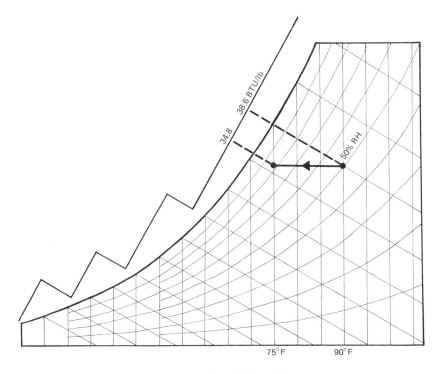

Figure 3.6. Sensible cooling.

ing or dehumidification process would take place with no change in the dry-bulb temperature of the moist air mixture, so it is represented by a vertical line on the psychrometric chart (Fig. 3.7). Again, the energy required for the process may be determined by the change in enthalpy times the mass of air.

Example: The volume of air in the house from the previous example, 16,000 ft³, is to be dehumidified from 75°F and 80% RH to 75°F and 40% RH. Find the energy required.

The mass of dry air in the house at 75°F and 80% RH is 16,000 ft³/13.8 ft³/lb = 1160 lb. The latent heat removed in the dehumidification process is

$$Q = (34.4 - 26.2) \text{ Btu/lb} \times 1160 \text{ lb}$$
$$= 9510 \text{ Btu}$$

Evaporative Cooling

Evaporative cooling takes place when water changes from a liquid to a vapor; an often-used example is the cooling effect felt when your moistened hand is waved in the air. About 1050 Btu of heat is absorbed by each pound of water

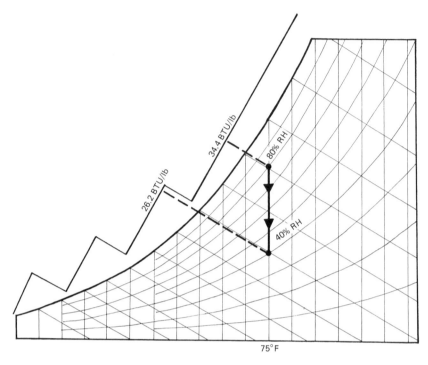

Figure 3.7. Perfect latent cooling or dehumidification.

that evaporates. The sensible heat in the air decreases, and the latent heat increases, leaving the total heat or enthalpy of the air unchanged. In evaporative cooling processes, the point on the chart describing the condition of the moist air moves up and to the left along or parallel to a constant enthalpy line. The amount of moisture in the air increases and the RH increases, while the dry-bulb temperature decreases. The latent heat added is exactly equal to the sensible heat removed.

Evaporative cooling can be effective for comfort cooling if the outdoor air conditions are appropriate. Consider the average July air conditions in Atlanta and Albuquerque as examples (Table 3.1).

For the Atlanta conditions, the wet-bulb temperature is approximately 71°F,

Table 3.1. Daily Average Weather Conditions, July.

	Dry-Bulb Temperature, °F	RH, %
Atlanta	77	75
Albuquerque	75	50

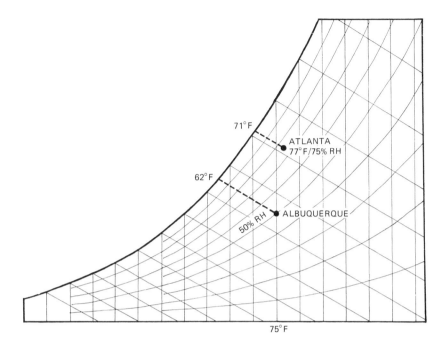

Figure 3.8. Psychrometric plot of July average weather conditions for Atlanta and Albuquerque.

indicating conditions near the upper limit of the normal comfort range and a limited potential for evaporative cooling. In Albuquerque, however, the average conditions are much more comfortable and offer a much greater opportunity for evaporative cooling, with a wet-bulb temperature of 62°F (Fig. 3.8).

Further information on evaporative cooling is contained in Chapter 17.

Dehumidification

Dehumidification is not a cooling process; it is actually the exact opposite of evaporative cooling and could be called *condensation heating.* A reduction in latent heat is exchanged for an increase in sensible heat. As moisture condenses it gives up the sensible heat associated with its phase change, about 1050 Btu for each pound of moisture. As dehumidification proceeds, the latent heat content of the air decreases, but the sensible heat content increases. In an ideal dehumidification process, the sum of the latent and sensible heat in the air remains constant. Such a process is said to be *adiabatic;* enthalpy is constant throughout the process; there is no change in total energy.

Air may be dehumidified either by a mechanical cooling system or by chemical means. Chemicals that can be used to dehumidify are called *desiccants*. They remove water from the air either by a chemical reaction or by causing it to condense on their sufaces. Mechanical dehumidification occurs in any refrigeration system when air is cooled below its dewpoint temperature. Although the actual processes are different, the end result is essentially the same. Neither process is actually a perfect constant enthalpy (adiabatic) process; with real equipment additional sensible heat is added to the air. In the case of chemical dehumidification, the chemical reaction by the desiccant releases more sensible heat than the amount generated by the change in phase of the water. With a refrigerant system, there is always additional sensible heat added from the operation of fans and the compressor.

Example: The air inside a building is to be dehumidified from 80% RH to 50% RH. The initial temperature is 75°F. Find the final temperature of the air. Assume adiabatic dehumidification; that is, no additional heat is added to the process other than the heat of condensation from the moisture.

In adiabatic dehumidification, the enthalpy of the air remains constant, and the process is represented by a straight line, identical to the process lines for evaporative cooling.

Plot the initial point on the psychrometric chart (Fig. 3.9). Any dehumidifi-

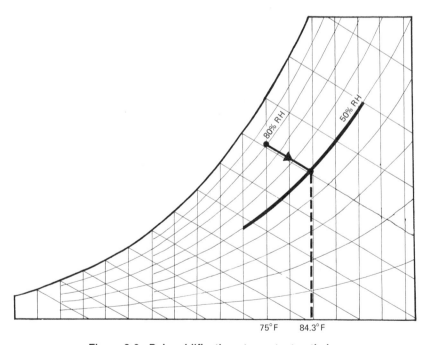

Figure 3.9. Dehumidification at constant enthalpy.

cation process will occur along a sloped line of constant enthalpy through this point. The final condition is the point where that line crosses the 50% RH line. The dry-bulb temperature at that point is 84.3°F. Obviously, dehumidification alone is not effective for comfort conditioning; in most cases sensible cooling is also required to produce comfortable conditions.

Dehumidification by Cooling below Dewpoint

Air conditioners and mechanical dehumidifiers remove latent heat by cooling moist air to a temperature below its dewpoint in the evaporator. When moist air passes over the evaporator surface (at about 55°F), it is cooled to its dewpoint and then cooled further along the saturation line (100% RH). As this occurs, both sensible and latent cooling are done. In a real machine, some air passes through the evaporator and receives only sensible cooling. The net result is a mixture of low-temperature air leaving the evaporator with low moisture content but high relative humidity. In most small air conditioning systems this air normally has a temperature of 57 to 60°F and a relative humidity of about 90%. The air from the evaporator then mixes with room air to provide the desired conditions.

Combined Sensible and Latent Cooling

Most cooling processes done by mechanical refrigeration cooling systems like air conditioners and heat pumps produce both sensible and latent cooling. Combined sensible and latent cooling processes appear on the psychrometric chart as sloped lines between the initial and final air conditions (Fig. 3.10).

Example: The air leaking into a building is cooled from the outdoor conditions of 90°F and 82% RH to the indoor conditions of 70°F and 50% RH by the air conditioner. If 100 lb of air enters each hour, what is the cooling load? How is the load divided between sensible and latent cooling?

The two air conditions are plotted on the psychrometric chart and the total cooling load is found as

$$Q = (h_i - h_f) \times m$$
$$= (49.4 - 25.4) \text{ Btu/lb} \times 100 \text{ lb/h}$$
$$= 2400 \text{ Btu/h}$$

The sensible portion of the load is represented by the horizontal length of the process line and the latent portion by the vertical length. The two components may be found by scaling the lengths of the two sides of the triangle shown on the chart or by reading the enthalpy values associated with the two sides.

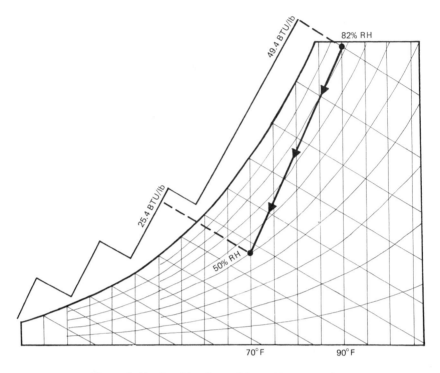

Figure 3.10. Combined sensible and latent cooling.

The latent load is:

$$Q_{latent} = \text{change in enthalpy due to latent cooling} \times m$$
$$= (49.4 - 30.4) \text{ Btu/lb} \times 100 \text{ lb/h}$$
$$= 1900 \text{ Btu/h}$$

The sensible load is:

$$Q_{sensible} = \text{change in enthalpy due to sensible cooling} \times m$$
$$= (30.4 - 25.4) \text{ Btu/lb} \times 100 \text{ lb/h}$$
$$= 500 \text{ Btu/h}$$

The cooling load is $(500/2400) \times 100\% = 24\%$ sensible and 76% latent. Another method of arriving at this split is shown later.

The room sensible heat fraction, or RSHF, is defined as the fraction of the total cooling load in a space that is made up of sensible heat gains. The RSHF of residential cooling loads is usually 60 to 85%. Commercial office buildings tend to have higher RSHFs as a result of the greater internal sensible heat gains from lights and equipment. Restaurants have lower RSHFs from the addition of moisture by cooking and large numbers of people.

In the example above, the sensible fraction of the infiltration cooling load was somewhat lower. Solar heat gains and conduction gains are 100% sensible heat gains and average the total cooling load in buildings up to a higher value.

A similar term, the sensible heat ratio, or SHR, is used to describe the cooling capacity of air conditioning equipment. Most systems have SHRs of 70 to 80%, indicating that 70 to 80% of their total cooling output is sensible cooling and 20 to 30% is latent cooling.

Air Mixtures

The psychrometric chart may also be used to determine the effects of mixing two volumes of air. First, plot the points representing the initial conditions of the two air volumes. Any mixture of the two air volumes must be represented by a point on a line drawn between these two points. The mixture point will lie closest to the point that represents the air volume with the greater mass. The actual location is determined by either measuring an appropriate distance along the line with a scale or by using a ratio of the dry-bulb temperatures.

Example: A room is cooled to 70°F dry-bulb and 50% RH, and the outdoor conditions are 90°F dry-bulb and 85°F wet-bulb. A window is opened for several minutes, allowing outdoor air to enter, so that the air inside the room contains $\frac{2}{3}$ indoor air and $\frac{1}{3}$ outdoor air. What are the temperature and RH of the mixed air?

Plot the two points on the psychrometric chart and draw a line connecting them (Fig. 3.11). Because indoor air makes up the majority of the mixture, the mixture point will lie closest to the room air point.

The outdoor air constitutes $\frac{1}{3}$ of the mixture, so the mixture point will lie $\frac{1}{3}$ of the distance to the outdoor point along the line. A scale may be used to find the point or it may be determined by taking a ratio of the two air temperatures

$$\text{Mixture temperatures} = \tfrac{2}{3}(\text{indoor dbt}) + \tfrac{1}{3}(\text{outdoor dbt})$$

$$= \tfrac{2}{3}(70°F) + \tfrac{1}{3}(90°F)$$

$$= 76.7°F$$

The mixture air dry-bulb temperature is then plotted on the line, and the RH is read directly as 66%.

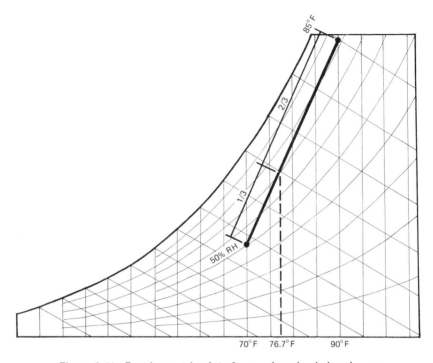

Figure 3.11. Psychrometric plot of example, mixed air volumes.

Other Uses of the Psychrometric Chart

The psychrometric chart may also be used for a variety of purposes in evaluating cooling concepts and cooling needs. A few examples are provided.

Example: An earth cooling tube is used to cool outdoor air at 85°F and 70% RH for use in a house at 75°F and 60% RH. If the air can be cooled to within 5°F of the tube surface temperature, how low must the tube temperature be for any dehumidification to occur? For the air to be dehumidified to the point that it would not increase the amount of moisture in the house?

Plot the outside air condition on the chart. The dewpoint temperature of the air is read as 74°F by moving horizontally left to the 100% RH line. Because the air moving through the tube is cooled only to within 5°F of the tube wall temperature, the tube wall temperature must be (74 − 5)°F, or 69°F. At higher temperatures no dehumidification will occur.

At 75°F and 60% RH, the indoor air contains about 78 grains of moisture per pound of dry air. For outdoor air to be dehumidified to the point that it would not add moisture, it must be chilled to its dewpoint temperature and then further cooled at 100% RH until its moisture content reaches 78 grains/lb.

Reading along the saturation line to the point where the moisture content is 78 grain/lb of dry air, the air must be cooled to about 60°F, requiring a tube surface temperature of 55°F. At higher temperatures, moisture would be added to the house.

Example: The air conditioning system in a building has been turned off, allowing the indoor conditions to stabilize at 85°F and 60% RH. Would it be advantageous to ventilate the building with night air at 70°F and 90% RH?

Plot the building air condition and the outdoor air condition. Because both the temperature and the moisture content of the outdoor air are significantly lower than the temperature and moisture content of the indoor air, it would definitely be advantageous to ventilate the building.

Example: The air inside a basement is at 75°F and 70% RH. How cold may an uninsulated water supply pipe be without sweating?

Condensation will occur when the pipe surface is cooled to the dewpoint temperature. From the psychrometric chart, the dewpoint temperature at 75°F and 70% RH is approximately 64.5°F.

Air Conditioning Supply Air Calculations

The psychrometric chart may be put to good use in calculating the required air conditioning supply air conditions for cooling a building. Even if you will not be conducting such calculations for design purposes, it is useful to understand them to gain insight into the effects of other building design and operating decisions.

The air conditioning process will be illustrated by an example.

Example: A building is operating with interior conditions of 75°F and 50% RH while outdoor conditions are 90°F and 70% RH. The heat gain to the building includes a sensible load of 35,000 Btu/h and a latent load of 15,000 Btu/h.

In commercial buildings the air that is cooled by the air conditioning coil (the return air) is normally a mixture of air from the building interior and outdoor air. The amount of outdoor air required is determined by the building type, the number of occupants, and such other factors as the presence of smokers. In residences and smaller buildings, the fresh air requirements are adequately met by air leakage into the building, and no outside air is mixed with the return air.

The indoor and outdoor air conditions are plotted on the psychrometric chart in Fig. 3.12 as points *A* and *B*. The return air conditions are determined by the relative amounts of indoor and outdoor air in the mixture. In the example, if the mixture is $\frac{2}{3}$ indoor air and $\frac{1}{3}$ outdoor air, the dry-bulb temperature of the mixture is 80°F, point *C*.

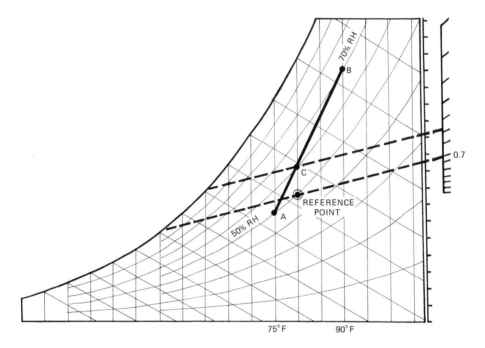

Figure 3.12. Psychrometric plot of a typical air-conditioning system.

Using the method described earlier, we find the cooling load on the building to be 70% sensible and 30% latent; its sensible heat fraction, or RSHF, is 0.70, calculated as

$$\text{RSHF} = \frac{\text{sensible load}}{\text{total load}} = \frac{35,000 \text{ Btu/h}}{35,000 + 15,000 \text{ Btu/h}} = 0.70$$

A line of constant RSHF may be drawn on the chart with the aid of the sensible heat ratio scale along its right and upper edges. The scale indicates sensible heat ratio values of 0.02 to 1.00 and is used in conjunction with the reference point located near the center of the chart at 78°F and 50% RH. A constant RSHF line may be drawn by connecting the reference point and the appropriate point on the scale. Any line on the chart that is parallel to the line will have the same constant sensible heat fraction.

The 0.70 RSHF reference line is drawn between the reference point and the 0.70 value on the sensible heat ratio scale. A line drawn parallel to this line and through the return air point represents the air conditioning process line. The process line in this example is also a line of 0.70 RSHF.

The RSHF line describes how the conditions inside the building will change as the cooling load acts on it. In this example the increase in dry-bulb temperature and moisture content in the example reflect a load that is 70% sensible and 30% latent. Because air mixtures are described by a line connecting the two points, the point describing the cool air delivered by the cooling system must lie on the RSHF line to the left of the room conditions.

As the return air passes through the cooling coil, its dry-bulb temperature and moisture content are both reduced. Because it is necessary to cool a portion of the air to saturation conditions to cause condensation of moisture, the RH of the air from the coil (point D) is quite high, usually about 90%. A portion of the return air is cooled to saturation by the coil, a portion is cooled only to a temperature above the saturation temperature, and a portion usually bypasses the cooling coil. The path from C to D is the average of the actual paths.

To properly meet the cooling load on the building, the point representing the conditioned air must lie on the RSHF line. The 90% RH curve crosses the RSHF line at 65°F dry-bulb. Assuming that the conditioned air from the coil is at 90% RH, the dry-bulb temperature should be 65°F. Air at these conditions may be mixed with the return air being drawn from the space to offset the building cooling load with the proper proportion of sensible and latent cooling and provide room air at the desired conditions.

4

THERMAL COMFORT

A building that does not provide comfortable interior conditions for the occupants cannot be considered a successful building. Unfortunately, the energy consumption of mechanical heating and cooling systems varies directly with the factors that control comfort. In general, stricter requirements for comfort lead to higher energy costs.

Human comfort occurs when the heat flows in the human thermal system are balanced and the internal body temperature is within a narrow range near 98.6°F. The body gains or loses heat through the skin by conduction, convection, and radiation with the air and the objects around it (Fig. 4.1). Heat is produced internally at a rate of about 360 btu/h when one is sitting quietly. Other modes of heat loss include evaporation of moisture from the skin and evaporation of moisture into exhaled air. Depending on the temperature of the air, respiration can also account for sensible heat gains or losses, as air moves in and out of the interior of the body. If heat is absorbed and produced substantially faster than it is lost, body temperature will rise, and we will feel uncomfortably hot. Conversely, if the rate of heat loss exceeds the rate of heat gain and production, we begin to feel cool.

The human body also has an intricate system of unconscious mechanisms that help balance the human thermal system at a comfortable temperature without conscious effort. When heat losses rise and body temperature begins to fall, the body compensates by increasing the rate of heat production through increases in physical activity, even shivering if necessary. To conserve heat, blood flow to the extremities is reduced. Fingers, toes, hands, and feet all have relatively large surface areas for heat loss and are not as essential to the body's survival as the internal organs. Cold, numb fingers and toes are a sure sign that the system has become unbalanced and heat losses are high. Goosebumps are a vestigial response to cold weather, one that originally fluffed the hair on the body to increase its insulation qualities.

When the rate of heat gain and internal heat production exceeds the rate of heat loss, the body calls on a different set of responses. Perspiration is produced

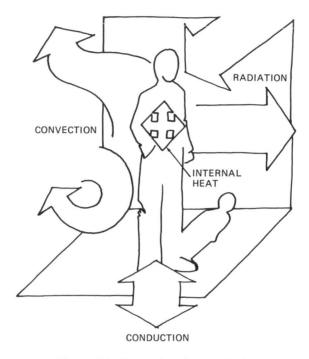

Figure 4.1. Human heat loss and gain.

to take advantage of evaporative cooling at the surface of the skin. To reject more heat from the body, additional blood flow is directed to the skin surface, resulting in higher skin temperature, increased heat losses, and the red, flushed appearance of an overheated person. When overheated, we tend to feel lethargic and automatically reduce our activity level and consequently, the rate of internal heat production.

The human thermal balance is affected by both environmental factors, such as air temperature, and personal factors, activity level and clothing. Any factor that affects heat transfer to or from the body or the rate of internal heat production has an effect on physical comfort. The major environmental determinants of comfort are air temperature, relative humidity, air motion, and mean radiant temperature (MRT). Any combination of these factors that balances the body's thermal system within the proper temperature range produces human comfort. For instance, increases in air temperature can be offset by an increase in air motion or a decrease in relative humidity or mean radiant temperature. Other factors that also influence comfort are solar radiation, activity level, clothing, and such psychological factors as light level and color.

Table 4.1. Clo Values of Typical Clothing (Ref. 4.1).

Men		Women	
T shirt	0.09	Bra & panties	0.05
Briefs	0.05	Half slip	0.13
Shirt, long sleeve	0.22	Blouse, light	0.20
with tie		Blouse, heavy	0.29
Shirt, short sleeve	0.14	Dress, light	0.22
with tie		Dress, heavy	0.70
Trousers, light	0.26	Skirt, light	0.10
Trousers, heavy	0.32	Skirt, heavy	0.22
Jacket, light	0.22	Jacket, light	0.17
Jacket, heavy	0.49	Jacket, heavy	0.37
Shoes, oxfords	0.04	Shoes, pumps	0.04

(Adapted with permission from *ASHRAE Standard 55-1981.*)

The effects of clothing and activity level are measured by two terms developed by ASHRAE, the *clo* and the *met*. The clo is a measure of the insulating characteristics of clothing. One clo is equal to 0.88 ft^2 h°F/Btu or an *R*-value of 0.88. The higher the clo value, the higher the insulating effect of the clothing and the higher the tolerance of the wearer to cold temperatures. Clo values for typical clothing are shown in Table 4.1.

The effect of clothing on the air temperature necessary for comfort is shown in Fig. 4.2, taken from ASHRAE Standard 55-1981. ''Thermal Environmental Conditions for Human Occupancy.'' Where clothing styles are flexible and the clo value of the occupants' clothing is reduced, cooling thermostats can be set up significantly. For instance, a reduction of clo value from 0.75 to 0.5 allows an increase in air temperature from 73 to 76°F.

The met is a measure of the rate of heat production by the body, the metabolic rate. One met is defined as 18.4 Btu/ft^2 h, roughly equal to the rate of heat production of a seated person at rest. For the average person, with a surface area of about 19 ft^2, this is equal to a total heat production of approximately 360 Btu/h. The met values corresponding to several activities are listed in Table 4.2.

OLGYAY BIOCLIMATIC CHART

Several methods of quantifying the effect on comfort of various combinations of conditions have been devised. One of the simplest and most useful in visualizing the problem is the bioclimatic comfort charts developed by Victor Olgyay.

The Olgyay bioclimatic chart (Ref. 4.2) provides a plot of the five major comfort factors and describes the set of combinations of conditions that produce

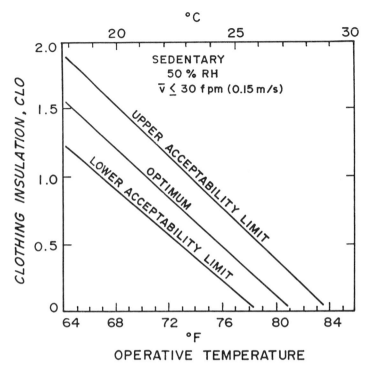

Figure 4.2. Effect of clothing on air temperature necessary for comfort. (Reprinted with permission from *ASHRAE Standard 55-1981*.)

comfort for the "average" person with light clothing. The two most significant factors are air temperature and relative humidity, plotted on the vertical and horizontal axes, respectively. The subject is assumed to be in the shade and air motion is less than 20 ft/min. The oblong shaded area in the center of Fig. 4.3 encloses the combinations of temperature and humidity that would produce

Table 4.2. Met Values for Typical Activities (Ref 4.1).

Activity	Metabolic Rate, Mets
Reclining	0.8
Seated, quiet	1.0
Sedentary activity (office, residence, school)	1.2
Standing, relaxed	1.2
Light activity, standing	1.6
Medium activity, standing	2.0
High activity	3.0

(Adapted with permission from *ASHRAE Standard 55-1981*.)

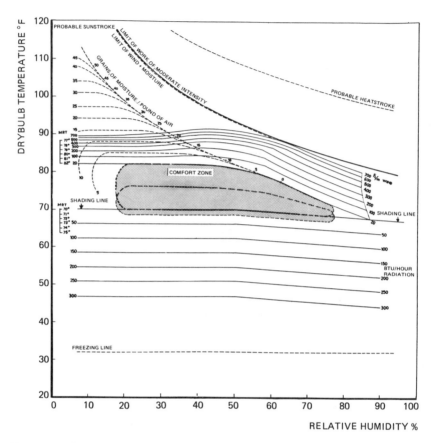

Figure 4.3. Olgyay bioclimatic chart. (Source: *Climatic Database*, Tennessee Valley Authority Solar Outreach and Technology Group.) Typical monthly climatic conditions from Jackson, MS are plotted.

comfort during the summer. For example, with relative humidity at 60%, comfort can be provided by air temperatures from 70 to 80°F. If the humidity climbs to 70%, temperature must be limited to 75°F to provide comfort.

The oblong area enclosed by the dashed line is the comfort zone for the winter. The body acclimates itself somewhat to the climate conditions, and differences in clothing from winter to summer are significant. The cooling effects of air motion are described by the series of lines above the upper boundary of the comfort zone and parallel to it. They show the possible upward extension of the comfort zone as a result of increased air motion. Consider the possible comfort points with humidity constant at 70% RH; the maximum temperature for comfort is 75°F. If a fan is used to provide air motion of 300 ft/min (fpm), comfort is possible at 81°F. Further increases in air motion can provide comfort at temperatures of up to 88°F. Some inconvenience begins to occur at 160 fpm, when papers and other very light objects begin to be disturbed. The great value of ceiling fans, whole-house fans, and natural ventilation is apparent from the chart.

Below the comfort zone are a number of lines that indicate the effect of solar radiation on comfort. The lines show the downward displacement of the winter comfort zone as a result of radiation heat gain by the body. As the body is exposed to higher levels of solar radiation, lower temperatures are required (allowable, from a heating viewpoint) to maintain comfort. An air temperature of 60°F is comfortable if solar radiation of approximately 130 Btu/h is provided. The solar radiation lines also demonstrate the critical need for shading in minimizing the effects of the sun during summer.

The fifth factor addressed by the bioclimatic chart is mean radiant temperature (MRT). The two small scales along the air temperature scale above and below the comfort zone are the MRT scales. Using the upper scale as an example, note that the lower end is set at 82°F, corresponding to an air temperature of 82°F. For increased air temperatures, the MRT scale shows the mean radiant temperature that must be provided to maintain comfort. With air temperature at 85°F, a mean radiant temperature of 79°F will produce comfort.

ASHRAE COMFORT STANDARDS

The American Society of Heating, Refrigerating and Air-Conditioning Engineers, ASHRAE, has developed a standard of human comfort that is used in designing HVAC equipment for buildings (Fig. 4.4). Standard 55-81, "Thermal Environmental Conditions for Human Occupancy," Ref. 4.1, discusses the major factors that affect comfort and specifies the limits of conditions acceptable for use in system design. It has been adopted by several governmental and institutional groups as the standard for building design and operation. Standard 55-81 is intended to describe conditions that will be acceptable to at least 80% of the building occupants. The comfort chart for Standard 55-81 also defines two comfort zones, a winter zone and a summer zone. It is assumed that typical winter and summer clothing are worn and that light activity, typical of an office or residence, is in progress. Air motion is limited to 30 fpm in winter and 50 fpm in summer.

To use and understand the chart, a new term is required, *operative temperature*. The operative temperature takes into account both the air temperature and the mean radiant temperature and weights them to arrive at a single temperature that describes both effects. By definition, the operative temperature is the temperature of a uniform enclosure that is a perfect radiator and absorber of radiant heat that would produce the same effects as the actual nonuniform

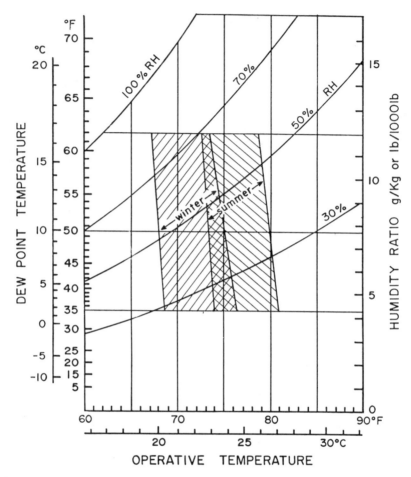

Figure 4.4. ASHRAE comfort chart. (Reprinted with permission from *ASHRAE Standard 55-1981*.)

environment. To simplify, for mean radiant temperatures less than 120°F and air motion of 80 fpm or less, the operative temperature is approximately the average of the dry-bulb air temperature and the mean radiant temperature. This average is also known as the *adjusted dry-bulb temperature*. A two-axis plot is used, with operative temperature on the horizontal axis and dewpoint temperature on the vertical axis. Relative humidity lines run diagonally across the plot. Any combination of conditions that lies inside the appropriate comfort zone, winter or summer, will produce comfort. The boundary of the summer comfort zone may be extended somewhat by increased air motion. Temperature may be increased by 1°F for each increase of 30 fpm in air motion, up to 160 fpm. The

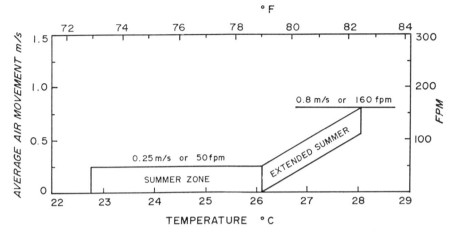

Figure 4.5. ASHRAE extended summer comfort zone. (Reprinted with permission from *ASHRAE Standard 55-1981*.)

ASHRAE summer comfort zone extended for air velocity effects is plotted in Fig. 4.5.

The analysis of air motion effects described above was based on very uniform airflow from a perforated ceiling. Ceiling fans and most other interior fans produce a more variable or turbulent type of flow that is apparently more effective in removing heat from the skin surface. Recent tests by the ASHRAE researchers have shown that the summer comfort zone can be expanded even further by the use of ceiling fans. The expanded zone, with comfort at temperatures of 85°F at 200 fpm air speeds, is superimposed on the ASHRAE extended summer zone in Fig. 4.5.

Table 4.3 summarizes the optimum and allowable temperatures for the 80% comfort satisfaction level. The people are assumed to be clothed in heavy slacks, long-sleeved shirt, and sweater in winter and light slacks and short-sleeved shirt in summer. The minimally clothed category is self-explanatory. Air motion is assumed to be less than or equal to 30 fpm, and humidity is 50% RH.

Table 4.3. Operative Temperatures for Thermal Acceptability.

Condition	Clo	Optimum Operative Temperature, °F	Operative Temperature Range for 80% Comfort, °F
Winter	0.9	71.0	68.0–74.5
Summer	0.5	76.0	73.0–79.0
Minimally clothed	0.05	81.0	79.0–84.0

(Adapted with permission from *ASHRAE Standard 55-1981*.)

As energy prices have risen, comfort standards have been relaxed somewhat. When operating a building for the highest possible energy efficiency, expanding the range of comfort conditions to be tolerated can allow significant savings. However, such modifications should be done with appropriate judgment; strong dissatisfaction with the comfort conditions in a building can lead to attempts to override the HVAC system controls, potentially resulting in performance problems or higher costs.

Comfort factors other than air temperatures can be used to advantage to reduce cooling energy consumption and costs. Solar radiation control and increased air speeds are the two most important.

5

COOLING LOADS AND COOLING LOAD REDUCTION

BUILDING ENERGY FLOW AND COOLING LOADS

Throughout the year, buildings, like other thermal systems, are subject to the constant flow of heat. Heat flows in and out across the boundary of the thermal system—into the building and out of the building. When natural heat flows do not maintain comfortable conditions inside the building, mechanical systems are relied upon to alter the net flow of heat and adjust the indoor conditions. A good understanding of what the various heat flows are, how to estimate their magnitude, and how to influence them is essential to designing buildings and mechanical systems that are both energy-efficient and comfortable.

Four major kinds of heat flows take place in buildings: (1) conduction through the building envelope, (2) air infiltration and ventilation, (3) solar heat gains, and (4) internal heat generation. Mechanical systems introduce a fifth type of heat flow into the system due to system inefficiencies, such as waste heat from fan motors and the leakage of conditioned air from ducts.

Conduction and infiltration and ventilation heat flows are directly related to the difference between the indoor temperature and humidity and the outdoor temperature and humidity. In a similar manner, moisture flow takes place according to the difference in the concentration of water vapor in the air inside and outside the building. The magnitude and direction of both the heat flow and the moisture flow are determined by the difference in temperature and the difference in vapor pressure, respectively. Higher differences, or gradients, mean higher heat and moisture flow rates.

Solar heat and internal heat generation always introduce heat into the building, regardless of the season. These gains are highly desirable in winter, but undesirable in summer. Obviously, manipulating the solar and internal heat gains to a building represents an opportunity to reduce the expense of purchased energy used by the mechanical system.

In winter, as the outdoor temperature drops, the conduction and infiltration and ventilation losses increase. The solar and internal heat gains are not directly related to the temperature differential. As the outdooor temperature falls, the losses from conduction and infiltration and ventilation eventually become exactly equal to the internal heat gains. This is the building's balance point. When the outdoor temperature is above the balance point, cooling will be required to maintain comfortable interior temperatures. As the temperature drops below the balance point, heating becomes necessary to maintain the interior temperature. The balance point for houses is usually between 50 and 65°F, though a commercial building, having greater internal heat gains and smaller relative surface areas for heat loss, may have a balance point of 35°F or lower. A calculated balance point figure, using an assumed level of internal heat gains, is a useful figure. For example, in a commercial building with significant internal heat gains, the balance point may be 50°F, so that cooling is required not only during the summer, but during the spring and fall as well. The heating season is drastically reduced and the cooling season lengthened, so that the conventional concept of heating and cooling loads and seasons may not be valid. In some cases, the internal heat gain is so high that it becomes desirable to reduce the insulation qualities of the building to take advantage of "free" cooling by increased conduction.

$$\text{Balance point} = T_{\text{inside}} - Q_{\text{int}}/OLC \ (°F)$$

where

T_{inside} = normal inside air temperature
Q_{int} = internal heat gain rate (Btu/h)
OLC = overall building loss coefficient (Btu/h per °F)
  = heat loss rate/design temperature differential

Both temperature heat gains (sensible heat gains) and humidity gains (latent heat gains) require the expenditure of energy to control them with a mechanical system. In residences, the total load is normally about 60 to 80% sensible and about 20 to 40% latent. The cooling strategies to be used in a building must recognize both these types of loads and the balance between them to provide comfort for the building occupants.

Cooling Load Estimates

Cooling load estimates are used to improve the building design, to design the mechanical system, to explore energy conservation and natural cooling alternatives, and to predict the energy consumption in the building. Several types of cooling loads are discussed: instantaneous loads, design loads, and seasonal loads. Estimating the cooling load on a building is not a straightforward matter. The actual rate of heat gain by a building is constantly changing, varying with the changes in weather conditions, solar radiation, and building use. This actual total rate of heat flow into the building at any given time is called the *instantaneous rate* of heat gain. But not all the heat that flows into a building contributes to the immediate cooling needs or cooling load. Only the portion of the heat gain that goes to the air inside the building is a cooling load. Thus the capacity of a mechanical cooling system does not need to be as large as the maximum instantaneous cooling load on the building.

For example, radiation from the sun passes through the air inside a building, is absorbed by the walls, floors, and furnishings, and is converted to heat. Only a portion of that heat then flows into the inside air; the balance is stored in the object that absorbed it. The fraction of the heat that goes to the air as a cooling load may be estimated with cooling load factors, or CLFs, from standard cooling load calculation methods. Cooling load factors that recognize this split between immediate heat loads and stored heat loads are applied to solar heat gains through glazing and to most internal heat gains. Infiltration and ventilation heat gains, latent internal heat gains, and most conduction gains go directly to the air in a building.

A set of assumed conditions, called the *design conditions*, is used to calculate a cooling load that is subsequently used to select the cooling capacity of the cooling system. These design conditions are based on the climate at the building site and on the design, construction, and function of the building. The resulting load is the design cooling load, expressed in Btu/h at the specified conditions.

In addition to providing information to size the mechanical system, the design cooling load represents a convenient means to judge the thermal success of the building design itself. Cooling load calculations can be used to evaluate the desirability of various building and equipment design alternatives, as well as the effects of changes in the building operations. Even in buildings that do not use mechanical cooling, the design load can be used as a performance benchmark.

Calculated loads are also used to judge the total cost and energy consumption of the mechanical system over the cooling season.

The balance of this chapter will deal with describing the various individual components of building loads and the factors that determine their magnitude. Fundamental methods and equations for estimating load components will be provided. Complete cooling load calculation methodologies are not included in this book.

The recommended load calculation methods are those published by the American Society of Heating, Refrigerating, and Air Conditioning Engineers, Inc., or those based on their research. (Ref. 5.1, 5.2, and 5.3) ASHRAE has developed two separate calculation methods: a commercial method and a simplified residential method. The commercial method provides a detailed procedure for calculating the individual components of building heat gain and allows the designer to account for a wide variety of individual factors that affect heat gains. The residential method is a simplified method that assumes that the building being analyzed is a small building with its heat gain pattern dominated by heat transfer through the building envelope and an operating pattern and design typical of residences. It is not as flexible as the commercial method, but is simpler to use and generally provides better figures for selecting residential mechanical cooling equipment.

Cooling Load Components

Each of the five load components is examined in further detail here. Common examples, fundamental equations for estimating their magnitude, and methods of reducing or ameliorating them are provided. To provide an understanding of the relative size of each component, two examples are provided. The first is the 1536-ft^2 residence described earlier. The standard version is used, with its front side facing south. The house, typical of many being built today, has the minimum insulating and weatherization features required by most codes.

The second example to be used is a 10,000-ft^2, two-story office building, also typical of current standard practice. It is described further in Table 5.1.

The cooling load components of both buildings are shown in Tables 5.2 and 5.3. Both buildings are assumed to be oriented with their long axes running northeast/southwest. The internal gain, infiltration, and occupant categories include both sensible and latent heat effects.

Conduction Loads

Conduction cooling loads are purely sensible loads that occur as a result of the difference between the outdoor and indoor air temperatures. Conduction heat

Table 5.1. Example Office Building Details.

Base dimensions	80 × 125 ft, 10,000 ft^2
Floor-to-floor height	10 ft
Ceiling height	8 ft
Ventilation rate	0.15 cfm/ft^2
Occupants	50
Roof/ceiling insulation	R18
Wall insulation	R10
Glazing	Clear glass/double
Equipment heat gain	7.5 kW

Table 5.2. Residential Cooling Load Components.

	Heat Gain, Btu/h	% of Total
Conduction, opaque surfaces	5410	27
Glazing heat gains, conduction and solar	8220	41
Internal gains	1200	6
Ventilation and infiltration gains	4150	21
Occupants	900	5
Total	19,880 Btu/h	100

Table 5.3. Commercial Office Building Cooling Load Components.

	Heat Gain, Btu/h	% of Total
Conduction, opaque surfaces	16,100	6
Glazing heat gains, conduction and solar	78,400	28
Internal gains	123,700	43
Ventilation and infiltration gains	38,800	14
Occupants	26,900	9
Total	283,900 Btu/h	100

transfer takes place through walls, ceilings, floors, doors, glazing, and any other building surfaces. Conduction cooling loads are increased by solar gains on the outside of the building that raise the external skin temperature and increase the temperature differential across the envelope.

Conduction loads are sensitive to three primary factors: the temperature difference, or delta T, across the building section; the insulating characteristics of the section; and the thermal capacitance of the building section. The delta T and the insulating characteristics determine the magnitude of the heat gain, and capacitance and conductivity determine the timing of the heat's arrival at the building interior. Estimating the magnitude of steady-state heat gains is a straightforward process (Fig. 5.1). A steady-state condition exists when the thermal system is in balance and changes in heat storage effects in the building section are small

$$Q = U \times A \times \Delta T$$

where

Q = steady-state heat gain, Btu/h
U = overall heat transmission coefficient, Btu/h ft^2 °F
A = area of building section, ft^2
delta T = temperature difference across the section °F

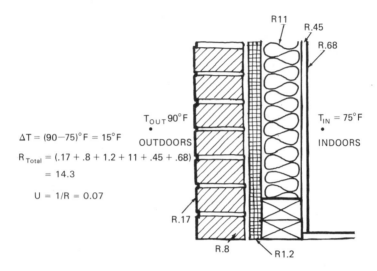

Figure 5.1. Conduction heat transfer through the walls of a building.

In almost all cases of actual building operation, steady-state conditions do not exist; solar heat gains and outdoor temperatures change rapidly. The amount of heat stored in the building envelope becomes significant and must be accounted for, particularly with heavy-weight masonry walls. Higher mass building sections absorb heat and slow the flow of heat to the building interior. In the ASHRAE residential cooling load calculations, the time lag, solar effects, and other factors are accounted for in an equivalent temperature difference, which is used in the conduction equation. The more complex commercial loads methods provide more detailed information for a wider variety of materials and factors.

In the energy-conserving example residence, conduction loads through the opaque portions of the building (walls, doors, and ceiling, but not glazing) account for 27% of the total load. In the office building example, they represent only about 6% of the total load. Individual conduction components for both examples are shown in Table 5.4.

In most residential cooling load calculations, conduction heat gain through glazing is included with solar heat gains in a single heat gain factor.

Controlling conduction heat gains involves:

- adding insulation
- reducing surface area and
- reducing the temperature of the exterior surface

In all but the most southern locations, the amount of insulation normally recommended for the heating season is adequate for the cooling season as well.

Table 5.4. Conduction Cooling Load Components.

	Residence		Commercial Building	
	Load, Btu/h	% of Total Conduction Load	Load, Btu/h	% of Total Conduction Load
Roof	2670	32	6,900	26
Walls	2360	28	6,300	23
Floor	0	0	0	0
Doors	390	5	2,000	7
Glazing	2890[a]	35	11,900	44
Total	8310 Btu/h	100%	27,100 Btu/h	100%

[a]Does not include solar heat gain.

Figure 5.2 provides a generalized recommendation for ceiling, wall, and floor insulation. Added insulation is subject to diminishing returns—as more insulation is added, less benefit is derived from each new increment. Figure 5.3 shows how the heat loss and heat gain through 100 ft^2 of wall decrease as insulation is added. Once the R value has been increased to about R20, further increases provide greatly reduced effects.

A more detailed set of recommendations is provided by the work of researchers at Los Alamos National Laboratories. Optimum insulation levels are calculated for 90 locations. These figures are applicable for residences and small commercial buildings having internal heat gain rates of 30 to 60 Btu/ft^2 per day or less. For each location, a conservation factor, CF, is obtained from the table see (p. 108) and substituted into simple equations to obtain the suggested insulation level for walls, floors, and ceilings. Two sets of conservation factors are given, one for "low" fuel costs and one for "high" fuel costs. Choose a practical insulation level that can be obtained with common materials and construction techniques within 20% of the recommended figure.

> R *Values*
> Walls: 14 × CF
> Basement and crawlspace floors: (16 × CF) − 8
> Slab floor perimeter insulation: (13 × CF) − 5
> Ceilings: 22 × CF

Example: For Lexington, Kentucky, the conservation factor assuming high fuel costs is 1.60.

> *Recommended* R *Values*
> Walls: 14 × 1.60 = 22.4
> Basement and crawlspace floors: (16 × 1.60) − 8 = 17.6
> Slab floor perimeter insulation: (13 × 1.60) − 5 = 15.8
> Ceilings: 22 × 1.60 = 35.2

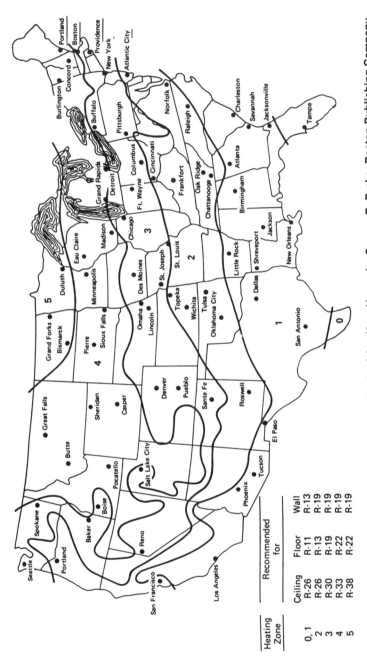

Heating Zone	Recommended for		
	Ceiling	Floor	Wall
0, 1	R-26	R-11	R-13
2	R-26	R-13	R-19
3	R-30	R-19	R-19
4	R-33	R-22	R-19
5	R-38	R-22	R-19

Figure 5.2. Insulation level recommendations. (*Weatherizing Your Home*, by George R. Drake, Reston Publishing Company, Inc., A Prentice-Hall Company.)

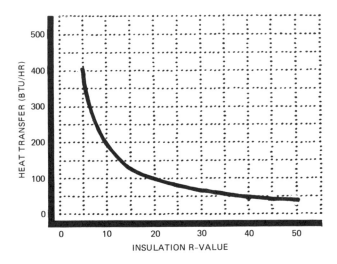

Figure 5.3. Diminishing Return on Insulation.

Infiltration and Ventilation

Infiltration and ventilation cooling loads are a result of the flow of warmer and more humid outdoor air into the building interior. They have both sensible and latent heat components. Outside air may be intentionally brought into the building to maintain internal air quality, especially in commercial buildings. And there is unintentional infiltration or uncontrolled air leakage due to door openings and flow through cracks and openings in the building envelope. In most residences, outdoor ventilating air is not required during periods of air conditioner operation, because infiltration provides enough fresh outdoor air for the occupants. Note that when internal heat and solar gains drive the building temperature above the outdoor temperature, infiltration and ventilation may act to reduce cooling loads.

When outdoor temperature and humidity conditions are acceptable, as they often are, ventilation provides an effective and economical method of cooling. Such opportunities must not be overlooked, particularly in residences. It should be possible to open the building for ventilation cooling when desired and also possible to seal it when mechanical cooling is employed or when heating becomes necessary. A key element of energy efficiency is *control* of infiltration and ventilation.

Infiltration is normally described quantitatively in terms of air changes per hour, or ACH. One air change occurs when a quantity of air equal to the volume of the building flows into the building. Of course, at the same time, the same volume of air must leak out of the building through other openings. In the example house with 1536 ft^2 of floor area and an 8-ft flat ceiling, an infiltration rate of 0.35 ACH would correspond to an air leakage rate of

$$1536 \text{ ft}^2 \times 8 \text{ ft} \times 0.35 \text{ ACH} = 4300 \text{ ft}^3/\text{h}$$
$$= 72 \text{ ft}^3/\text{min}$$

This flow rate corresponds to a typical residential bathroom vent fan running continuously. The rate of air infiltration in a building depends on many factors, and accurately estimating or measuring infiltration is extremely difficult. In load calculations, the infiltration rate is usually a guess at best.

The most significant factors contributing to air infiltration are building design, construction details and quality, temperature differential, wind, and the actions of the occupants. Building design and construction influence the character and number of openings available for leakage. Temperature difference and wind provide the forces that cause infiltration. Occupants increase infiltration by operating windows, doors, and exhaust fans. During the summer, infiltration rates in most air conditioned homes range from 0.25 ACH for well-sealed houses to 0.75 ACH for older, leaky houses. For residential cooling load calculations and system sizing, ASHRAE recommends a nominal design value of 0.5 ACH. A slightly lower value might be appropriate where careful infiltration control measures are taken. Summer infiltration rates are sometimes estimated as one-half the winter rate.

In commercial buildings, positive ventilation is usually necessary to provide enough fresh air to ensure adequate oxygen for the occupants and to remove carbon dioxide and odors. The number of people in a given building area is higher in commercial buildings, and the relative size of the exterior surfaces that allow air to leak into the building is smaller.

Until recently, ventilation air design practices have been rather antiquated, based on standards developed nearly 50 years ago when bathing habits and the lack of air conditioning called for higher ventilation rates. Ventilation design rates of 25 to 30 cubic feet per minute (cfm)/person have been the norm. ASHRAE standards (Ref. 4.1) now set the minimum level at 5 cfm/person for non-smoking general office areas and 20 cfm for areas where smoking is allowed. Higher levels are specified for restrooms and other odor-producing areas. Designers should be extremely careful to avoid specifying excessive ventilation air quantities when designing systems. If possible, the actual flow through the completed system should be checked and fine-tuned. Reducing excess infiltration and ventilation is usually the simplest and least costly conservation measure.

The cooling load that results from ventilation and infiltration includes both sensible and latent components. The magnitude of the total load, as well as the split between sensible load and latent load, depends on the difference between the indoor and outdoor levels of air temperature and humidity. The use of the psychrometric chart to estimate the cooling load effects of infiltration and ventilation was discussed in Chapter 3. Approximate alternative calculation methods are presented below.

Sensible heat gain in Btu/h from infiltration and ventilation is calculated with the following equation

$$Q_{sensible} = 60 \times 0.075 \times V \times (0.24 + 0.45 \times W/7000) \times \Delta T$$

where

  60 = min/h
0.075 = density of dry air, lb/ft^3
  V = rate of air infiltration or ventilation, ft^3/min
0.24 = specific heat of dry air, Btu/lb°F
0.45 = specific heat of water vapor, Btu/lb°F
  W = average humidity ratio for the two conditions, grains of water/lb of dry air
7000 = grains/lb
  ΔT = temperature difference between inside air and outside air, °F

For most air conditioning problems, W is approximately equal to 70 grains/lb, so that

$$Q_{sensible} = 1.080 \times V \times \Delta T$$

The latent gain in Btu/h is calculated by the following equation

$$Q_{latent} = 60 \times 0.075 \times 1076 \times V \times \Delta W/7000$$
$$= 0.692 \times V \times \Delta W$$

where

  60 = min/h
0.075 = density of dry air, lb/ft^3
1076 = energy content of water vapor in 50% RH air at 75°F minus the energy content of water at 50° F, Btu/lb
  V = rate of air infiltration or ventilation, ft^3/min
  ΔW = the difference in the humidity ratio of outdoor air and indoor air grains of water/lb of dry air
7000 = grains/lb

The 1076 term accounts for the difference in the energy content of moisture in the air at the interior conditions and moisture discharged from the system as condensate.

The effects of air infiltration and ventilation on design cooling loads are shown by Table 5.5. Indoor conditions of 75°F and 50% RH are assumed; outdoor

Table 5.5. Heat Gain Resulting From 100 cfm of Outdoor Air at 2-1/2% Design Conditions; Indoor Air Conditions are 75°F and 50% RH.

Location	% sensible	% latent	Total load, Btu/h
Albuquerque, N.M.	—[a]	—[a]	500
Atlanta, Ga.	44	56	4000
Boston, Mass.	46	54	2900
Denver, Colo.	—[a]	—[a]	−1000
Houston, Tex.	38	62	5600
Jacksonville, Fla.	38	62	5200
Kansas City, Mo.	57	43	4000
Knoxville, Tenn.	38	62	3600
New Orleans, La.	31	69	5600
Pittsburgh, Pa.	50	50	2900

[a]The outdoor air is hotter and drier than the indoor air. Ventilation and infiltration would remove moisture from the building, because the latent cooling effect exceeds the sensible heat gain.

conditions are the $2\frac{1}{2}$% design dry-bulb temperature with the mean coincident wet-bulb temperature. The split between sensible and latent load is also indicated. Values are calculated using the change in enthalpy method discussed in Chapter 3.

Time lag effects are not significant with infiltration and ventilation heat gains, because the heat gain occurs directly to the air inside the building.

For the energy-conserving example residence, an air infiltration rate of 0.35 ACH constitutes 21% of the total cooling load. Poor quality control during construction and lax operation can easily triple the load from infiltration. In the office building, ventilation of 1000 cfm accounts for 14% of the total load. Because the building is pressurized by the ventilation system, infiltration is essentially zero.

In typical homes, the small cracks and openings in the envelope combine to yield a total open area for infiltration of several square feet. Specific locations through which air leaks occur are shown in Fig. 5.4. For moisture and infiltration control, a 4- or 6-mil polyethylene vapor barrier should be installed on the inside of the insulation in all ceilings and walls. Vapor barriers are installed on the exterior side of the insulation only in extreme southern locations where heating loads are almost negligible. Contact a local builders association or building codes department if you have any doubts. It would be desirable to also have a polyethylene vapor barrier at the floors, but installation is difficult. To further reduce air leakage, an infiltration barrier, such as Dupont's Tyvek, may be installed on the exterior of the walls behind the exterior siding material. Such materials block air motion but allow moisture to pass.

The same guidelines used for minimizing heating energy consumption through

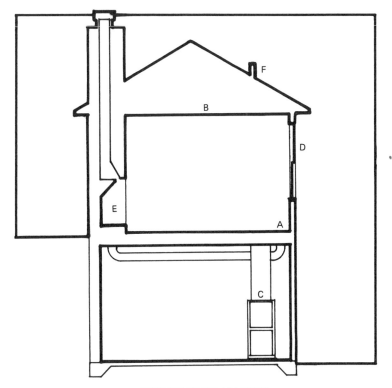

SOURCES OF AIR LEAKAGE

	COMPONENT	RANGE	AVERAGE
A	WALLS AND FLOORS	18–50%	35%
B	CEILING	3–30%	18%
C	MECHANICAL SYSTEM	3–28%	15%
D	WINDOWS AND DOORS	6–22%	15%
E	FIREPLACE	0–30%	12%
F	VENTS	2–12%	5%

Figure 5.4. Infiltration leak sources.

infiltration control apply to low-energy cooling. Careful caulking and sealing can greatly reduce air leakage; commercial sealing contractors can apply foam sealers (not urea formaldehyde foam insulation) to all the major leakage points for as little as $0.10 per ft^2 of floor area. Infiltration is most easily reduced during the construction of a building by appropriate detailing and careful quality control.

If contaminants exist in a building, drastically reduced air infiltration rates may lead to indoor air quality concerns; the smaller volume of airflow through the building cannot dilute indoor contaminants as well. Sources of contaminants include cigarette smoking; inadequately vented combustion appliances; and carpets, fabrics, and building materials that release formaldehyde. Information on how to avoid contaminant generation and what level of airflow is required to provide adequate dilution of contaminants is very limited. However, indoor air quality problems seem to be more the exception than the rule, even in well-sealed energy-conserving houses. If an air quality problem is identified, straightforward solutions are available to increase the flow of air into the building.

Further information on indoor air quality is available in the references. Commercial services that offer low-cost monitoring methods for formaldehyde and radon are also identified.

If an air quality problem does arise, it is always possible to increase the flow of fresh air into the building by opening a window or modifying the forced-air system. Another alternative is an air-to-air heat exchanger, discussed later.

Solar Loads

Radiant solar heat contributes to cooling loads both directly, by transmission through windows, skylights, and glazed doors; and indirectly by increasing the exterior surface temperature of walls and roofs. Solar gains are purely sensible loads, they contribute no moisture to the building.

During the summer, solar radiation transmission through windows can exceed 200 Btu/h per ft^2 of glazing. An old, but not recommended, rule of thumb for air conditioner system design suggests 1 ton (t) of capacity for every 500 ft^2 of building area, or 24 Btu/h ft^2. (One ton per 700 ft^2 is more appropriate for modern houses.) The solar gain on the outer surface of a single-story building's roof can be more than 200 Btu/h ft^2, an order of magnitude greater than the installed cooling capacity. Obviously, the sun is a powerful force to be considered. The difficulty in dealing with solar gain is increased by the fact that the heat gains are somewhat desirable for offsetting heating loads in winter. Once again, the best building solution calls for flexibility in the manner in which the building interacts with its environment.

Solar loads are most critical on the transparent or translucent portions of the building envelope—the windows, doors, and skylights. Normal clear glazing materials allow 50 to 90% of the solar radiation that strikes them to pass through to the building interior, depending on the angle of the rays. In Atlanta, maximum total daily solar radiation heat gain through single glazing during the summer months ranges from about 500 Btu/h ft^2 for a vertical north-facing surface to about 2200 Btu/h ft^2 for a horizontal surface.

Figure 5.5 graphs the design solar heat gain values normally used for July at 32° north latitude. Included are curves for south, east, west, north and horizontal glass. Note that horizontal, east, and west glass create the greatest cool-

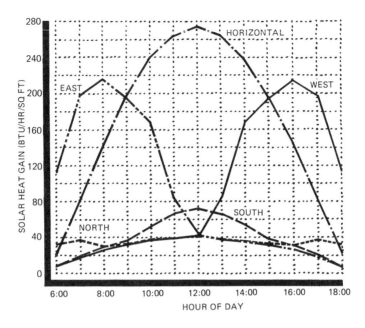

Fig. 5.5. Design solar radiation values for various surface orientations.

ing loads; during summer, south-facing glass transmits very little solar radiation at this latitude.

Solar heat gains through glazing are estimated by the following equation. Simplified methods for residences are detailed in the ASHRAE loads calculation procedures and in *Manual J*.

$$Q_{solar} = A \times SC \times SHGF \times CLF$$

where

A = net area of glazing, ft^2
SC = shading coefficient, dimensionless
$SHGF$ = solar heat gain factor, Btu/h ft^2
CLF = cooling load factor, dimensionless

The shading coefficient, SC, describes the effectiveness of the fenestration, or glazing and shading systems, in blocking solar radiation gains. It is defined as

$$SC = \frac{\text{Solar gain through fenestration}}{\text{Solar heat gain through clear } \frac{1}{8}\text{-in. double-strength glass}}$$

Table 5.6. Shading Coefficients.

	Single-glazing	Double-glazing
Clear glass	1.0	0.88
venetian blinds		
Medium	0.64	0.57
Light	0.55	0.51
Roller shades		
Dark	0.59	0.60
White	0.25	0.25
Translucent, light	0.39	0.37
Drapes		
Open-weave, medium color	0.67	0.57
Semiopen-weave, medium color	0.60	0.52
Closed-weave, medium color	0.55	0.48
Semiopen-weave, light color	0.55	0.48
Semiopen-weave, dark color	0.67	0.57
Louvered sun screens		
Black, 23 louvers/in.	0.15–0.35	0.10–0.27
Light, 23 louvers/in.	0.20–0.33	

(Adapted with permission from *ASHRAE Handbook—1985 Fundamentals.*)

The lower the value of the shading coefficient for a material the less radiation it allows to enter the building. Shading coefficients for various materials are given in Table 5.6.

Solar radiation striking the opaque surfaces of a building also increases the cooling load by raising the temperature of the outer surface and increasing conduction through the envelope. This effect is usually accounted for in the conduction equation by the use of an equivalent temperature difference that includes both air temperature and solar effects. Such factors include the design equivalent temperature differential, or DETD, in the ASHRAE residential calculations and the cooling load temperature difference, or CLTD, in the commercial building calculation methods.

Controlling solar heat gains is a matter of keeping the sun out of the building and off the exterior surfaces. The highest priorities for sun control are horizontal glazing and east and west glazing. Other glazing areas are second in priority and, finally, the opaque walls and roof.

The most desirable method of reducing solar gains is to block the sun's rays before they reach the building. Trees are excellent shading devices and should be jealously guarded during site work and construction. Adjacent buildings may provide protection from low east and west sun in densely built areas. A variety of plantings and structures may also be used, including trellises, arbors, and fences. Elements of the building may also shade the primary spaces from solar gains; carports and storage spaces on the west side of houses are good examples. Porches, decks, overhangs, and wing walls also offer shading possibilities.

Other exterior shading devices for glazing include operable hinged shutters, roll-down shutters, and a variety of metal, wire, and woven shade screens. All are effective, because they block the sun's rays before they reach the glass and may protect the entire window area.

A less effective method of solar gain control involves blocking or reflecting the sun's heat at the glazing itself, using reflective or heat-absorbing glass and reflective films. Such measures are less effective than exterior shading, because the glazing temperature rises and conducts heat to the interior. Still, they are a straightforward and simple solution; in commercial office buildings, heat-absorbing and reflective glass are a standard feature. Films should be approached with some degree of caution. If improperly used, they may cause the glass to be heated and to crack as it expands. Peeling and bubbling of the film may also occur. Use a reliable contractor who offers good materials and guaranteed work, and look at previous projects.

The final and least effective line of defense against unwanted solar heat is offered by interior window treatments. Curtains, drapes, and blinds provide some protection by reflecting a portion of the solar gain back out the window. They can also reduce the conduction heat gain through the glazing by partially confining the hot air near the glass.

In high-mass buildings that are occupied only during the day, interior window treatments can actually increase the impact of solar heat gains. They convert the solar radiation that is not reflected to heat that goes directly into the air. Without the window treatment, the radiation might be scattered around the space and absorbed into the high-mass objects and structure rather than heating the air. The heat stored in the mass could then be dissipated during the night.

The effects of orientation, glazing type, and window treatment on solar heat can be judged from tabular listings of Table 5.7, heat gain rates for residential cooling system design in the ASHRAE *Fundamentals Handbook*. Ref. 5.1. The values represent the total of the conduction and solar heat gains through glass in Btu/h per ft^2. The heat gain through a window is found by multiplying the appropriate factor by the area of the glass. If a glazed area is shaded, use the value for north-facing glass to estimate its heat gain. Again, the horizontal and east and west glazing are the first priority for reducing undesirable summer heat gain.

Internal Heat Gains

The presence of people and the use of electrical and mechanical equipment result in the release of heat to the building interior. These internal gains may include both latent and sensible portions. The heat given off from a light bulb is a sensible heat gain. Human respiration, bathing, and the combustion process in a gas range are examples of latent load sources.

Table 5.7. Design Cooling Load Factors Through Glass (Btu/h · ft²).

Outdoor Design Temp.	Regular Single Glass						Regular Double Glass		
	85	90	95	100	105	110	85	90	95
No Awnings or Inside Shading									
North	23	27	31	35	39	44	19	21	24
NE and NW	56	60	64	68	72	77	46	48	51
East and West	81	85	89	93	97	102	68	70	73
SE and SW	70	74	78	82	86	91	59	61	64
South	40	44	48	52	56	61	33	35	38
Horiz. Skylight	160	164	168	172	176	181	139	141	144
Draperies or Venetian Blinds									
North	15	19	23	27	31	36	12	14	17
NE and NW	32	36	40	44	48	53	27	29	32
East and West	48	52	56	60	64	69	42	44	47
SE and SW	40	44	48	52	56	61	35	37	40
South	23	27	31	35	39	44	20	22	25
Roller Shades Half-Drawn									
North	18	22	26	30	34	39	15	17	20
NE and NW	40	44	48	52	56	61	38	40	43
East and West	61	65	69	73	77	82	54	56	59
SE and SW	52	56	60	64	68	73	46	48	51
South	29	33	37	41	45	50	27	29	32
Awnings									
North	20	24	28	32	36	41	13	15	18
NE and NW	21	25	29	33	37	42	14	16	19
East and West	22	26	30	34	38	43	14	16	19
SE and SW	21	25	29	33	37	42	14	16	19
South	21	24	28	32	36	41	13	15	18

(Adapted with permission from *ASHRAE Handbook—1985 Fundamentals.*)

In residences, most internal gains arise from appliances, cooking, and bathing. In commercial buildings, lighting and occupants become more important; individual pieces of equipment, such as a computer, can create very large loads. The magnitude and importance of these heat gains vary widely with the type of building, becoming a major force in commercial buildings and superinsulated homes.

In the past, lighting systems in commercial buildings were commonly designed to provide illumination levels well over 100 footcandles. Lighting power consumption rates of 5 W/ft² of floor space were normal. Recent changes in lighting standards have allowed reductions to 70 footcandles or less for most general office spaces. Such levels provide perfectly acceptable lighting in most circumstances and significantly reduce interior heat gains. More efficient lamps and ballasts offer further reductions, so that lighting systems using less than 2

Regular Double Glass			Heat Absorbing Double Glass						Clear Triple Glass		
100	105	110	85	90	95	100	105	110	85	90	95
No Awnings or Inside Shading											
26	28	30	12	14	17	19	21	23	17	19	20
53	55	57	27	29	32	34	36	38	42	43	44
75	77	79	42	44	47	49	51	53	62	63	64
66	68	70	35	37	40	42	44	46	53	55	56
40	42	44	19	21	24	26	28	30	30	31	33
146	148	150	89	91	94	96	98	100	126	127	129
Draperies or Venetian Blinds											
19	21	23	9	11	14	16	18	20	11	12	14
34	36	38	20	22	25	27	29	31	24	26	27
49	51	53	30	32	35	37	39	41	38	39	41
42	44	46	24	26	29	31	33	35	32	33	34
27	29	31	15	17	20	22	24	26	18	19	21
Roller Shades Half-Drawn											
22	24	26	10	12	15	17	19	21	13	14	15
45	47	49	24	26	29	31	33	35	34	35	35
61	63	65	35	37	40	42	44	46	49	49	50
53	55	57	30	32	35	37	39	41	41	42	43
34	36	38	18	20	23	25	27	29	25	26	26
Awnings											
20	22	24	10	12	15	17	19	21	11	12	13
21	23	25	11	13	16	18	20	22	12	13	14
21	23	25	12	14	17	19	21	23	12	13	14
21	23	25	11	13	16	18	20	22	12	13	14
20	22	24	11	13	16	18	20	22	11	12	13

W/ft^2 are possible. Not only do excessive lighting and equipment power consumption increase power consumption directly, they also increase cooling costs.

Internal Latent Gains

Internal latent heat gains are associated with water vapor. Sources of internal heat latent gains include human respiration, cooking, bathing, clothes washing and drying, and house plants. Such gains are a major portion of total internal gains and are particularly important in well-insulated residences. Almost all conservation efforts result in reductions of sensible heat gains, leaving internal heat gains largely unchanged. Latent loads become a larger portion of the total cooling load and may exceed the dehumidification capacity of the air conditioning equipment, resulting in comfort problems. This problem is discussed in more detail in Chapter 11.

Not only do latent heat gains increase the load on the air conditioning equipment, they increase relative humidity and reduce comfort levels. In extreme cases, higher moisture levels may result in mildew, mold, or condensation on cool surfaces.

Typical values of moisture production rates and latent heat gains from normal residential activities are provided in Table 5.8. The heat gain figures are developed by multiplying the moisture production figures by 1050 Btu/lb.

ASHRAE suggests a value of 0.7 lb/h of moisture production for a typical family of four, equivalent to a latent heat gain of 735 Btu/h. The actual rate is strongly influenced by the habits and conservation efforts made by the occupants. Moisture production rates over twice the typical value can easily occur.

House plants can be a surprisingly large source of interior moisture, particularly leafy plants in direct sunlight. The figure 0.04 lb/h in Table 5.8 assumes a normal collection of seven plants that require about 1 pt of water per day. The water added to the plants is essentially completely evaporated, producing sensible cooling and an equivalent latent heat gain. Each pint of water added to the pots or sprayed on the leaves adds 1.04 lb of moisture to the building interior. During the cooling season, the evaporation of water inside a building

Table 5.8. Moisture Production for Various Residential Operations.

Activity	Moisture gain, lb	Latent heat gain, Btu
Floor mopping (80-ft^2 kitchen)	2.40	2,440
Clothes drying (not vented)^a	26.40	26,800
Clothes washing^a	4.33	4,400
Cooking (not vented)^a		
Breakfast	0.34	350
Lunch	0.51	520
Dinner	1.17	1,190
Bathing, tub	0.12	120
Bathing, shower	0.50	510
Dishwashing^a		
Breakfast	0.20	200
Lunch	0.15	150
Dinner	0.65	660
Adult, resting	0.20	200
Adult, average activity	0.40	410
Adult, working hard	0.60	610
House plants	0.04	40

^{a}Based on a family of four.
(Adapted with permission from *ASHRAE Handbook—1979 Equipment.*)

is normally a liability. However, in dry climates where the relative humidity is well below the comfort range, the evaporative cooling effect can be beneficial.

Internal heat gains from equipment deserve particular attention, because they exact a multiple energy penalty. Not only does the electricity, natural gas, or oil used to power the equipment constitute an initial energy expense, it is completely or partially converted to heat inside a building. In a mechanically cooled building, additional energy must be purchased and consumed to remove that heat.

The power consumption resulting from a piece of equipment entirely inside the conditioned space may be estimated by the following evaluation. It is assumed that all the output goes directly as a cooling load.

Power consumption for cooling = Power rating of equipment

$$\times \frac{\text{(number of months that air conditioning is used)}}{(12) \times \text{COP of air conditioner}}$$

For a 4-month cooling season and an air conditioner with a COP of 2.25, an appliance that requires 1000 kWh of electricity over the course of a year would cause an additional electrical load of 150 kWh. The added cooling effect should be considered when evaluating the operating costs of alternative pieces of equipment. As a rule of thumb, increase the rated load by 3 to $3\frac{1}{2}\%$ per month of cooling season.

The heat gain from a piece of equipment is calculated by converting its power consumption to a thermal equivalent and adjusting for the number of hours it operates and the portion of the heat that goes into the building interior. Unless a device is vented directly to the outdoors, all the energy it consumes is released to the building interior as heat. Even vented pieces of equipment, such as clothes dryers and ranges, lose a large portion of their heat to the interior. Cooling load design references provide guidelines for making estimates for specific pieces of equipment.

For design purposes, the heat gain from the people in commercial buildings is estimated as 510 Btu/h, half sensible heat and half latent heat gain. The residential cooling calculation method usually assumes a sensible heat gain of 225 Btu/h per person, with the latent heat gain lumped into an overall assumption for the building. The actual rate of heat production by people varies widely with their activity level, from a total heat output of approximately 350 Btu/h at rest to 1800 Btu/h when very active, as in a racquet ball game.

For initial analysis, the figures in Table 5.9 may be used to estimate the interior heat gains from people, lighting, and equipment in the offices.

Reducing internal heat gains is simply a matter of reducing or eliminating the source of heat. If appliances, lights, and equipment are not needed, turn them off. Make sure that heat-producing equipment (both sensible and latent) in kitchens and bathrooms and clothes dryers are vented.

Table 5.9. Internal Heat Gain Estimates for Offices.

Load	Density	Heat Gain, Btu/h/ft^2
People	one per/150 ft^2 to one per/450 ft^2	0.5 to 2.1 (sensible only)
Equipment		
Typical	1.0 W/ft^2	3.4
High	1.5 W/ft^2	5.1
Lighting		
Energy-conserving	1.5 W/ft^2	5.1
Current practice	2.25 W/ft^2	7.7
Older buildings, poor design, or high		
Illumination requirements	5.0 W/ft^2	17.1

Mechanical System Gains

Inefficiencies and losses during the operation of a mechanical cooling system are responsible for heat gains that add to the cooling load on a building. The two major sources of system heat gains are the fans, pumps, and blowers and the ductwork or piping used to distribute cooled air or water. In combination, they can increase the base building cooling load by as much as 25%. Phrased another way, proper design can result in large savings.

The motors used in fans, pumps, and blowers are not perfectly efficient in converting electric energy into mechanical energy; typical efficiencies range from 35% for a $\frac{1}{15}$-horsepower (HP) motor to 87% for a 20-HP unit. Blower and fan motors normally used in residential systems have an efficiency of less than 70%. Thus, at least 30% of the motor's power consumption is immediately converted into heat and usually added directly into the conditioned airstream. In addition, the work done by a fan, pump, or blower is eventually converted into heat as the fluid is moved through the distribution system and the building. For a $\frac{1}{4}$-HP motor, typical of a small residential air conditioning system, the heat gain resulting from operation of the motor is approximately 1180 Btu/h. New motors offering efficiencies of more than 90% are now available and should be considered in larger commercial systems where motor choice is an option. There are generally no choices offered for motors in smaller systems. The general equation for estimating the heat gains from motors is

$$\text{Heat gain} = \frac{\text{Horsepower}}{\text{Motor efficiency}} \times 0.746 \text{ kWh/HP} \times 3413 \text{ Btu/kWh}$$

Heat gains into the ducts or distribution piping depend on the insulation on the ducts or pipes and their location. Poorly insulated ducts that run through an attic can impose an additional load equal to 15% or more of the building's cooling load. The losses occur by both conduction through the duct walls and by air leakage from the ducts. Wherever possible, it is desirable to route ducts and piping through the conditioned space, essentially eliminating losses. Good insulation and careful joining and sealing of ductwork are essential for ducts located in unconditioned areas. It is also necessary to use a vapor barrier on the outer side of insulation on cool ducts and pipes to avoid the condensation of moisture in the insulation. Duct systems should be inspected periodically to check for damage and deterioration of sealing materials.

In residential and small commercial systems, duct heat gains are normally estimated by multiplying the calculated cooling load for the home by a factor determined by the location of the ducts and the amount of insulation used. The duct heat gain is then added to the building cooling load to determine the required system capacity. If ducts are poorly installed and leak excessively, the amount of energy loss may be much greater than indicated by the factors.

Using Cooling Loads

Traditionally, load calculations have been thought of as a step that takes place only after the building design is complete. The architects finish their work, and the plans are passed on to the mechanical engineers. If the final building design is to be efficient, simple load calculations and consideration of cooling loads must be an integral part of every stage of the design process (Fig. 5.6). Energy and comfort must be considered at the very first stages of the design process, when the design program is being developed. By understanding the source and nature of load components, the building designer can often reduce or even eliminate portions of the load.

Cooling Design Temperatures

The conduction and infiltration heat loads on a building increase directly with increases in outdoor design temperature. Obviously, the choice of temperatures

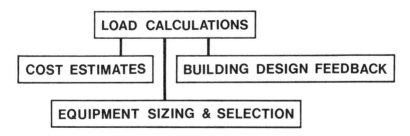

Figure 5.6. Using cooling load calculations.

used in load calculation has a great effect on the calculated equipment capacity. Outdoor cooling design temperatures are presented in three forms, 1%, $2\frac{1}{2}$%, and 5% figures. These percentages represent the fraction of the period from June through September during which the outdoor temperature is at or above the design temperature. For instance, the 1% design temperature for Atlanta is 94°F. For the 2904 h in June, July, August, and September, the outdoor temperature is normally above 94°F for only 29 h. The $2\frac{1}{2}$% and 5% figures are defined similarly, and they are 73 and 145 h, respectively. The highest temperature to be expected during a typical year at a location is given by the median of annual extremes or the average of the highest annual temperatures for a period of years. Such figures are not used for design purposes.

Outdoor design conditions for several major cities are presented in Table 5.10. Because the peak outdoor temperature and the peak outdoor moisture level seldom occur simultaneously, it is useful to consider the outside moisture level when the temperature is at the design condition. The mean coincident wet-bulb (MCWB) temperatures in Table 5.10 indicate the average wet-bulb temperature at the time that the dry-bulb temperature is at the given design condition. Note the variation in humidity levels indicated by the MCWB temperatures.

In the past the 1% design temperature was normally used for almost all residential and most commercial cooling system design. With the increased awareness of energy costs and availability, most designers substitute the $2\frac{1}{2}$% figures. ASHRAE's Standard 90 requires their use, as do most state and municipal building energy codes. In most cities, a switch from the 1% figure to the $2\frac{1}{2}$% figure results in reducing the size of a typical residential air conditioning system by 4 to 6%.

The use of a $2\frac{1}{2}$% design temperature does not mean that the building will be uncomfortable for $2\frac{1}{2}$% of the cooling season. Several factors combine to almost always preclude such an event. Most importantly, the mass of a building and its furnishings provide significant thermal storage mass and create a flywheel effect, which slows the rate of temperature change in the building. This allows the building to "coast" through periods of severe cooling loads without extreme temperatures and loss of comfort control.

Table 5.10. Summer Outdoor Design Conditions.

	Design Dry-bulb & MCWB			Mean Daily	Design Wet-bulb		
	1%	2.5%	5%	Range	1%	2.5%	5%
Atlanta	94/74	92/74	90/73	19	77	76	75
Boston	91/73	88/71	85/70	16	75	74	72
Chicago	94/74	91/73	88/72	20	77	75	74
Dallas	102/75	100/75	97/75	20	78	78	77
Denver	93/59	91/59	89/59	28	64	67	75
Seattle	86/68	82/66	78/65	19	69	67	65

(Adapted with permission from *ASHRAE Handbook—1985 Fundamentals.*)

OVERHANGS FOR SOLAR GAIN CONTROL

Fixed overhangs might seem to be the ideal passive measure for controlling solar gains through glazing. Working with the natural cycles of the sun's position during the year, we can design a fixed overhang to admit direct sunlight in the winter and exclude it in the summer. The principle has been used for thousands of years by the Romans, the American Indians, and others. The simplicity and natural function of fixed overhangs make them a very compelling design feature (Fig. 5.7).

The geometry of selecting fixed overhang lengths is straightforward; the position of the sun can be described with great precision for any time. Sun angles may be calculated from simple equations or looked up in tables or charts available in a variety of references. Sizing a projection to provide a certain shadow length at a particular time is a matter of applying one or two trigonometric equations. Such methods are found in numerous publications. But in attempting to apply a fixed overhang to an actual building, complications begin to arise. The most significant is the tradeoff between heating and cooling considerations during the year. Although an overhang admits more sunlight in winter than in summer, the effect is not well matched to the cooling and heating requirements

Figure 5.7. Fixed overhang for sun control.

of buildings. Overhangs admit more or less sunlight according to the position of the sun. The difficulty in design arises because the position of the sun during the year and the outdoor air temperature are not in phase. The altitude angle of the sun reaches its minimum value on about December 21 and its maximum value on about June 21. Thus the shadow from a fixed overhang is shortest on December 21 and longest on June 21.

Unfortunately, the minimum outdoor temperature and the greatest heating loads occur several weeks later, during January in most locations. Maximum air temperatures usually occur in July, again several weeks after the shading from the overhang begins to decline. The greatest building cooling loads take place even later, a result of higher outdoor humidity and greater solar gains as the sun's position in the sky moves lower. The plots of heating and cooling degree days for Atlanta and solar declination in Fig. 5.8 illustrate the phase difference between the sun's altitude angle and the air temperature.

This phase difference leads to significant differences in building heating and cooling loads in months with similar sun angles. Equal solar altitude angles occur on the 21st of the month for each of these five pairs of months

> May and July
> April and August
> March and September
> February and October
> January and November

Even though the solar position is equivalent in April and August and in February and October, the cooling and heating needs of a building are quite differ-

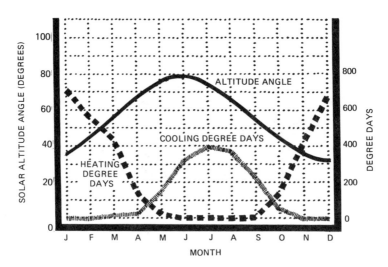

Figure 5.8. Phase difference between solar altitude and air temperature, Atlanta.

ent. A fixed overhang provides the same shading in April as in August, so that designing a fixed overhang where both heating and cooling must be considered is a matter of compromise to minimize the total of the heating and cooling costs for the year.

For practical purposes, overhangs are effective only for windows that face within about 30 to 45° of south. During the morning and afternoon, when the sun is striking east and west walls, it is so low in the sky that an overhang of practical length gives only partial protection. Only an extremely wide overhang, a carport or porch for example, can provide protection during the late morning or early afternoon. But in the early morning and late afternoon the low sun passes under even the widest overhang.

Shading from Overhangs

Overhangs are not nearly as effective for blocking summer heat gains as commonly thought. Solar radiation consists of direct, diffuse, and reflected radiation; an overhang is effective against only the direct component of the radiation. But direct radiation is not always a large fraction of total solar radiation. Diffuse radiation is a much larger portion of total solar radiation in the East and South than in the arid Southeast. The amount of diffuse radiation that a surface, such as a window, receives depends on the fraction of the sky that the surface "sees." Vertical surfaces, including windows, normally see half of the sky; an overhang of reasonable length reduces this figure only slightly. Reflected radiation bounces off the ground and passes under the overhang to strike the window (Fig. 5.9). In certain cases, solar radiation is reflected by an overhang onto the surface it shades.

Another factor that restricts the potential benefit of overhangs is the increased reflection of solar radiation off glazing materials at high incidence angles. (Note that the incidence angle is the angle between the beam of radiation and a line perpendicular to the surface. A beam striking a surface directly or head-on has an incidence angle of 0°. An incidence angle of 90° indicates that the beam is moving parallel to the surface.) The effect is much like a rock skipping off the surface of a pond when thrown at a shallow angle. Figure 5.10 shows how the transmittance of solar radiation decreases as the radiation strikes the glass at shallower angles (greater incidence angles). Notice that reflection of solar radiation increases sharply above angles of 50 to 60°.

During summer when the sun is high, the incidence angle on vertical surfaces is great. At noon on June 21st in Atlanta, the solar incidence angle on a vertical surface is only slighty less than 80°. From Fig. 5.10 45 to 55% of the direct radiation striking an unshaded window would be reflected. Only about 30 to 40% would be transmitted through the glass (some is absorbed). Adding an overhang could eliminate all the remaining direct radiation, but would have only a small effect on the cooling load of the building, because most of the direct

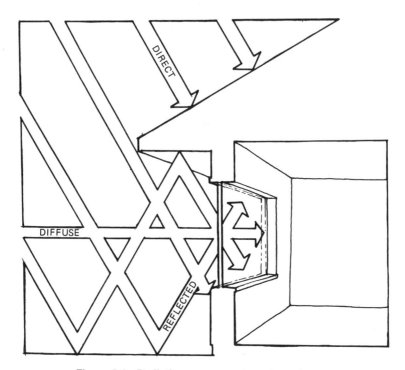

Figure 5.9. Radiation components and overhangs.

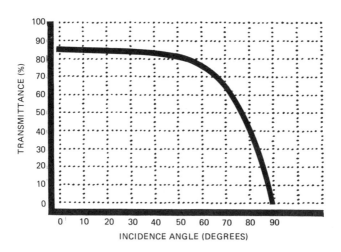

Figure 5.10. Transmittance vs. incidence angle.

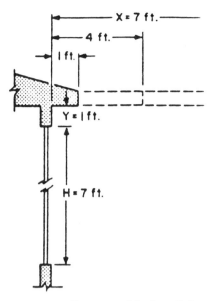

Figure 5.11. Overhang geometry. (Courtesy of Andrew S. Lau and *Solar Age Magazine*.)

radiation would be reflected anyway and diffuse and reflected radiation are not affected.

The effect of fixed overhangs in reducing heat gains is shown for Atlanta in Figs. 5.11 and 5.12. (Ref. 5.5) The overhang length is set at 1 ft, 4 ft, and 7

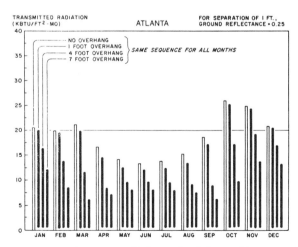

Figure 5.12. Effect of overhang on radiation gain, Atlanta. (Courtesy of Andrew S. Lau and *Solar Age Magazine*.)

ft, with a constant 1-ft separation from the top of the window. The bars on the chart indicate the total amount of solar radiation transmitted through 1-ft^2 of vertical, south-facing, double-glazing per month. The first of each group of four bars represents a completely unshaded window. The other three represent the heat gains for the three overhang lengths.

The effect of the overhangs is certainly positive during the summer; the amount of radiation transmitted through the glass is reduced. However, even the unreasonably large 7-ft overhang eliminates less than half of the undesirable gains at the middle of the cooling season. The amount of shading is greatest during the heating season, when solar heat gains are desirable.

Figure 5.13 shows the breakdown of total solar transmission through a vertical, south-facing surface in Atlanta during each month of the year. Similar results would be obtained for most other nonarid areas of the country. A ground reflectance of 0.25, typical of most residential sites, is assumed.

The net effect of fixed overhangs as shading devices on south glass is rather small and certainly not nearly as great as the pervasive simple sun angle plots imply. And their already limited effects are reduced even further for surfaces facing east or west of south. But even though fixed overhangs are not extremely effective in controlling total solar gains, they do provide a measure of protection, and should be used where appropriate. Fortunately roof overhangs are beneficial for other purposes, such as rain protection, and are considered as standard building features. However, other measures must be used for truly effective sun control.

Designing Overhangs

Almost all the overhang design tools available consider direct radiation and geometry to calculate shadow lengths. Because they do not consider diffuse and

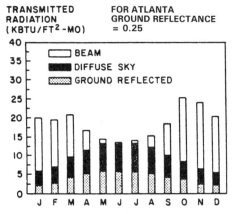

Figure 5.13. Radiation components—vertical south-facing surface (Atlanta). (Courtesy of Andrew S. Lau and *Solar Age Magazine*.)

reflected radiation, the value of the summer shading in reducing the cooling loads, or the heating value of the winter solar gains allowed to pass under the overhang, simple geometric design methods are severely limited. The method described below attempts to address these concerns without becoming overly complicated.

Overhang Alternatives

Several quite different overhang geometries may be used to achieve the same shading effects, as illustrated in Figs. 5.14 and 5.15. In Figure 5.14 the sun angle is the summer solstice angle, June 21st, for Atlanta; the window faces due south.

Both overhang geometries provide the same shadow length and might be considered to be equally desirable. But consider their performance during the heating season. Figure 5.15 illustrates the sun's angle at noon on December 21st, the winter solstice, in Atlanta.

The second overhang provides much better heating season performance, because it exposes the entire window to the sun. The first design shades a large portion of the window. The difference is the separation between the overhang and the top of the glass.

As indicated in Fig. 5.16 any of an infinite combination of overhang width and separation dimensions will provide complete shading against direct summer sun. The sun angle plotted is the noon summer solstice angle in Atlanta. As the

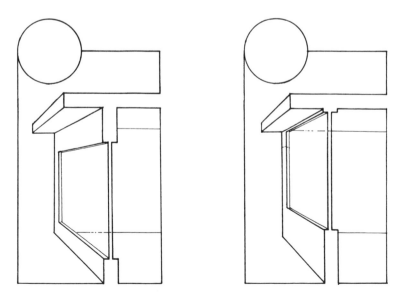

Figure 5.14. Overhang design alternatives (summer, Atlanta).

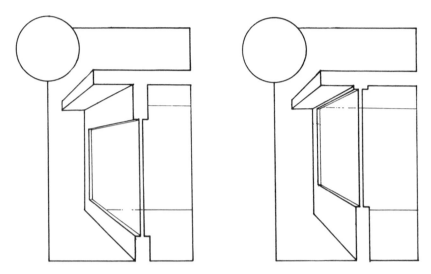

Figure 5.15. Overhang design alternatives (winter, Atlanta).

separation is increased, the width of the overhang must be increased to form the same angle. Using a separation between the top of the glass and the overhang causes the winter shadow to fall above the glass, leaving the entire window in sun.

A simple graphical procedure can be used to select a set of overhang and separation dimensions that provide both full sun in winter and full shading in summer. But two other factors must be considered first: the time of year that shading is desired and the changing position of the sun during the day.

To use a fixed overhang to shade during the latter part of the cooling season in September, shading must be tolerated in March. The designer must make a compromise, according to whether passive solar heating or summer shading is more important in lowering the energy costs in the building. For residential passive solar heating systems, a suggested period of full sun exposure is provided in Fig. 5.17. For conventional windows in residences, more shading could be tolerated than for passive heating systems. In commercial buildings, with higher internal heat gains and smaller heating loads, more shading is desirable.

Too often, overhang sizing is thought of only in two dimensions in terms of the noon sun angles, although the shading performance of an overhang can be quite different at other hours. In examining the shading effect of overhangs at times other than solar noon, it is useful to use the profile angle. The profile angle accounts for the sun's altitude and azimuth angles and considers the portion of the overhang that extends to the sides of the window. In a section view with a line drawn from the glazing surface toward the sun, the angle between that line and a horizon line in a plane perpendicular to the glazing surface is the

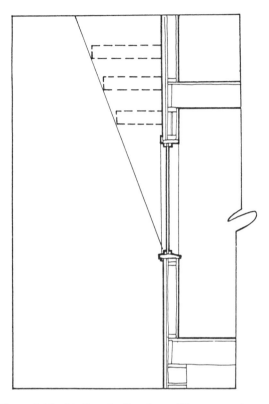

Figure 5.16. Similar shading from different overhangs.

profile angle. Profile angles are also called shadow line angles, because they are used to calculate shadow lengths. Figure 5.18 provides an illustration. Profile angles are tabulated by latitude in Reference 5.1. Blank spaces in the profile angle tables indicate that the sun does not shine on that surface at that hour. Notice that the profile angle is equal to the altitude angle at noon when the sun is due south.

Overhang Sizing Procedure

This procedure plots the shadow required for complete summer shading and the maximum shadow that is allowable for the full winter solar exposure. It then shows the combinations of overhang width and separation that may be used. Particular dimensions are then chosen to fit with the other design constraints on the building. As an example, consider a building near Jackson, Mississippi at latitude 32°N that requires full shading on its south-facing windows at noon on

Balance Temperature - 70°F

Balance Temperature - 60°F

Balance Temperature - 50°F

Figure 5.17. Recommended period of full solar exposure for residential passive solar heating systems. (Courtesy of Andrew S. Lau and *Solar Age Magazine*.)

August 21st and full sun at noon January 21st. The windows are 3 ft high with a sill 3 ft above the floor level.

Step 1.   Plot the desired summer shadow line. Make a scale drawing of a section through the wall with the window at a convenient scale; $\frac{1}{2}$ or $\frac{1}{4}$ in. = 1 ft

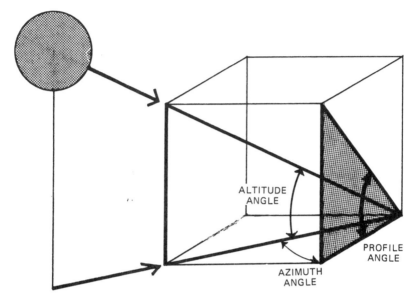

Figure 5.18. Profile angle.

is suggested (Fig. 5.19). Starting at the bottom of the glazing, plot the profile angle at the earliest or the latest time and date that shading is desired. For noon on August 21st at 32°N latitude, the profile angle is 70°. Any overhang that extends from the wall to this line or beyond will provide the necessary amount of shading (Fig. 5.20).

Step 2.   Plot the winter shadow line. The winter shadow line should fall at or above the top of the glazing at the specified time and date. At noon on January 21st, the profile angle for 32°N latitude is 38°. Plot a line at 38° above the horizontal, beginning at the top of the glazing. Any overhang that projects no father away from the wall than this line will not shade the glazing at noon on January 21st. Notice that the window frame shades a portion of the top of the glazing (Fig. 5.21).

   The zone between the winter and summer shading lines (Fig. 5.22) represents the desired location of the end of the overhang. If summer shading is a greater concern, the overhang should project to the outer edge of the zone. The point where the two lines cross represents the lowest overhang (minimum separation) that can be used with the desired results.

Step 3.   Select specific overhang and separation dimensions. The overhang length and separation dimensions must consider the design and construction of the building. In some instances, it will be difficult to select a set of dimensions

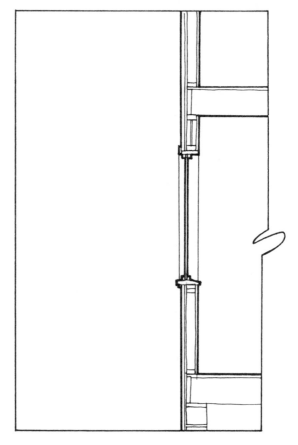

Figure 5.19. Wall section sketch for overhang sizing.

that fits the building design. Tall glazing or sliding glass doors in a house with a 7.5- or 8-ft ceiling height are examples. A conventional roof design does not allow adequate separation between the roof and the top of the glazing. In such cases, a compromise must be made.

Though noon angles are used more for simplicity, other times of the day may be considered with the same methods. The procedure described above is also applicable to non-south-facing walls. Continuing the example, consider the effect of changing the times for full shading and full exposure from noon to 10:00 A.M. on August 21st and January 21st. The profile angles then become 85 and 35°, respectively, and the summer and winter shadow lines are drawn accordingly. Notice that from April through August the profile angle for south-facing surfaces is greater in the morning and afternoon than at noon.

Most overhang discussions, including the one above, tend to treat the over-

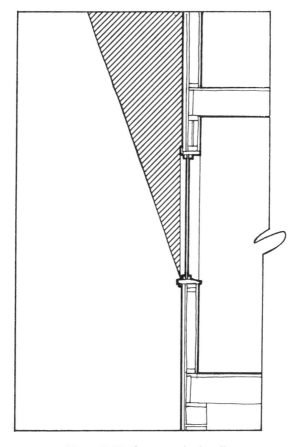

Figure 5.20. Summer shadow line.

hang as if it had an infinite length. If the overhang is only as wide as the window, significant discrepancies between actual shading patterns and the expected patterns will occur (Fig. 5.23). A simple analysis provides exact results for noninfinite overhangs only when the azimuth angle between the sun and the surface is zero; for south-facing surfaces, this occurs only at noon. At other hours, the shadow slants to the side, and an overhang that does not extend beyond the sides of the window will expose a portion of the window during the morning and afternoon. In many cases, an overhang may be considered to be effectively infinite. An example of such a case is a window in a wall shaded by a roof soffit. If the window is near the center of the wall, the assumption of an infinite overhang is reasonable. But if the window is near one end of the wall, the overhang appears infinite in only one direction.

For most purposes, if the overhang extends to each side of the window a

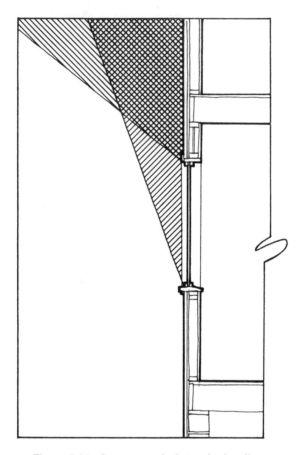

Figure 5.21. Summer and winter shadow lines.

distance equal to three times the height of the window plus the separation, it may be considered an infinite overhang. For windows, the following example provides a procedure that may be used to locate the shadow of a noninfinite overhang.

Example: Draw the 9:00 A.M. shadow for August 21st from a 3-ft-wide fixed overhang that extends 2 ft outward from a south-facing wall. The building is in Lexington, Kentucky, at 38°N latitude.

Solution: First draw the line that represents the lower edge of the shadow. (Fig. 5.24) As an alternative to the graphical method, the shadow length may be calculated

Shadow length = TAN (profile angle) × (overhang length)

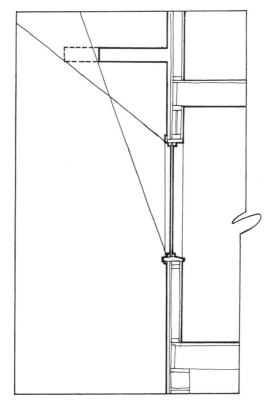

Figure 5.22. Selection of overhang design.

The profile angle at 9:00 A.M. on August 21st is 68°. The shadow length is

Shadow length at 9:00 =

TAN (68) × (2 ft) = 2.475 × (2 ft) = 4.95 ft

The shadow of a south-facing overhang will fall directly below the overhang only at noon. The distance that the lower edge of the shadow is shifted at other hours is calculated by using the sun's azimuth angle, approximately 69° at 9:00 A.M.

Distance shifted = TAN (azimuth angle) × (overhang length)

Distance shifted at 9:00 = TAN (69) × (2 ft)

= 2.605 × (2 ft)

= 5.2 ft

Figure 5.23. Shading from a non-infinite overhang.

The shadows of both edges are shifted an equal distance. Notice how the thickness of the overhang increases the shadow width at times other than noon. A 3-ft-wide window located directly below the overhang would have a large portion of its area exposed to the sun. For the window to be fully shaded at 9:00,

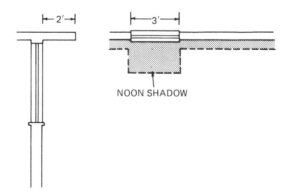

Figure 5.24. Shading example, August 21, Lexington, KY.

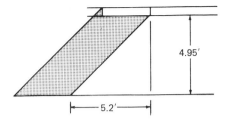

4.95′

5.2′

Figure 5.25. Shadow line at 9:00 AM.

it would be necessary for the overhang to extend at least 5.2 ft to the east side of the window.

The effect of overhangs in shading windows should not be overestimated; most of the literature leads one to believe that a simple overhang is the solution to any sun control problem. An overhang blocks *only* the direct portion of the sun's rays. Diffuse radiation and reflected radiation still reach the ''shaded'' surface. Overhangs should be thought of as only the first step in reducing undesirable summer heat gains.

CONTROLLING HEAT GAINS FROM PASSIVE SOLAR HEATING SYSTEMS DURING SUMMER

Passive solar heating systems can provide a building with large amounts of clean, low-cost heat during the winter and the summer. Unlike a conventional furnace, there is no on/off switch or thermostat to turn a passive solar heating system off when it is not needed. The shading provided by fixed overhangs and high summer sun angles is, at best, only a partial solution.

Passive systems add to summer cooling loads in two ways. The glazing in a passive solar heating system represents an area of reduced thermal resistance, or insulating value, in the building shell. Double glazing allows about 10 times the conduction heat transfer of an $R19$ wall. Even a thermal storage wall has much lower insulating qualities, with an R value of only about 6.

Secondly, passive heating systems can continue to act as heating systems during the cooling season. Even with an overhang the vertical glazing in a thermal storage wall, sunspace, or direct gain system receives sizable diffuse and reflected solar gains during the summer. Every state in the South and East has examples of buildings with passive solar heating systems that emulate southwestern designs and reward their owners with 95°F summer interior temperatures and record air conditioning bills.

Not all passive heating design efforts have a negative effect on summer performance. Often, cooling loads are actually reduced by redesigning the residence or small commercial building for small passive solar systems or suntempering. This can happen when glazing is relocated from east and west walls to the south walls. In such cases the total glazing area is increased only slightly or not at all. The increased insulation levels usually associated with passive solar buildings and, in most cases, the added thermal mass also have a beneficial effect during the summer. The greatest source of potential conflict is unwanted summer solar gains.

GUIDELINE VALUES OF CONSERVATION FACTOR (CF)

	Low-Fuel Cost	High-Fuel Cost		Low Fuel Cost	High Fuel Cost
	CF	CF		CF	CF
Birmingham, AL	.95	1.19	North Platte, NB	1.41	1.77
Phoenix, AZ	.70	.83	Ely, NV	1.41	1.70
Winslow, AZ	1.13	1.35	Las Vegas, NV	.86	1.02
Little Rock, AK	1.04	1.30	Reno, NV	1.23	1.47
Fresno, CA	.91	1.12	Concord, NH	1.51	2.01
Los Angeles, CA	.70	.81	Newark, NJ	1.27	1.65
Red Bluff, CA	.92	1.14	Albuquerque, NM	1.08	1.29
Sacramento, CA	.93	1.15	Los Alamos, NM	1.29	1.53
San Francisco, CA	.89	1.04	Albany, NY	1.47	1.95
Colorado Springs, CO	1.30	1.55	Binghamton, NY	1.50	1.99
Denver, CO	1.27	1.52	Buffalo, NY	1.47	1.94
Grand Junction, CO	1.27	1.56	New York (Central)	1.25	1.64
Hartford, CT	1.42	1.88	Asheville, NC	1.14	1.42
Wilmington, DE	1.25	1.62	Raleigh, NC	1.06	1.32
Washington, DC	1.26	1.64	Bismarck, ND	1.67	2.22
Apalachicola, FL	.69	.82	Cleveland, OH	1.39	1.84
Orlando, FL	.50	.59	Columbus, OH	1.34	1.78
Atlanta, GA	1.00	1.24	Oklahoma City, OK	1.07	1.33
Boise, ID	1.31	1.67	Medford, OR	1.22	1.56
Chicago, IL	1.39	1.83	North Bend, OR	1.11	1.35
Springfield, IL	1.32	1.73	Portland, OR	1.21	1.55
Evansville, IN	1.21	1.58	Philadelphia, PA	1.25	1.62
Indianapolis, IN	1.33	1.76	Pittsburgh, PA	1.37	1.81
Burlington, IA	1.39	1.82	Providence, RI	1.37	1.79
Mason City, IA	1.56	2.07	Charleston, SC	.84	1.03
Dodge City, KA	1.21	1.49	Rapid City, SD	1.48	1.90
Lexington, KY	1.23	1.60	Sioux Falls, SD	1.56	2.07
Lake Charles, LA	.72	.89	Memphis, TN	1.02	1.29
New Orleans, LA	.70	.85	Nashville, TN	1.10	1.42
Caribou, ME	1.72	2.29	Amarillo, TX	1.08	1.30
Portland, ME	1.52	2.02	Corpus Christi, TX	.58	.70
Baltimore, MD	1.23	1.58	Dallas, TX	.87	1.06
Boston, MA	1.33	1.75	El Paso, TX	.88	1.04
Detroit, MI	1.40	1.85	San Angelo, TX	.84	1.01
Traverse City, MI	1.54	2.04	Bryce Canyon, UT	1.49	1.77
Int. Falls, MN	1.80	2.39	Salt Lake City, UT	1.31	1.64
Minneapolis, MN	1.60	2.13	Burlington, VT	1.56	2.08
Jackson, MS	.86	1.06	Norfolk, VA	1.05	1.31
Columbia, MO	1.26	1.64	Roanoke, VA	1.16	1.47
Kansas City, MO	1.29	1.67	Seattle, WA	1.25	1.60
Saint Louis, MO	1.22	1.58	Spokane, WA	1.44	1.88
Billings, MT	1.47	1.91	Charleston, WV	1.21	1.58
Dillon, MT	1.55	1.98	Green Bay, WI	1.58	2.10
Great Falls, MT	1.51	1.97	Madison, WI	1.55	2.05
Omaha, NB	1.43	1.87	Casper, WY	1.44	1.78

Source: "Conservation and Solar Guidelines," LA-UR-83-2129, J. Douglas Balcomb, Los Alamos National Laboratory.

6

VENTILATION FOR COOLING

VENTILATION

Ventilation provides cooling by using moving air to carry away heat. The air movement may be natural, resulting from wind or thermal forces, or forced, the result of an electric fan. In either case, ventilation as a cooling mechanism may involve either the building or the human body.

Ventilation can be used simply to remove heat from the building, as with an exhaust fan, or it may cool the occupants directly, as a ceiling fan does. A whole-house fan may accomplish both functions simultaneously.

Cooling the Building

Ventilation is useful in cooling buildings when the interior temperature is above the outdoor temperature. Using the atmosphere as a heat sink, air flow through the building can effectively carry away an unlimited amount of heat. There is one important limitation: the ambient temperature sets a limit on the availability of the atmospheric heat sink. Ventilation can be used to cool a building only when the temperature of the surrounding air is lower than the temperature of the air inside the building.

Even so, ventilation can be extremely useful. Internal heat gains and solar heat gains often combine to raise the temperature inside a building above the outdoor air temperature during mild weather. When this occurs, the building may be cooled directly by simply ventilating it with cooler outdoor air. Throughout the entire United States, there are significant portions of the cooling season when ventilation alone provides adequate cooling. In some locations, it may be possible to rely exclusively on ventilation for the entire cooling season and avoid the cost of an air conditioning system. Even in the deep South, ventilation can make summers without air conditioning tolerable if not comfortable.

Opportunities for ventilating a building at night when the ambient air is cool and storing the cooling effect in the mass are discussed in more detail later in this chapter.

Table 6.1. Cooling Effect of Air Motion at 60% RH.

Airspeed, fpm	T_{DB} °F	ΔT_{DB}
Still (<50)	76.7	–
100	79.5	2.8
200	83.2	6.5
400	86.0	9.3
800	88.0	11.3

Cooling the Body

Ventilation is extremely effective for cooling people directly. Air motion reduces the insulating effect of the layer of still air at the skin surface and produces the wind-chill effect described in winter weather reports. Though a liability during winter, the increased heat loss from the body caused by moving air produces a very beneficial cooling effect in the summer. Air flow over the skin also increases the rate of evaporation of moisture from the skin, a very powerful cooling mechanism that allows a feeling of comfort even when the air temperature is above the normal comfort level. With evaporation, the limit on the use of the air as a heat sink becomes the wet-bulb temperature, rather than the dry-bulb temperature.

The total cooling effect of air flow over the body is shown in Table 6.1 (Ref 6.1.). The table shows the increase in the comfortable dry-bulb temperature made possible by air motion. It assumes that a typical individual is comfortable in light clothing at 76.7°F with little or no airflow. Relative humidity is assumed constant at 60%.

The relationship between air speed and comfort is not exact, and different researchers have arrived at different descriptions of the effects. However, it is agreed that there are significant opportunities to use airflow to provide comfort levels at higher air temperatures. As a general rule of thumb, each increase in air speed of 30 ft per min will allow comfortable conditions to be maintained at an air temperature 1° higher. However, papers may be disturbed at 160 fpm, and air speeds over 300 fpm become irritating and should usually be avoided.

Interior Versus Exterior Air Circulation

Ventilation cooling may make use of air from either the interior or the exterior of the building. Interior air circulation is used primarily for people cooling, while exterior air is circulated for either building cooling or simultaneous cooling of both the building and the occupants.

Ventilation with outdoor air can be used to remove excessive heat and humidity when outdoor conditions are favorable. When outdoor conditions are unpleasant, ventilation with outdoor air may be undesirable, because it could introduce even more heat and humidity into the building interior. Indoor air circulation, however, does not change the interior conditions, but only makes them more comfortable for the building occupants. Interior fans are a simple means to reduce air conditioning energy costs by increasing the comfortable thermostat setting and reducing the air conditioner's run time.

Several of the most practical and most interesting ventilation concepts are discussed in this chapter. They include

wind-driven ventilation
electric fans
stack-effect ventilation
solar chimneys
whole-house fans
ceiling and space fans

Basic Analysis

The heat removal capacity of outdoor ventilating air is a function of both the rate of air flow and the temperature difference between the exhaust air and the supply air

$$Q = \rho \times C_p \times V \times (T_{exhaust} - T_{supply}) \times 60$$

where

Q = rate of heat removal, Btu/h
ρ = density of air, lb/ft^3
C_p = specific heat of air, Btu/lb°F
V = volumetric airflow rate, cfm
$T_{exhaust}$ = temperature of exhaust air, °F
T_{supply} = temperature of supply air °F
60 = conversion for minutes/hour

For normal conditions, ρ = 0.075 lb/ft^3, and C_p = 0.24 Btu/lb°F. The product of these two figures is 0.018 Btu/ft^3°F and is often substituted in calculations for simplicity. Thus

$$Q = 0.018 \times V \times (T_{exhaust} - T_{supply}) \times 60 \text{ (Btu/h)}$$

Example: Calculate the heat removed from a house at 80°F by a fan producing a flow rate of 1500 cfm with outdoor temperature at 72°F

Q = 0.018 (Btu/ft^3°F) × 1500 (ft^3/min) × (80 − 72) (°F) × 60 min/h
Q = 12,960 Btu/h

Second, the volume of air flow may be estimated if the velocity of the flow and the area of the flow path are known

$$F = V \times A$$

where

F = volumetric air flow rate, cfm
V = air flow velocity, ft/min
A = area of flow path, ft^2

Example: If an attic fan moves 6000 cfm of air and only two 3- × 4-ft casement windows are open to allow air to enter the house, what is the air speed through the windows?

$F = V \times A$ may be rewritten as $V = F/A$. The open window area is 2 × 3 ft × 4 ft, or 24 ft^2.

$$V = 6000 \text{ (cfm)}/24 \text{ (}ft^2\text{)}$$
$$= 250 \text{ ft/min}$$

Natural Versus Forced Ventilation

Ventilation may be created by either natural forces (natural ventilation) or by electric fans and mechanical equipment (forced ventilation). Although some passive energy enthusiasts have a strong predisposition against active alternatives, forced ventilation greatly expands the opportunities for using ventilation cooling.

Natural ventilation should be used whenever possible: at the beginning and end of the cooling season and even on mild days during the middle of the season. It should be considered a first line of defense against summer discomfort. However, extensive natural ventilation features impose significant design restrictions on a building, and, alone, they are not adequate to provide comfortable conditions in most of the country. Electric fans are a more powerful ventilation means and increase the range of conditions at which ventilation can be used. Electric ventilation is available on demand, and its power consumption is quite small. A sensible building ventilation plan makes use of natural ventilation when conditions allow and then uses forced ventilation before finally resorting to air conditioning when outdoor conditions are severe.

Natural Ventilation

As a research topic, natural ventilation has been extensively examined during the past several decades. The resulting abundance of flow patterns, optimum aperture aspect ratios, velocity distributions, and other details are enough to confuse even the best aeronautical engineers and leave the building designer speechless. Myriad cryptic arrows and dotted lines in building cross sections and plans, like the one in Fig. 6.1, abound in research publications.

What do they mean to the designer of a three-bedroom ranch house or a 5000-ft² office building? How does natural ventilation relate to the design of passive solar systems and heating energy conservation measures? Why do those people in the drawings live in one-room houses with no furniture? Natural ventilation is an issue that is characterized by uncertainty. Winds are extremely variable and unpredictable in most locations. The effects of the building's occupants are difficult to predict or account for. Furniture placement, window treatments, door and window operation, and individual preferences all have an effect on airflow and the usefulness of natural ventilation. Landscaping and adjacent buildings, fences, and other structures that influence the winds actually available at a building site can and do change over the years.

These uncertainties make meaningful design recommendations difficult. The very natures of natural ventilation airflow and its cooling effect make it difficult to quantify them and to communicate design information. Natural ventilation is, and should be, a secondary consideration in the overall building design. Interior space planning, window locations, window areas, landscaping, building form, architectural features, and exterior design are governed by other con-

Figure 6.1. Natural ventilation explained.

siderations of equal or, usually, greater importance than natural ventilation. Cooling itself is a secondary consideration to heating in almost all of the country, including the majority of the South.

This section, then, focuses on simple, cost-effective natural ventilation concepts and features that can be easily incorporated into small buildings. Despite its limitations, natural ventilation is the only purely passive cooling technique that can be practically used throughout the country. However, in warm, humid areas, unless the occupants of a building have an extremely good tolerance for high temperatures or have a limited budget, natural ventilation will not be relied on as a complete substitute for air conditioning. Natural ventilation is not a universal panacea for summer cooling needs.

How Natural Ventilation Works

Natural ventilation occurs as a result of differences in the distribution of air pressures around a building. Pressure differences cause air to flow through the building in much the same way that temperature differences cause heat to flow through a wall or roof. Air always flow from areas of high pressure to areas of low pressure.

A pressure differential may be created either by winds or by buoyancy forces that arise from the difference in the density of air at different temperatures. The term *stack effect* is used to describe flow pressure differences that result from temperature and density differences. For practical purposes, wind-induced ventilation is the dominant type of natural ventilation. Stack-effect ventilation is not a powerful ventilation mechanism and has several limitations that reduce its applicability.

Wind-Induced Ventilation

A simple explanation of how wind-induced ventilation functions is provided by Fig. 6.2. The drawings show the path of the wind flowing around a building. The building creates an obstruction around which the wind must flow. The air striking the upwind or windward side of the building is slowed and diverted around the sides or over the top of the building. After being pushed aside by the structure, the air streams eventually rejoin some distance downstream and continue their normal path. The effect is quite similar to water flowing around a rock in a stream.

The action of wind blowing against a surface creates a higher pressure at the surface; the force of the wind on an open umbrella is a good example. Where the wind strikes a building, a zone of high pressure is created, while the eddy on the downwind, or leeward, side of the building establishes a low-pressure zone. Low-pressure zones are also created along the sides of the building and on the roof, where wind velocities are higher.

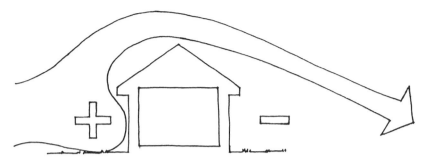

Figure 6.2. Wind-induced ventilation potential.

If a window is opened on a side of a building adjacent to a high-pressure zone and another on a side adjacent to a low-pressure zone, flow through the building will take place. Air flows into the building from the high-pressure zone and through the building to the low-pressure zone. The wind does not actually "blow" through a building, it flows through according to pressure differences. In following the pressure differential, it may move perpendicular to the wind direction or even opposite it.

The pressure due to the speed of the wind is estimated by the following equation Ref. 5.1.

$$P_v = 0.000482 \times (Vw)^2$$

where

P_v = velocity pressure, in. of water
Vw = wind velocity, MPH

The pressures around the building will usually be some fraction of the velocity pressure of the wind, either positive (high pressure) or negative (low pressure). For square or rectangular buildings, the pressure on the windward side normally varies from 0.5 to 0.9 times the velocity pressure of the wind, Pv. On the downwind side, the pressures are negative and range from −0.3 to −0.9 Pv. See Fig. 6.3.

The fundamental equations for predicting wind-induced ventilation through a space are provided below. In applying the equations, the designer should keep in mind that they are only approximate. Wind-driven ventilation depends upon many variables that defy simple analysis.

Two equations are provided, one for winds perpendicular or nearly perpendicular to the openings, and one for winds that strike the building surface obliquely.

For perpendicular winds
$F = 48 \times R \times A \times V$

For oblique winds
$F = 26 \times R \times A \times V$

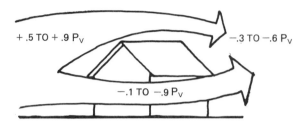

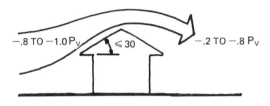

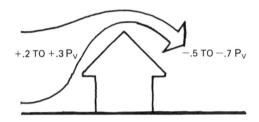

Figure 6.3. Wind velocity pressure patterns around buildings.

where

F = airflow rate, cfm
R = factor for relative inlet/outlet areas, dimensionless
A = free area of smaller opening, either inlet or outlet, ft^2
V = wind speed, MPH

$$48 \text{ and } 26 = \frac{88 \text{ ft/min}}{1 \text{ MPH}} \times \text{opening effectiveness}$$

(Opening effectiveness = 0.50 to 0.60 for perpendicular winds or 0.25 to 0.35 for oblique winds.)

The inlet/outlet area ratio factor is taken from Table 6.2, using the ratio of the larger opening area (either inlet or outlet) to the smaller opening area. An equation for calculating these factors is presented later.

Table 6.2. Inlet/Outlet Ratio Factor.

Ratio of Larger Area to Smaller Area	Factor R
1.00	1.00
1.25	1.11
1.50	1.18
1.75	1.23
2.00	1.27
2.50	1.32
3.00	1.34
4.00	1.37
5.00 & above	1.38

The inlet and outlet areas to be used are the net *free* area of the opening, not simply the total ventilation area. The flow-reducing effects of louvers or screens must be taken into account. Use the values in Table 6.3 to estimate the free area.

Wind speed information is available from a variety of sources. But do not use annual average figures for serious analysis; wind speeds during the summer are normally somewhat lower than in winter. For design purposes, a wind speed equal to one-half the summer average value is suggested to ensure that the calculation results are applicable to the majority of the cooling season.

Example: Estimate the rate of wind-induced ventilation through the example house defined in Chapter 2, Fig. 6.4. Assume that the windows are double-hung windows, fully opened and that screens are in place. Use Atlanta wind data (Table 6.4), and assume that there is no blockage of winds by buildings

Table 6.3. Free Area For Various Ventilation Configurations.

Configuration	Free area, %
1/4-in. mesh hardware cloth	100
1/8-in. mesh screen	80
No. 16 mesh screen, with or without plain metal louvers	50
Wood louvers & 1/4-in. mesh hardware cloth	50
Wood louvers & 1/8-in. mesh screen	45
Wood louvers & no. 16 screen	33

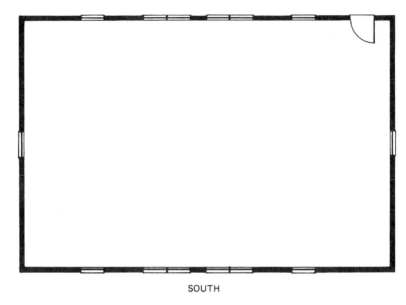

SOUTH

Figure 6.4. Window location for example.

or trees at the site. (As discussed later, this is usually not a realistic assumption in actual building projects.)

Atlanta's average summer wind direction—southeast—implies that the equation for oblique winds is appropriate for evaluating flow entering through the south and east windows and exiting through the north and west windows. Note the double-hung windows provide an open area of only half their total area. The following values are used

$R = 1.0$

$A = (77 + 15)/2 \times 0.5$

$\quad = 23 \text{ ft}^2$ (double-hung windows with 50% open area; screens restrict flow, reducing net free area by 50%)

$V = 7.8/2 = 3.9$ MPH

Table 6.4. Atlanta Wind Data.

	Speed	Direction
May	8.6	NW
June	7.9	NW
July	7.4	SW
August	7.1	NW
September	8.0	ENE
Average	7.8	NW

$$Q = 26 \times R \times A \times V$$
$$Q = 26 \times 1.0 \times 23 \times 3.9$$
$$= 2330 \text{ cfm}$$

For comparison, this ventilation effect is slightly less than the ventilation supplied by a 20-in.-diameter, portable window fan drawing 185 W on low speed. The operating cost of the fan would be about $0.014/h (power cost = $0.075/kWh). The ventilation rate at average wind conditions would be higher by a factor of 2, or 4660 cfm.

Of course, the ventilation rate at any particular time will vary as the wind speed and direction change. These estimates are quite optimistic, because weather stations measure winds in unobstructed sites at some height above the ground. Actual wind speeds at nearby building sites are almost always lower due to the effects of trees and buildings.

Notice the decrease in ventilation when the window configuration is rearranged for sun-tempering. If half the north window area and all the east and west windows are moved to the south side, the flow rate drops to 1330 cfm.

Though the potential wind-induced ventilation is reduced by about a half, the loss is more than compensated for by the improvements in heating performance and reduced heat gain through east and west windows. The loss in natural ventilation performance is easily compensated for with a small electric fan.

Factors That Influence Wind-Induced Natural Ventilation

Window Areas

The amount of wind-induced flow through a building increases directly as the window area increases. Larger open areas provide greater air flow. For this reason, windows that open fully for ventilation through their entire area are desirable. Casement and awning windows are full opening, while double-hung and slider windows open only 50% of their total area. Jalousie windows also provide 100% opening, but they allow extremely high infiltration and should be used only in areas that are not conditioned, such as sun porches.

The distribution of the open area between inlets and outlets is also important. As shown in the calculation procedure, the amount of flow can be increased by increasing the area of either the outlets or inlets. But the maximum flow for a given total open area is achieved by making the inlet and outlet areas equal. When inlet and outlet areas are not equal, the effective ventilation area may be calculated as

$$A_{\text{eff}} = \frac{A_o/A_i}{(A_o^2 + A_i^2)^{0.5}}$$

where

A_{eff} = effective ventilation area
A_i = inlet area
A_o = outlet area

Although the greatest airflow *volume* is obtained with equal inlet and exit areas, an imbalance may provide more favorable air *velocity*. Larger outlets mean greater air speeds near the inlets, and larger inlets cause greater air speeds near the outlets. The ratio of inlet area to outlet area and thus the air speeds in certain areas of a building can be changed by simply opening and closing windows. For example, the maximum air speed through an individual room on the windward side of a building may be achieved by closing all windward windows except those in the room and opening all leeward windows.

Window Shapes and Types

Wide windows, those with a high width-to-height ratio, perform better for oblique winds than either square or vertical windows. With winds perpendicular to the window, all three shapes produce roughly equivalent interior wind velocities. But for winds at an angle to the windows, the wide window is far superior. Interior air speeds actually increase to a maximum when winds are from a 45° angle. At a 60° wind incidence angle, the wide window produces about twice the interior air velocity that square or vertical windows do.

Casement windows are particularly effective for oblique winds; the window itself can help channel flow into the opening. Both casement and awning windows are a good choice for areas with high heating loads, because they seal well to reduce air infiltration. Casement windows can be adjusted to provide some control of the distribution of air horizontally through the interior. Awning windows give some control of vertical air flow distribution.

Window Treatments

Almost any window treatment added to a bare window will reduce the flow of air through the window. Because window treatments are necessary for significant aesthetic, functional, and energy reasons, they should be used, but chosen to minimize their adverse effects on ventilation. Curtains and drapes can cause great reductions in flow and may also be a nuisance when winds are strong. Perhaps more important, their presence makes windows less accessible and reduces the likelihood that natural ventilation will be used. Standard blinds or the miniblinds that have become popular in recent years are a good alternative to curtains and drapes. Window screens also greatly reduce air flow through windows, but they are almost a necessity. A frequently used factor suggests that they reduce air flow by 50%. Other researchers (Ref. 6.2) report reductions of 21% for bronze wire screen and 29% for plastic-covered fiberglass screens.

Architectural Features

Architectural features are one of the major determinants of pressure differences around a building and thus have a large effect on wind-induced natural ventilation. Wing walls, end walls, roof eaves, decks, balconies, and shading overhangs will usually increase pressure differences and air flow through windows. The effect is greatest for features located near windows and greater for oblique winds. Wing walls can be very effective in increasing air flow and velocities in rooms with windows on only one wall. In one model test (Ref. 6.2), a wing wall configuration improved interior air velocities by 50% for perpendicular winds. With oblique winds of 22.5 and 45°, the improvement was more than 150%. The function of the wing walls could be duplicated, although with less dramatic flow improvements, by open casement windows or tall shrubs.

Adjustments by Occupants

Adjustments made by the building occupants can do much to improve the effectiveness of wind-induced ventilation. Figures 6.5 through 6.8 provide examples.

Wind as a Cooling Resource

The wind at almost all sites in the United States is a very uncertain cooling resource. Variations in both speed and direction are large; only in a few coastal and mountain locations is there a steady wind with a predictable direction. Designing a building with a strong reliance on the wind for ventilation and cooling without other supplemental or backup systems is risky. Also, acquiring useful wind data for design purposes for a particular building site is very difficult. Local terrain features—bodies of water, buildings, hills, trees and landscaping, paved areas—exert a large influence on the winds at a given location. Variations from site to site can be large, even over distances as short as a few hundred yards.

Further uncertainties in winds arise from variations with height; winds are normally greater at higher altitudes, and buildings and trees can induce even greater differences. The majority of wind-monitoring stations take data with an instrument mounted in a relatively flat, unobstructed area, such as an airport, at some height above the surface. Attempting to use this information for a one-story building located 20 miles away in a grove of trees on hilly terrain can be

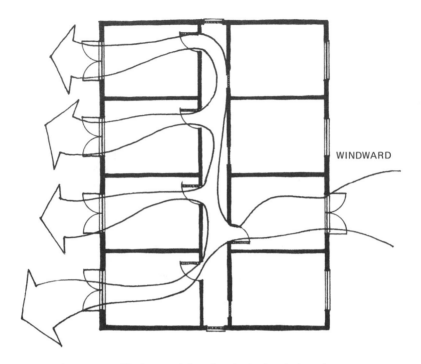

Figure 6.5. Maximum airflow & velocity in windward room.

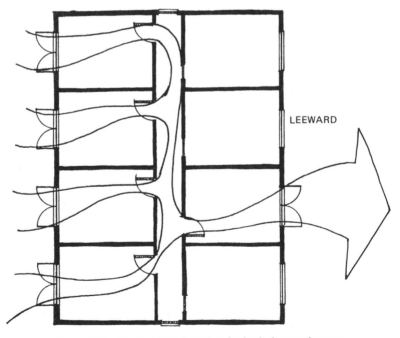

Figure 6.6. Maximum airflow & velocity in leeward room.

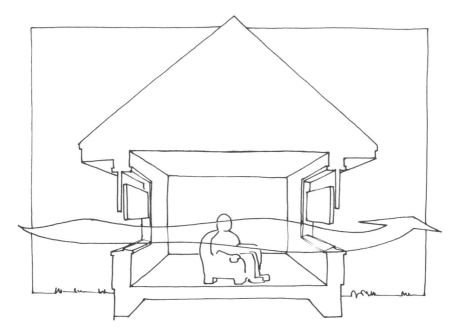

Figure 6.7. Window opened for flow at best level.

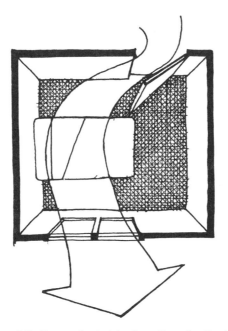

Figure 6.8. Door adjusted for best flow distribution.

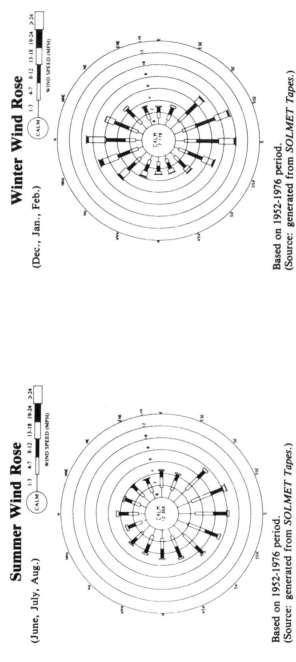

Figure 6.9. Summer and winter wind roses for Chattanooga. (Source: *Climatic Database*, Tennessee Valley Authority Solar Outreach and Technology Group.)

very misleading. Winds at a building site are normally much slower and only rarely faster than at monitoring sites. Weather station wind data reports are usually optimistic estimates of the wind resource at a nearby building site.

In many cases the prevailing wind direction for a location is provided as a design input. Use such information with caution; "prevailing" does not imply the direction that the wind blows for the great majority of the time, but merely the direction it blows more than other directions. Also, when studying ventilation cooling options, be sure to consider only summer wind data, rather than annual average figures.

As an example, consider the average wind data for Chattanooga, Tennessee, Ref. 2.4. The wind rose in Fig. 6.9 shows the distribution of wind speeds and directions normally experienced during the summer (June, July, and August) and during the winter (December, January, and February). The prevailing summer wind direction for Jackson is listed as south-southeast, and indeed the wind is normally from within $22\frac{1}{2}°$ of south-southeast for 24% of the summer hours.

But the wind is likely to be from any other 45° sector for 12% of the summer each. Calm conditions are also likely to prevail for 12% of the summer. A building designed to respond only to south-southeast winds would *not* perform well for most of the summer. Summarized summer wind data for several other southern locations are given in Table 6.5. (Ref. 2.4.)

It is interesting to note that there is a significant portion of the summer when the winds are calm in each of these locations. More than 20% in several cities and 39% in Asheville, North Carolina. In most cases, there is a similar period during which the winds are less than 4 MPH, providing only limited driving force for ventilation. Such information reinforces the attractiveness of electric fans for dependable ventilation.

Table 6.5. Summer Wind Data For Southern Cities.

Location	Average Speed, mph	% Calm	Major Wind Direction, %	Major Opposing Wind Direction, %
Asheville, N.C.	7.8	39	NNW/25	SSE/15
Chattanooga, Tenn.	6.3	21	S/27	NNE/19
Huntsville, Ala.	8.0	21	SSE/22	N/14
Jackson, Miss.	7.6	12	SSE/24	ANY/12
Knoxville, Tenn.	7.3	12	WSW/30	NE/24
Memphis, Tenn.	9.1	6	SSW/33	NNE/16
Nashville, Tenn.	8.0	7	S/32	NNE/16
Paducah, Ky.	7.6	18	SSW/33	NE/15
Tri-Cities, Tenn.	5.6	23	WSW/20	ENE/18

(Source: *Climatic Database*, (Various locations), Tennessee Valley Authority Solar Outreach and Technology Group.)

Stack-Effect Ventilation

As air is heated it expands, becoming less dense and tending to rise above nearby cooler air. Warmer air is more buoyant; it "floats" on top of the denser cool air. The greater the difference in temperature, the greater the force associated with the upward flow. The stack-effect principle may be used to create flow through a building during periods when there is little wind. However, it is a weak form of ventilation and provides only low flow velocities,

The general equation for stack-effect flow with air is

$$F = C \times A \times \{h \times (T_c - T_a)/T_c\}^{0.5}$$

where

F = volumetric flow rate, cfm
C = constant of proportionality, dimensionless
A = free area of inlets and exits, ft^2
h = height from inlet to exit, ft
Tc = average temperature of warm air column, °F
Ta = ambient air temperature °F

For most conditions the following values or sources of data may be used

C = 9.4 when inlets and exits are optimal (65% effective)
C = 7.2 when inlets and exits are obstructed or restricted (50% effective)
A = net free area of inlets *or* exits; assumed to be equal
H = the *vertical* height between the center of the inlet and the center of the exit

The basic elements required for stack-effect flow are a warm column of air, a cool column of air, and a path for flow between them (Fig. 6.10). As the equation indicates, the area of the openings has a greater effect on the air flow than either the temperature difference or the height between the openings. Air flow increases directly with area and only by the square root of temperature difference and height.

In both examples below, the outdoor air forms the cool air column; the chimney and the building itself form the warm air column. In the occupied parts of the building high temperatures cannot be tolerated, limiting the buoyancy forces and the air flow.

In very tall buildings, unwanted stack-effect flow through stair towers and elevator shafts can be a problem. In low-rise buildings, the height of the air columns is much smaller, placing yet another limit on the flow forces. As an example, consider a three-story building with five 3- by 4-ft casement windows

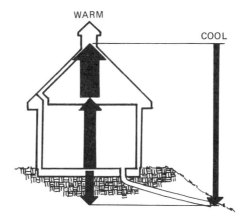

Figure 6.10. Warm/cool air column.

without screens, fully open on both the first and third levels. If the wind is calm and the average air temperature inside the building is 75°F and the outdoor air is 65°F, what is the total air flow due to the stack effect and the average air velocity through the windows?

The height of the air columns is the vertical distance between the two rows of windows, about 18 ft. Substituting this and the other values into the equation for stack-effect flow yields

$$Q = C \times A \times (h \times (T_c - T_a)/Tc)^{0.5}$$
$$= 9.4 \times 60 \text{ ft}^2 \times (18 \text{ ft} \times (75 - 65)°F/75)^{0.5}$$
$$= 874 \text{ cfm}$$

The total volume of air flow is 874 cfm; if window screens were in place, the net free area would be reduced by one-half, and the flow would be only 437 cfm. The average air velocity through the windows is obtained by dividing the flow volume by the window area. The resulting velocity is applicable only at the windows; inside the building the air stream spreads out, and velocities will be much lower

$$\text{Velocity (ft/min)} = \frac{874 \text{ cfm}}{60 \text{ ft}^2} = 14.6 \text{ ft/min}$$

Stack-effect ventilation is not an extremely powerful means of ventilating a building. The flow volumes that can be obtained are rather small compared with those available with electric fans. It should be kept in mind when designing buildings, but it is not one of the most important considerations.

Guidelines for Using Stack-Effect Ventilation for Cooling

1. Consider stack-effect ventilation only as a secondary means of ventilation.
2. Locate skylights, vents, and windows so that stack-effect ventilation can be used to help remove heat from high interior spaces.
3. Maximize the vertical distance between the lower and upper openings for greatest air flow.
4. Design so that wind-induced ventilation and stack-effect ventilation work in harmony to create both horizontal and vertical flow in the building.

Natural Ventilation Recommendations

Because wind-induced ventilation can provide reasonable ventilation rates when winds are available, residential buildings and some commercial building (if appropriate to the building function) should be designed to be capable of taking advantage of it. However, extreme measures to enhance the use of wind-induced ventilation are not justified in most of the United States.

In locations with mild temperatures and consistent winds, such as coastal areas along the northern Gulf and southern Atlantic, more extensive natural ventilation features are appropriate. The work of the Florida Solar Energy Center provides an excellent source of information for more detailed calculation methods. Ref. 6.2.

Stack-effect ventilation should be used where it fits with the other design features of the building. For example, an operable skylight or second-floor windows can be used to provide vertical air motion through the building. More exotic stack-effect devices, such as the solar chimney (to be discussed in detail later in this chapter), are not generally advisable.

Natural Ventilation Design Guidelines

The following guidelines will assist in successfully applying natural ventilation features to small building designs.

1, Design the building to respond well to winds from *any* direction.
2. Provide both an inlet and an outlet for air flow from each space; locate them so that the air flows through the portion of the space most likely to be occupied, and avoid creating stagnant areas.
3. Make use of both horizontal and vertical flow through the building.
4. Use full-opening windows—casement, awning, and hopper windows. Similarly, French doors open to provide more ventilation area than sliding glass doors. (Infiltration is lower, too.)
5. Ensure that the natural ventilation features are accessible and easy to use.

Select window treatments that facilitate access to the windows and ventilation; blinds are a good choice.

6. Avoid blocking windows with exterior objects, such as shrubs and fences, but do not compromise shading; it is a higher priority.

7. Double-glazed windows are preferable to single-glazing with storm windows; storm windows are usually left in place all year and interfere with ventilation.

8. Concentrate ventilation openings in spaces most likely to require cooling.

9. Provide the occupants with guidelines for using natural ventilation, and be certain that they understand the potential savings. Switch from air conditioning to natural ventilation whenever possible.

10. Use overhangs, porches, and eaves to protect ventilation openings from rain, and increase the period of time that they can be left open.

11. Be certain that all ventilation openings can be effectively sealed during winter and when air conditioning.

12. Design so that wind-induced and stack-effect ventilation work together; a particular problem is backflow through the exits of stack-effect devices resulting from wind.

13. Use electric fans to supplement natural ventilation.

Forced Ventilation—Electric Fans

Electric fans are the most consistently effective means of providing ventilation in buildings. Although electric ventilation does not operate without cost, like natural ventilation, its advantages usually outweigh the small amount of energy it consumes. Electric ventilation is also available at the touch of a switch and requires few special provisions in the design of a building. Where the budgets for both construction and operating costs are limited, electric fans provide a low-cost alternative to air conditioning. The initial cost of a whole-house fan and several ceiling fans is less than one-half the cost of a central air conditioning system. Later, if air conditioning is added, the fans can still be used to reduce operating costs.

The equation below may be used to estimate the hourly cost of operating a fan

$$\text{Hourly operating cost (\$/h)} = \frac{\text{Wattage (watts)} \times \text{power cost (\$/kWh)}}{1000 \ (\text{W/kw})}$$

For example, with electric power at \$0.08/kWh, a 250-W ceiling fan costs \$0.02/h to operate

$$\text{Hourly operating cost} = \frac{250 \ \text{W} \times \$0.08/\text{kWh}}{1000 \ \text{W/kW}} = \$0.02/\text{h}$$

Table 6.6. Typical Motor Efficiencies.

Horsepower	Type	Full Load Efficiency, %
0.05	Shaded pole	35
0.08	Shaded pole	35
0.125	Shaded pole	35
0.16	Shaded pole	35
0.25	Split phase	54
0.33	Split phase	56
0.50	Split phase	60
0.75	Three-phase	72
1.00	Three-phase	75
2.00	Three-phase	79
3.00	Three-phase	81
5.00	Three-phase	82

(Adapted with permission from *ASHRAE Handbook—1985 Fundamentals.*)

Where only the horsepower of a fan is known, the wattage can be estimated

$$\text{Wattage} = \frac{\text{Horsepower (HP)} \times 746 \text{ W/HP}}{\text{Efficiency}}$$

Typical electric motor efficiencies are provided by Table 6.6. Ref. 5.1.

Annual operating hours range from about 100 h/yr for a ceiling fan in a seldom-used room to more than 2000 h/yr for a whole-house fan used as the sole means of cooling in a hot area. For most residential applications, a figure between 800 and 1200 h/yr is appropriate for a fan used as a primary cooling means. For fans used only during mild periods of the cooling season, 200 to 500 h/yr is a reasonable estimate. The potential savings in energy and costs by substituting electric fans for air conditioning are obvious when operating costs are compared. Even a large whole-house fan uses only about 10 to 15% of the electric power used by a central air conditioner. Annual cooling energy savings of more than 60% are easily achieved when electric fans are used diligently as a substitute for air conditioning. But like many energy conservation measures, the actual saving associated with fans for cooling is strongly influenced by the way the building occupants use them. Field tests have shown that energy savings from whole-house fans can vary by a factor of 3 from one household to another.

INTERIOR VENTILATION

Interior fans are used to provide air circulation inside a building as opposed to ventilating the building with outdoor air. They do not remove heat from the building, but from the occupants themselves, providing improving comfort con-

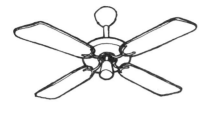

Figure 6.11. Interior fans.

ditions without changing the interior temperature. Interior fans (Fig. 6.11) are very effective people-coolers, making them a highly effective and economical means of reducing air conditioning usage and improving comfort conditions. Unlike natural ventilation, electric fans can provide air motion inside a building without introducing exterior air.

Approximate hourly operating costs for several common interior fans are shown in Table 6.7 for power costs of $0.04, $0.06, $0.08, and $0.10 per kWh.

The fans described in Table 6.7 are commercially available models with the following speeds, flow rates, and wattages.

Box fan—20-in. diameter; three speeds (1050/920/720 RPM); 2900/2550/2000 cfm; 180/120/60 W

Oscillating portable fan—12-in. diameter; three speeds (1400/1100/900 RPM); 1800/1480/1325 cfm; 44/21/12 W

Ceiling fan—52-in. diameter; three speeds (175/130/50 RPM); 7000/5200/2000 cfm; 85/35/17 W

Note the differences in power consumption and airflow rates for the three fans. On high speed, the box fan provides only 16 cfm of ventilation per watt of power consumed. The oscillating fan and the ceiling fan provide more air motion for the power they consume, 32 and 82 cfm per W, respectively. But, because the power consumption is small in all cases, the difference in the cost

Table 6.7. Approximate Hourly Operating Costs for Fans.

| Fan Type | Electric Power Cost, Cents/Hour (Highest Operating Speed) | | | |
	$0.04	$0.06	$0.08	$0.10
Box	0.72	1.08	1.44	1.80
Oscillating	0.18	0.26	0.35	0.44
Ceiling	0.34	0.51	0.82	1.02

of electricity may not be significant unless several fans are used or operating hours are very high.

Possible Problems

Interior fans are simple to apply and use; the only potential problems that may arise are inconvenience due to excessive air speeds and noise. Excessive air speeds can produce problems for building occupants, particularly in offices. Speeds of 150 fpm or more may cause paper to blow about; speeds above 300 fpm may be annoying to many people. Common sense in selecting fan locations will preclude most problems. Fan speed controls allow the selection of lower speeds to minimize problems. Fan noise can come from three sources, the blades, the motor, and vibrations transmitted to the building structure.

Vibration noise is usually avoided by proper mounting and common sense. Higher quality fans usually do not produce bothersome motor noise. However, a hum may be produced when ceiling fans or whole-house fans are used with certain controls to regulate the speed of the fan. Be sure that particular fans and controls are compatible before buying.

Lower quality fans sometimes use very high speeds to increase air flow rather than using a larger, more expensive blade and motor rotating at a slower speed. If quiet operation is a concern, a fan with a slower operating speed should be chosen.

Ceiling Fans

Who can walk into a room with a ceiling fan without briefly assuming Humphrey Bogart's role in *Casablanca* and humming a few bars of "As Time Goes By"? Or perhaps another scene from any number of films, plays, or novels set in Central America, the South Pacific, or the American South? While the fans slowly turn, romances develop, revolutions are plotted, and business deals are closed. This imagery certainly has contributed to the increased popularity of ceiling fans, or paddle fans, in recent years. For a modest price a bedroom in Cincinnati can be transformed into a sensual Moroccan boudoir.

Besides having romantic appeal, ceiling fans are also a very effective method of improving summer comfort conditions in buildings. They are efficient air movers and are easily incorporated into almost any residence and many other buildings. Test results have shown that significant reductions in air conditioning costs are possible if fans are used properly. By allowing us to comfortably tolerate higher temperatures, ceiling fans create several energy savings opportunities

1. as a substitute for air conditioning
2. in conjunction with air conditioning to allow a higher thermostat setpoint

3. to extend the ''coasting'' period of a building cooled by nocturnal ventilation

Sizing a ceiling fan is normally a matter of selecting between two or three sizes. If the budget allows, it is desirable to install a larger fan, so that a greater range of air flow settings is available and ventilation is provided over a larger area without excess velocities. Larger fans can provide an equivalent amount of airflow with less noise and usually use only slightly more power than similar smaller units. For example, one company's 52-in., 7000-cfm fan uses 90 W of power, and its 36-in., 5000-cfm model requires 50 W. Over 1000 h of operation, with an electric power cost of $0.08/kWh, the 40-W difference results in an operating cost difference of only $3.20. The difference in purchase price is approximately $40.00. There are fairly large variations in both power consumption and noise levels from one brand to another. Very inexpensive models may give poor performance.

A separate ceiling fan should be used to serve each frequently occupied space in the building. Larger rooms will require more than one fan. Guidelines for selecting fan sizes are provided in Table 6.8.

Ceiling fans should be located to provide airflow to areas most likely to be occupied within a room, such as the seating area in a den. Although it is convenient to simply mount a fan with an integral light to replace a ceiling light fixture, such fixtures are not always in the preferred location for ventilating a large room. It is normally possible to mount a ceiling fan with a light kit in a room with an 8-ft ceiling. A fan/light combination should be considered for applications in new residences in particular, for the savings that accrue from not buying a separate light fixture can partially offset the cost of the fan.

The horizontal and vertical distribution of airflow and speed for a ceiling fan in a typical room are shown in Fig. 6.12. The presence of furniture in a room can alter the pattern somewhat. With high ceilings, it is beneficial to extend the fan hanger to lower the blades to 7 to 8 ft above the floor. This increases the air speed over the occupants.

Ceiling fans should be equipped with variable speed controls or should have two operating speeds to allow air velocities to be matched to cooling needs. Reverse airflow is a desirable feature, but not a necessity. Upward flow is useful in providing general air motion in the room without high speeds in the area immediately under the fan.

Table 6.8. Fan Size Selection.

Area Served, ft^2	Fan Diameter, in.
150	42
225	48
375	52

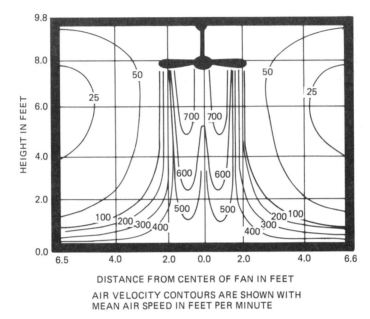

DISTANCE FROM CENTER OF FAN IN FEET

AIR VELOCITY CONTOURS ARE SHOWN WITH
MEAN AIR SPEED IN FEET PER MINUTE

Figure 6.12. Air flow and speed from ceiling fan. (Aynsley, 1977)

Although ceiling fans have been advertised as offering energy savings during the winter, they provide little benefit in most applications. Only where ceilings are quite high, more than 12 ft, is there sufficient stratification to warrant the use of a fan to redistribute the heat. Industrial buildings provide possible applications. But in residences, ceilings are lower, and the cooling effect of moving air overcomes any benefits of circulating heat that accumulates near the ceiling. An exception is a room with a wood stove or large passive solar glazing area; a ceiling fan set on a low speed may be useful to distribute heat and prevent localized hot and cool spots. The actual air conditioning energy savings from the use of ceiling fans are greatly influenced by the building occupants. A test conducted in single-family homes in Orlando, Florida, showed savings of 0 to 31% when ceiling fans were installed to supplement existing air conditioning systems (Ref. 6.3 and 6.4). The average figure was 13%, but if four households that apparently did not use the fans often and relied on air conditioning more often are disregarded, the average savings figure climbs to 20%.

Ceiling fans even produce a psychological cooling effect. During tests at Kansas State University using 256 people, researchers found that the test subjects reported a cooling effect with ceiling fans producing air velocities of only 30 fpm. Such slight air motion is undetectable, indicating that the effect was a result of the sight of the moving fan blades.

For interior air circulation, ceiling fans are probably unmatched for effectiveness, ease of use, and appearance.

Air Conditioning Supplemented With Interior Air Circulation

Even when air conditioning is in use in a building, interior circulating fans can provide energy conservation opportunities. In residences, the use of ceiling fans can allow an increase in the thermostat setting from 78 to 85°F. Such an increase can reduce air conditioning energy consumption by 30 to 45%, even with the cost of electricity for operating the fans considered. This operating mode also allows the air conditioning unit to provide some dehumidification of the indoor air. This is particularly valuable in areas where very high humidity is a problem.

Interior circulating fans also allow downsizing of the air conditioning equipment. The downsized capacity can be estimated by using 82°F, or the assumed comfort temperature with the fans in operation, in the design load calculations. The benefits of downsizing include equipment cost reduction, peak electrical demand reduction, and improved humidity control. In existing buildings with air conditioning systems that cannot maintain comfortable conditions, interior fans are an alternative to installing increased air conditioning capacity.

Attic Ventilator Fans

Attic ventilator fans are one of the more widely used cooling retrofit devices for residences. Advertised as a simple, afternoon do-it-yourself project, they are often featured in the energy products department of hardware and building supply stores. The fans simply exhaust hot air from the attic and draw cooler outdoor air into the space through vents and infiltration leaks. Attic ventilators must not be confused with whole-house fans, once often referred to as *attic fans*. The whole-house fan moves great quantities of outdoor air through the living area and exhausts it through the attic. An attic ventilator is much smaller and ventilates only the attic or ceiling cavity (Fig. 6.13).

Attic ventilators are normally mounted directly through the roof within a small exhaust duct that penetrates the roof deck. Controls and operation are simple. A thermostatic switch turns the fan on whenever the attic air temperature reaches a certain level. The setpoint is either fixed at approximately 100°F or variable, with a control mounted on the unit. Once turned on, the fan con-

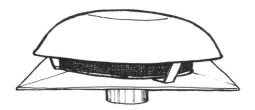

Figure 6.13. Attic ventilator fan.

tinues to run until the attic temperature drops to a temperature about 15° below the set point, typically 85°F. By reducing the attic air temperature, the ventilator reduces undesirable heat gain through the ceiling into the occupied space. Tests have shown reductions in ceiling heat gain of 20 to 30% with powered attic ventilators. Refs. 6.5, 6.6, 6.7. However, as pointed out later, such savings figures need to be interpreted carefully.

The fan motors in attic ventilators are usually small, from $\frac{1}{15}$ to $\frac{1}{5}$ HP, with power requirements of 250 to 420 W. Airflow capacity ranges from 900 to 1700 cfm at 0.03 in. of water, a standard rating point. In less expensive models, the efficiency of the fan motor and the fan are low; thus the volume of air moved per watt of power consumed is also low. Performance figures for several attic ventilators are shown in Table 6.9. Manufacturers recommend that 0.7 cfm of flow capacity be provided for each square foot of attic floor area if standard louvers are used. The area of the openings allowing air to enter the attic must be at least 1 ft^2 for each 300 cfm of flow capacity.

Performance and Energy Savings

Although we can show that electric ventilators do provide a significant decrease in attic temperature, the reduction in air conditioning costs is not necessarily large, and the power consumed is not a negligible cost by any means. There is a considerable amount of disagreement on the overall savings attainable from electric ventilators. Manufacturers suggest that savings are substantial, but test results around the country and computer simulations consistently indicate otherwise (Refs. 6.5–6.10).

A reduction in attic air temperatures will certainly reduce air conditioning costs or improve comfort. But in most houses and small commercial buildings, the ceiling or roof heat gain is already a small portion of the total cooling load, usually less than 15%. So, even a substantial reduction in ceiling heat gains result in only a small reduction in total cooling load. For the example houses defined earlier, the ceiling cooling load represents only about 12% of the total load. A 25% reduction in ceiling cooling load reduces total cooling load about 3%.

Table 6.9. Attic Ventilator Performance Data.

Power Requirement, W	Air Flow at 0.03 in. Water, cfm	cfm/W
255	900	3.5
185	905	4.9
415	1200	2.9
215	1420	6.6
303	1720	5.7

In most cases, the power consumption of the attic ventilators is equal to or greater than the savings in air conditioning costs. Rigorous tests on residences in Florida, Washington, D.C., New Jersey, Nebraska, and Texas have all produced this conclusion. Both peak power demand and total power consumption increased slightly when fans were used. The air conditioning savings were not adequate to offset the additional power consumed by the fans.

In these tests, attic ventilators reduced *peak* attic temperatures by 10 to 15°F, from 120–125 to 105–115°F. This does not mean that the *average* attic temperature is also reduced 10 to 15°F. The attic temperature drops at night even without the ventilators. The net effect on the average attic temperature over the full 24-h day is a reduction of only 2 to 3°F.

Savings are strongly influenced by the amount of insulation installed in the ceiling. As the insulation level increases, the total ceiling heat gain decreases and the potential saving from an attic ventilator also decreases. Attic ventilation is most effective when insulation levels are very low, less than $R11$. But the same can be said of additional ceiling insulation, and additional insulation also provides benefits during the heating season.

The insulation value of a naturally ventilated attic with 0.2 cfm/ft^2 of area is roughly $R3$. If an attic ventilator is used to boost the ventilation rate to 1.0 cfm/ft^2, the effective R value climbs to $R9$, an increase of $R6$. Thus, in an attic with $R11$ insulation, the attic ventilator increases the total R value for the ceiling/attic combination from about 14 to $R20$. The reduction in ceiling heat gain for a given ceiling area and temperature difference is $[1 - (\frac{1}{20})/(\frac{1}{14})]$, or 30%. With $R30$ insulation, the ceiling heat gain is lower, and the reduction is a smaller fraction $[1 - (\frac{1}{39})/(\frac{1}{33})]$, or 15%.

The monthly power consumption in kilowatt-hours per month (kWh/mo) of an attic ventilator may be estimated by multiplying the wattage by the run time. In tests, the daily hours of operation for properly sized ventilation varied from 6 to more than 12 h/day. An estimate of 8 to 9 h/day is suggested as a seasonal average. If the thermostatic control is not properly adjusted, the fan can run long into the night after its usefulness has diminished.

If air conditioning ducts are routed through the attic, then attic ventilators can provide additional savings by reducing duct losses. The reduction is also proportional to the difference in the attic temperature and the temperature of the air in the duct with and without the fan in operation. Both ceiling heat gain savings and duct gains savings were considered in the tests described here.

Decreased ceiling temperatures are sometimes cited as a further justification for powered attic ventilators. Besides reduced heat gain to the interior, a decrease in ceiling temperature improves comfort by decreasing the mean radiant temperature inside the building. But the effect of an attic ventilator on ceiling temperatures is rather small, except at very low insulation levels.

Table 6.10 shows the change in ceiling temperature associated with a reduc-

Table 6.10. Effect of Attic Ventilation on Ceiling Temperature.

	Insulation R Value, h °F ft^2/Btu		
	R7	R19	R30
Ceiling temperature with attic air at 135°F, °F	81.1	77.6	76.7
Ceiling temperature with attic air at 100°F, °F	78.6	76.5	76.0

inside air temperature of 75°F is assumed. A peak attic temperature reduction of 10°F, rather than 25°F, is more representative of most installations where power vents are added to existing natural ventilation that meets code requirements. Ceiling temperature reductions would be only 40% of the amount shown in Table 6.10. Field test results indicate that a typical attic ventilator reduces ceiling temperatures by only 1.0 to 1.5°F. Ref. 6.7 Because the ceiling is only of six surfaces that determine the mean radiant temperature in a normal room, a 1.5°F reduction at the ceiling results in a much smaller reduction in mean radiant temperature. A maximum benefit of no more than 0.5°F should be expected.

Attic ventilators may provide noticeable benefits if poorly insulated air conditioning ducts are routed through the attic or if there is excessive infiltration from the attic to the ducts or the living space below. Air leaks in the ceiling between the attic and the building interior also increase cooling loads directly. The consequences of duct leaks or ceiling leaks are much more severe than for leaks around windows and doors, because the temperature of the air that leaks in is so much higher. Where air leakage is high, attic ventilators would yield good results, but so would a simple repair of the ducts or the ceiling leaks. And eliminating the leaks also reduces heating loads.

Controls and Effectiveness

Attic ventilators consume a fixed amount of power as they run; the speed is not varied with the need for ventilation. When the attic temperatures are high, a ventilator removes large amounts of heat. As the attic temperature falls, the rate of heat removal also drops, reaching zero when the attic temperature is equal to the outdoor temperature. At some point, when the attic temperature is still above the outdoor air temperature, it is better to shut the fan off rather than continue operating it. Unfortunately, many attic ventilators are supplied with thermostats that allow the fan to continue to operate when it is removing little heat from the attic, doing almost nothing to reduce the cooling load and consuming electricity needlessly.

Most fans have thermostats that switch the fan on at 100°F and leave it running until the attic temperature drops to 85°F. When the outdoor temperature is above 85°F, the fan will continue to operate, even after the attic has been cooled to the outdoor temperature and further ventilation is completely useless. Some units are sold with thermostats that can be set to turn the fan on at temperatures as low as 70°F, so that the fans could run during the entire spring, summer, and fall if the controls are improperly adjusted. A further possibility for inefficient operation is the wide variation in the actual temperature settings of the thermostat in an attic ventilator. Calibration errors of nearly 10°F have been found.

Attic Ventilation Alternatives

If excessive ceiling heat gains create a problem in an existing building, there are several effective attic ventilation alternatives, other than power vents, that may be used. In new buildings, effective natural ventilation features may be designed into the building to preclude the need for powered attic ventilation. In some cases, natural ventilation features may be used instead of powered attic ventilation in existing buildings. Additional gable and soffit vents can usually be installed. Ridge vents have been successfully retrofitted to existing roofs, although the process is not simple. Certainly, whenever powered vents can be installed, natural draft turbine vents can be used as easily. Installing additional ceiling insulation is also a very effective measure to reduce ceiling heat gains in buildings that are poorly insulated.

Applications of Powered Attic Ventilators

Powered attic ventilators are most applicable to situations where excessive ceiling heat gains result from poor ceiling insulation and attic ventilation, and insulation and natural ventilation cannot be easily increased. Such conditions might be encountered in a building where much of the attic space is not accessible.

Recommendation

Powered attic ventilators are usually not an effective cooling energy conservation measure in most buildings. Tests indicate that the power consumed by the fan is roughly equal to the air conditioning energy savings. In cases where excessive ceiling heat gain is a problem, additional ceiling insulation or natural attic ventilation should be considered before powered attic ventilation.

Whole-House Fans

Function

Whole-house fans, or attic fans, as they were once called, are an economical way to reduce air contitioner usage and costs throughout the United States. Whole-house fans simultaneously provide large quantities of ventilating air to the living space of a house and remove hot air from the attic. Figure 6.14 illustrates a typical installation and describes the airflow patterns the fan creates. The whole-house fan pulls air from the interior of the house and discharges it into the attic, creating a negative pressure inside the house. Air enters the house through open windows to relieve the low pressure, flows through the living space, and is then drawn into the attic and exhausted. Louvers, which open automatically when the fan is started, are normally installed in the ceiling below the fan. The flow of outside air through the house and the attic removes heat and lowers the interior temperature to or near the outside temperature. Attic temperatures are also reduced, decreasing heat gains from hot ceilings. More importantly, air motion through the living space creates a cooling effect at the occupants' skin surfaces, allowing them to be comfortable at higher than normal

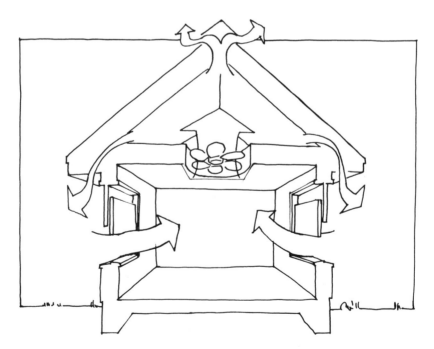

Figure 6.14. Whole-house fan installation.

temperatures. Offering interior air speeds of 100 to 200 ft/min, a whole-house fan can provide acceptable comfort at temperatures above 82°F with reasonable humidity levels.

For many years, whole-house fans were the most sophisticated cooling system available for homes. Today they provide both a good substitute for air conditioning during most of the cooling season and, in some locations, a complete replacement for air conditioning for conservation-minded homeowners. By preventing the house from creating a cooling problem during mild or moderate summer weather the whole-house fan shortens or eliminates the air conditioning season. While a typical house might require air conditioning whenever the outdoor temperature rises above 72°F, a house with a whole-house fan might require air conditioning only when the outdoor temperature is above 82°F. Reductions in the air conditioning season of 30 to 50% are easily achieved.

Limitations and Potential Problems

Whole-house fans cannot remove humidity from the air and they cannot reduce the temperature of the air. When humidity and temperature rise to extreme levels, conventional comfort conditions cannot be provided inside the home. Thus, many people in the South would be unwilling to give up their air conditioners and rely exclusively on whole-house fans.

Other concerns include

1. Dust and pollen. Because a whole-house fan circulates large quantities of outdoor air through a building, it can bring in dust and pollen if they are present. One potential solution is the use of conventional window screens or filter units made for the purpose. These are installed in the windows, where they remove dust and other particulates from the air as it enters the house.
2. Noise. Many people consider the sounds of a fan a perfect way to cover up the noise of restless dogs, incompatible neighbors, and nearby traffic. Such "white" noise is sometimes used in offices to mask other sounds. Other people find the noise of an attic fan to be disturbing.

Mechanical sounds have several origins, normally associated with either poor fan design, improper installation, or damage to the fan. Excessive noise can arise if the fan is designed to operate at too high a speed. Where quiet operation is a concern, a fan having an operating speed of 700 RPM or lower should be selected. Severe noise problems can arise if the fan blades are not balanced or have become bent or damaged during installation; vibrations may be transmitted from the fan housing through the house's structure. Other possible sources of noise include loose mounting of either the fan or the louvers and inadequate airflow paths. Louvers should be chosen to match the size of the fan, following manufacturers' recommendations. Oversized louvers will not open fully and often will rattle during operation. Conversely, undersized louvers may restrict airflow and increase airflow noise levels.

Sizing and Selection

Whole-house fans should be sized to provide between $\frac{1}{2}$ and 1 air change per minute (30 to 60 air changes per hour) of ventilation for the space they serve. This represents 10 to 20 times the air exhange rate in a typical house with the windows open. The $\frac{1}{2}$ air change per min value is recommended for installations where the fan will be used only on mild days as a substitute for air conditioning. In an air conditioner is not installed or if the occupants wish to maximize the period in which they can comfortably use the fan, the upper value should be chosen.

$$\text{Recommended flow rate} = \text{floor area} \times \text{ceiling height} \times f \, (\text{CFM})$$

where: $f = 0.5$ for fans installed with air conditioning, and $f = 1.0$ for fans used as the only cooling source
The fan should be rated to provide the required airflow at a static pressure of 0.1 in. of water. This is a typical rating value used by manufacturers and approximates the flow resistance encountered in most residential installations.

Differences in power consumption between models are normally not a major concern. For example, with a power cost of \$0.075/kWh and 1000 h of annual operation, a reduction in power consumption of 50 W results in savings of only \$3.75/yr. However, high power consumption may indicate poor motor and bearing quality.

Installation

Whole-house fans are simple to install, but a few rules must be followed, if performance, comfort and safety are not to be compromised. The fans are normally installed in a horizontal position in the ceiling below an attic. Other alternative installations in gables and monitors are possible if ceiling mounting is not possible. In any position, louvers are usually used to hide the fan and close the opening when the fan is not in use. The inlet to the fan should open directly into the living space, and at least 3 ft of clearance should be provided between the discharge of the fan and any obstructions, such as the lower side of the roof. Of course, the ceiling structure must be reinforced to compensate for any framing cut during installation. Fans are available with mounting systems that eliminate the need to cut framing members.

The fan should be controlled by a switch in the living area. Timers are a useful feature, for they allow operation of the fan during the early portion of the night, when interior temperatures are still high, and automatic shutdown later in the night, when temperatures drop. The use of a thermostat to turn the fan on when the house temperature rises above the setpoint is not recommended. The fan may be damaged if it is run when windows or doors are not open to allow air to enter the house. Also, a simple interior thermostat may turn the fan on when the outdoor temperatures are much higher than the indoor temperature and ventilation is not appropriate. More sophisticated thermostatic control based on both interior and exterior temperature is advantageous, but such controls are not available as a standard unit and must be assembled from components.

A firestat, or a fusible link in the fan power circuit, should be used to interrupt power to the fan in the event of a fire. It may be required by some building codes.

The fan must have adequate flow areas at the inlets to the house and the exits from the attic. The free areas of both the inlet and exit vent should be equal to 1.5 to 2.0 times the area of the fan opening. The air speed should be kept below 750 fpm through the inlets and exits. The free area is the actual area of the vent adjusted for any restrictions, such as louvers or screen. Table 6.3 provides factors to calculate the free area of several common vent configurations.

Operation

The operating strategy for a whole-house fan is quite simple; it is turned on when the inside temperature is higher than the outside temperature or when airflow is desired, and turned off when it is no longer required. By running the fan as much as possible during the cool nights, the mass of the house may be used to store "coolth" for the next day. Windows and doors should be kept closed in the morning as outdoor temperatures begin to rise. The fan should not be used until the inside temperature reaches an uncomfortable level. Figure 6.15

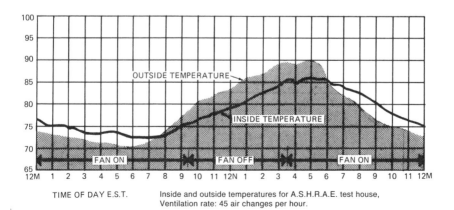

TIME OF DAY E.S.T.   Inside and outside temperatures for A.S.H.R.A.E. test house,
                            Ventilation rate: 45 air changes per hour.

Figure 6.15. Typical operating pattern. (Adapted from HVAC, May 1944, p. 300)

illustrates a typical operating pattern for a whole-house fan in Atlanta. Ref. 6.9. In some cases, the house can coast through the entire day until the following night when temperatures fall again. The higher mass of passive solar houses is beneficial for this effect.

The louvers used with whole-house fans should not be relied upon for good sealing against infiltration when the fan is not in use. During winter and the portion of the summer when the air conditioner is being used, the fan opening should be positively sealed with an insulated and gasketed or weatherstripped panel. When operated briefly with most of a home's windows and doors closed, whole-house fans are quite effective in highlighting undesirable air infiltration paths into the home. Leakage around plumbing and electrical lines, window and door frames, and wall joints is easily felt with a bare hand or seen with cigarette smoke or incense. Be certain to close the damper in the fireplace flue before operating the fan.

Economics: Costs and Savings

Average quality whole-house fans may cost from about $180 for a 24-in.-diameter, $\frac{1}{3}$-HP model to $320 for a 36-in.-diameter, $\frac{3}{4}$ HP model. The prices of higher or lower quality models differ by about 25%. Louvers add an additional $30 to $60. Timers cost $10 to $25. Total installation costs range from $285 to $575.

As there is no refrigeration compressor and only an electric motor, whole-house fans are extremely economical to operate, with power consumption levels of about 400 to 550 W for most large models. With electric power at $0.075 per kWh, a typical fan would cost less than $0.03 per hour to operate. In contrast, a 3-ton air conditioner with an EER of 8.0 costs about $0.34 per hour to run. Table 6.11 illustrates operating costs for air conditioning systems and whole-house fans with various power rates.

Table 6.11. Whole-House Fan and A/C Hourly Operation Costs.

	Electric Power Cost, Cents per kWh		
	5	7.5	10
8,000-Btu/h room air conditioner, EER = 6.0	6.6	10.0	13.3
36,000-Btu/h central air conditioner, EER = 8.0	22.5	33.8	45.0
36-in. Whole-house fan, low speed, 250 W	1.3	1.9	2.5
36-in. Whole-house fan, high speed, 550 W	2.8	4.1	5.5

Even in the hot and humid deep South, there are significant periods during the cooling season when outdoor temperatures are in a range that is ideal for the use of whole-house fans. Between 72 and 82°F, a whole-house fan can easily take the place of an air conditioner. If light clothing is worn (CLO = 0.5) whole-house fans can provide comfort conditions described as no worse than slightly warm all summer throughout the country. The useful operating period for a particular location may be estimated from temperature bin data, Ref. 2.5. Table 6.12 shows the distribution of cooling season temperatures for several locations. Ref 6.10. Also included is a calculation of the percentage of possible hours of whole-house fan operation, assuming the fan is used only when the outdoor temperature is between 72 and 82°F.

Whole-house fan operating costs may be estimated by multiplying the hours of operation by the fan wattage/1000 and the power cost. Hours of operation may be estimated as the number of hours in the 72 to 78°F range for a fan used in conjunction with an air conditioner or as the number of hours above 72°F for a fan used without an air conditioner. The savings effect may be visualized by examining the graphs in Fig. 6.16, which describe the cooling season in Atlanta. For an Atlanta house with a relatively efficient 3-ton air conditioning unit (EER = 8.0), a 550-W whole-house fan might be used for 1000 h in a normal year. With power costs of $0.08/kWh, a cost of $44/yr would result.

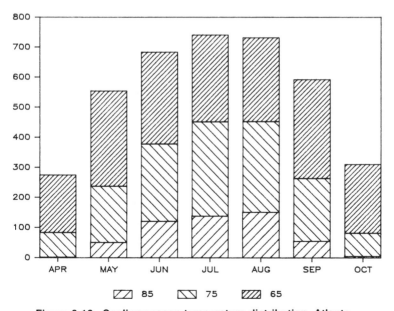

Figure 6.16. Cooling season temperature distribution, Atlanta.

Table 6.12. Annual Cooling Temperature Distributions.

Locations	Temperature Bins[a]					Percentage of Possible Whole-House-Fan Hours $\dfrac{\text{col 2} + \text{col 3}}{\text{col 5}} \times 100$
	col 1 65–71	col 2 72–77	col 3 78–82	col 4 above 82	col 5 above 72	
Atlanta, Ga.	1878	1217	663	439	2319	81%
Burbank, Calif.	1967	528	67	53	648	92%
Chicago, Ill.	1102	717	330	275	1322	79%
Fresno, Calif.	1087	745	526	1195	2466	52%
Ft. Worth, Tex.	1117	1378	934	1422	3754	62%
Houston, Tex.	1374	1808	1160	1244	4212	70%
Minneapolis, Minn.	906	704	389	452	1545	71%
Phoenix, Ariz.	1157	900	718	2422	4040	40%
Portland, Ore.	755	345	192	138	675	78%
Washington, D.C.	1110	1008	601	722	2331	69%

[a]The bin data were generated from ASHRAE TRY (Test Reference Year) weather data tapes.

Air conditioner usage of 570 h would be displaced, at a saving of about $205, for a net savings of $161. If the whole-house fan were substituted for the air conditioner during the entire season, savings would be approximately $335.

A field test program sponsored by the state of Florida in 1982 monitored the performance of whole-house fans installed with central air conditioning systems. Ref 6. The fan control was interlocked with the air conditioner thermostat and programmed to operate between 7:30 A.M. and 4:00 A.M., whenever the thermostat called for cooling and the outdoor temperature was below 82°F. The fans were observed to run for significant periods of time for each day during the 3-months test period. Based on the test data, the payback and rate of return resulting from a $460 investment in a whole-house fan were calculated for four locations in Florida. Refs. 6.3 and 6.4. In another program, a detailed computer

Location	Payback Period, yr	Rate of Return, %
Tallahassee	1.99	59.1
Gainesville	1.79	64.9
Orlando	1.68	66.8
Miami	1.13	98.4

simulation of whole-house fan performance was conducted by the National Bureau of Standards, using a computer simulation and annual weather tapes. Ref. 6.10 The program simulated the cooling performance and power consumption of a 450-W whole-house fan and an air conditioning system in a 1176-ft^2, three-bedroom ranch house for 10 locations in the United States. Two modes of operation were used.

The first maintained interior temperature at 78°F or less, and the second mode allowed interior temperatures to increase to 82°F, taking advantage of the cooling effects of the moving air. In the first mode, the fan was operated at full speed whenever it was possible to use outdoor air to maintain the 78°F thermostat setpoint. Air conditioning was assumed at other times. The second mode assumed the following

Outdoor temperature < 72°F	Cooling by natural ventilation only at 6 ACH
Outdoor temperature = 72 to 78°F	Cooling by whole-house fan at low speed (130 W), 30 ACH
Outdoor temperature = 78 to 82°F	Cooling by whole-house fan at high speed (450 W), 60 ACH
Outdoor temperature > 82°F	Cooling with air conditioning, 0.6 ACH

The house was a single-story unit with a 22.6° pitched roof having R19 insulation (R22 in Minnesota) and R11 wall insulation. Windows were 15% of the

Table 6.13.   Whole-House Fan Performance, Mode 1.

Locations	Annual Cooling, kWh		WHF Hours of Operation	Cooling Savings, kWh	Estimated Fan Power Consumption, kWh[a]	Net Savings Electric Energy	
	Without WHF	With WHF				kWh	%
Atlanta, Ga.	3098	2056	288	1042	130	912	29.4
Burbank, Calif.	1870	1444	107	426	48	378	20.2
Chicago, Ill.	1725	1189	173	536	78	548	26.6
Fresno, Calif.	2845	2342	182	503	82	421	14.8
Ft. Worth, Tex.	3894	2992	275	902	124	778	20.0
Houston, Tex.	4394	3172	361	1222	162	1068	24.1
Minneapolis, Minn.	1853	1332	162	521	73	448	24.2
Phoenix, Ariz.	4580	4078	182	502	82	420	9.2
Portland, Ore.	1347	1025	90	322	41	281	20.9
Washington, D.C.	2567	1859	201	708	90	618	24.1

[a] Assumed fan size 450 W.

Table 6.14. Whole-House Fan Performance, Mode 2.

Locations	Annual Cooling, kWh		WHF Hours of Operation	Cooling Savings, kWh	Estimated Fan Power Consumption, kWh[a]	Net Savings Electric Energy	
	Without WHF	With WHF				kWh	%
Atlanta, GA	3098	879	1880	2219	469	1750	56.4
Burbank, CA	1870	961	595	909	124	785	42.0
Chicago, IL	1725	629	1047	1096	249	847	49.1
Fresno, CA	2845	1722	1271	1123	341	782	27.5
Ft. Worth, TX	3894	2037	2312	1857	613	1244	31.9
Houston, TX	4394	1834	2968	2560	775	1785	40.6
Minneapolis, MN	1853	755	1093	1098	274	824	44.5
Phoenix, AR	4580	3356	1618	1224	449	775	16.9
Portland, OR	1347	655	537	692	135	554	41.3
Washington, DC	2567	1094	1609	1473	412	1061	41.3

[a] DB > 82, air conditioner with no whole-house fan, 0.6 AC/h.
82 > DB > 78, no air conditioner with whole-house fan, 60 AC/h.
78 > DB > 72, no air conditioner with whole-house fan, 30 AC/h.
72 > DB, natural ventilation, no air conditioner and no whole-house fan, 6 AC/h DB = outdoor temperature.

floor area and single glazed, except in Minneapolis, Chicago, Portland, and Washington, where double-glazing was assumed. An internal heat gain of 15.5 kWh/day was used. Floor construction was either slab, basement, or crawl space according to the location.

The results of the simulation are provided in Tables 6.13 and 6.14 and may be used to estimate the potential of whole-house fans in similar applications.

Conclusion

Whole-house fans are an example of another elegantly unsophisticated method of reducing space conditioning energy costs. Though they do have minor problems and require the building occupant to operate the fan and open and close the windows, they provide significant benefits. Savings of $100 to $200/yr are possible in the South, and in the cooler North, a $500 fan may make a $2000 air conditioning system unnecessary. As a remedy for comfort problems in a house without air conditioning or as a method of reducing air conditioner use, a whole-house fan should be seriously evaluated.

Nocturnal Ventilation and Interior Thermal Mass Storage

Interior Thermal Mass for Cooling

Interior thermal mass is widely used in passive solar heating systems to store excess solar heat during the day and release it at night when temperatures are lower. In certain cases the same concept can be applied to summer cooling, with heat taken from the building during the day and released to the cooler night air. Unfortunately, climatic variables place more severe limits on the successful use of thermal mass for cooling than for heating. The lack of a large temperature differential for heat transfer from the building is the primary difficulty.

The magnitude of the heat transfer into and out of thermal storage mass depends on the temperature differential between the mass and its surroundings. In cooling situations, the day-to-night variation in ambient temperature provides the driving force for the storage of "coolth." At night cool air from the outdoors is circulated through the building to flush out the heat and cool the mass to a lower temperature. As the outdoor air temperature rises the following day, the cool mass absorbs heat and stabilizes the building's interior air temperature. This strategy is known as *nocturnal ventilation.*

A ventilated, low-mass building tends to respond to solar gains and internal heat gains by creating daytime interior temperatures higher than the maximum daytime ambient air temperature and nighttime interior temperatures near the minimum nighttime ambient air temperature. Thermal mass reduces the interior daytime high temperatures and increases the nighttime temperatures, bringing the average building interior temperature closer to the average ambient temperature. With high night ventilation rates and effective control of heat gains during the day, the average building temperature could be decreased to a point below the average ambient temperature. However, in practice, a reduction to the average ambient temperature is a more realistic limit.

One important condition must be satisfied to effectively use nocturnal ventilation and thermal mass for cooling. The day-to-night, or diurnal, temperature variation must be adequate to allow significant heat transfer from the mass, and the minimum nighttime temperature must be below the desired interior building temperature. The fraction of the cooling season during which these conditions are met varies greatly from one location to another. But even in southeastern coastal areas, there are periods in the early and late portions of the cooling season when an opportunity exists.

Nocturnal ventilation and thermal mass can meet the peak summer cooling loads only in very mild climates or in locations where the diurnal temperature variation is large. Such large temperature variations occur in the Rockies and parts of the Southwest, where clear, dry air allows the atmosphere to cool quickly after sundown. Nighttime minimum temperatures are often 40 to 50° lower than daytime highs. Similar conditions also exist in winter, making interior thermal mass a highly desirable feature in these areas.

In most regions of the country, the desirability of high interior mass is less obvious. Where the average summer diurnal temperature swing is less than 20 to 25°F, and where average daily summer temperatures are above 75°F, it is usually not justified for cooling considerations only. In such areas, the normal mass of the house can supply some storage capacity during milder weather. As a rule of thumb, an effective thermal storage mass capacitance of 3 to 6 Btu/°F for each square foot of floor area may be assumed for residences, including the effects of furnishings. The mass included in a major passive solar heating system can easily double this figure. The total "coolth" storage potential from night ventilation may be estimated by multiplying the storage capacitance by the temperature change it undergoes. For example, in a conventional 1500- ft^2 house with a nighttime temperature reduction of 8°F, the storage is

$$1500 \text{ ft}^2 \times 4 \text{ Btu/°F ft}^2 \times 8°\text{F} = 48,000 \text{ Btu}$$

Interior thermal mass may be undesirable in certain circumstances. An extreme example is a building that is occupied only during the daytime. Thermal mass interferes with effective night temperature setbacks and setups by preventing the mechanical system from changing the interior temperature quickly in the morning. A second example includes locations where the average temperature during the cooling season is above about 75°F. The effect of thermal mass is to drive the building temperature toward the average daily temperature. At night temperatures are barely low enough for comfort without air conditioning, and there is little opportunity for heat rejection and storage of "coolth." The excess heat absorbed during the day can create uncomfortable conditions at night when it is released, requiring the use of mechanical cooling, whereas a lower mass building might get by with only ventilation.

Under conditions where nocturnal ventilation is appropriate, using it is a simple matter. Whole-house fans, window fans, and air conditioner economizer cycles are all effective in ventilating a building at night. If conditions are right, natural ventilation may also be used. When fans are used, the period of operation should not be excessive; once the temperature in the building is reduced, continued operation is only marginally beneficial. Distribution of airflow throughout the entire building is desirable; flow through high-mass areas is important.

The adequacy of the ventilation method being used can be evaluated with a simple test suggested by Steve Baer of Zomeworks. It requires an immersible thermometer and two identical water containers—1-gal milk jugs are good. Fill both containers with water, and allow the temperature to stabilize at room temperature. After dark, leave one container indoors on a chair or table in a central living area. Place the other container outdoors under a tree, porch, or carport where it cannot radiate directly to the night sky. The next morning, before the sun has begun to warm the outdoor container, measure the temperature of the water in both containers.

The difference between the two provides an indication of the cooling provided by the night ventilation system. If a difference of more than a few degrees is seen, more ventilation would be beneficial. The temperature of the outdoor water container indicates the usefulness of ventilation for those particular weather conditions. If it is not at least 5° below the highest interior temperature that can be tolerated during the coming day, attempts to use thermal mass will be only marginally effective.

Mass that is effective for passive solar heating is also effective for nocturnal ventilation cooling. Vertical surfaces are better for cooling than horizontal surfaces. Large surface area is essential; mass should be spread out as much as possible with a thickness of 2 in. or less if possible. Except in walls exposed to the air on both sides, a mass that is more than 4 in. thick is not very effective.

Solar Chimneys

Solar chimneys are stack-effect ventilators that use passive solar heat to boost their performance. Solar chimneys are also called *thermal chimneys* or *solar-enhanced ventilators*. Figure 6.17 illustrates the construction and operation of a typical device.

A solar chimney is essentially a passive solar collector with its inlet drawing air from the building interior and its outlet discharging to the outdoors. A glazed surface allows solar energy to heat the interior of the chamber. As the temper-

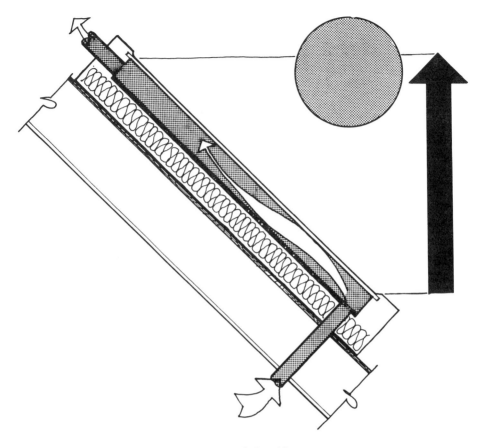

Figure 6.17. Solar chimney.

ature of the air inside the solar chimney increases, it becomes less dense and rises leaving the chimney and drawing more air through the inlet. As hot air leaves the solar chimney, air is drawn from the interior of the building, and outdoor air flows into the building through open doors and windows. The advantage of solar chimneys over other stack-effect systems is that the hot column of air is outside the occupied space of the building. Thus, its temperature can be driven up to increase airflow without creating discomfort for the occupants.

Two general types of solar chimneys have been built: the stack type and the roof panel type. Both are described in Fig. 6.18. The roof panel type is probably the better choice, for construction is simpler and there are fewer difficulties with wind loading and appearance. Large solar collection areas are more easily incorporated into the roof panel designs, a desirable feature if the solar chimney is to also be used as a solar collector in winter.

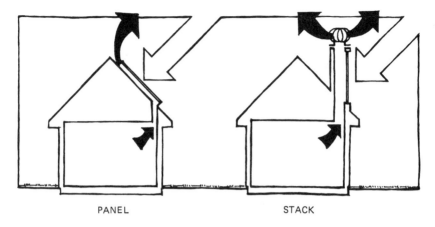

PANEL   STACK

Figure 6.18. Stack and panel type solar chimneys.

The airflow rate provided by a solar chimney can be estimated from the stack-effect equation described on page 126. From the equation, the important performance considerations may be identified. Only the cross sectional area, the height of the chimney, and the inside temperature may be manipulated in the design. The airflow through the chimney increases directly with increases in the cross-sectional flow area of the device. If the area is doubled, the flow doubles, all other things being equal.

Increases in height have a smaller effect, because flow changes with the square root of the height. Doubling h results in only a 41% increase in flow. (The square root of 2 is approximately 1.41.) To double flow rate, it would be necessary to increase h fourfold. A chimney with a large cross section is more desirable than a narrower tall chimney.

The effect of increasing the average temperature inside the chimney is not so straightforward. Considering the solar chimney as a thermal system, the flow of heat in the system (Fig. 6.19) may be described by the equation

$$Q_{air} = Q_{solar} - Q_{conduction} - Q_{infiltration}$$

The inside temperature and the airflow are related by the heat balance equation. As the airflow through the solar chimney increases, the volume of the airflow and the amount of heat carried away by the air also increase. This tends to drive the temperature inside the chimney down, reducing the forces driving the flow. Under stable conditions, the solar chimney would balance at a constant temperature and airflow. Actual airflow rates vary according to solar inputs, winds, and air temperatures.

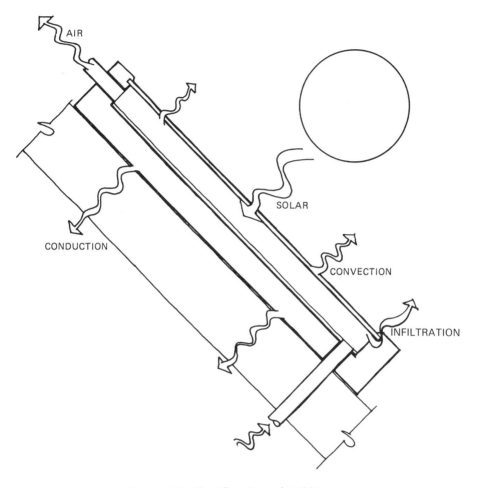

Figure 6.19. Heat flow in a solar chimney.

Applications of Solar Chimneys

The actual usefulness of solar chimneys for ventilating buildings is limited by several of their operating characteristics; most important is their inability to create high air velocities. The buoyancy forces created by a solar chimney are much too weak to force air through a building at speeds high enough to provide a noticeable cooling effect for the occupants. Thus, the solar chimney is more useful in applications where general building ventilation is required. Because it uses the outdoor air as its heat sink, a solar chimney can reduce the temperature in a building interior only to the outdoor temperature. Like other ventilation alternatives, the solar chimney is least effective as a cooling option during periods when it is needed most. And worse, during the portion of the day when the most sunlight is available to drive the solar chimney, the outdoor temperature is usually near its maximum for the day.

It is not practical to use thermal mass to store heat in a solar chimney for ventilation at night after outdoor temperatures have dropped. For even modest airflow volumes, unreasonable amounts of mass are required. A further problem is the rate of heat transfer from the interior of the thermal mass to the surface where it can heat the air.

Consider a rather ridiculous case where 1 ton of concrete is uniformly heated 20°F during the daylight hours. This situation would be most difficult to create in a real design, both from the heat collection and heat transfer standpoints, as well as for structural reasons.

The amount of heat stored is:

$$\text{Heat stored} = M \times C_p \times \Delta T$$

$$\text{Heat stored} = 2000 \text{ lb} \times 0.2 \text{ Btu/lb°F} \times 20°F = 8000 \text{ Btu}$$

For a chimney operating with only 10° difference in air temperature from inlet to exit, the amount of heat required for 8 h of ventilation is

$$\text{Heat used} = M \times C_p \times \Delta T \times t$$

$$= V \times \rho \times C_p \times \Delta T \times t \times 60 \text{ min/h}$$

where V = airflow rate, ft^3/min. The airflow rate is then

$$V = \frac{\text{heat available}}{(\rho \times C_p \times \Delta T \times t \times 60 \text{ min/h})}$$

$$= \frac{8000 \text{ Btu}}{0.075 \text{ lb/ft}^3 \times 0.24 \text{ Btu/lb°F} \times 10°F \times 8 \text{ h} \times 60 \text{ min/h}}$$

$$\cong 90 \text{ ft}^3/\text{min}$$

In a 1500-ft^2 house, 90 cfm represents only one air change each 130 h or 0.075 air change per hour, which is hardly noticeable and is somewhat less than that provided by a typical electric range vent fan. A small ventilator fan might provide 1000 cfm (10 times as much) of airflow while consuming only about 50 W of electric power, corresponding to a cost of only $0.005 per hour at an electicity cost of $0.10 per kWh.

Wind-Assisted Flow

The winds at a building site can either boost the flow through a solar chimney or reverse its direction, turning the device into an unwelcome solar heater during the summer. Even mild breezes produce enough pressure to overwhelm the thermal buoyancy forces created by a solar chimney. Figure 6.20 compares the velocity pressure forces due to winds of various speeds to the thermal buoyancy forces created by a solar chimney. The solar chimney is assumed to have inlet and exit areas of 8 ft² and a total vertical height of 16 ft. An outdoor temperature of 85°F is assumed.

With an average interior temperature of 110°F on a clear, sunny day, a buoyancy force of 0.0098 in. of water would be created. The distribution of wind velocity pressures around a building is described in Fig. 6.2. For a solar chimney with its air exit on the upwind wall of the building, so that the velocity pressure is only 0.5 times the velocity pressure in the free wind stream, a breeze on the site of less than 6.5 MPH would negate the thermal forces in the chimney. The result would be reverse flow in the chimney, with solar-heated air flowing backward into the house (Fig. 6.21).

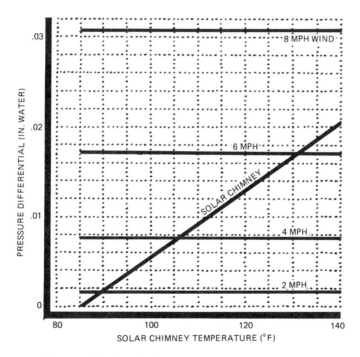

Figure 6.20. Stack effect pressure vs. wind pressure.

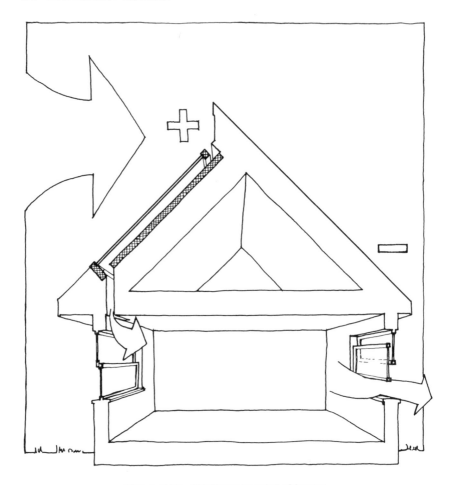

Figure 6.21. Backflow in solar chimney.

If the wind direction changed 180°, however, so that the solar chimney exit was in the low-pressure area on the downwind side of the building, the wind would boost the airflow through the chimney. With a design such as the one in Fig. 6.20, the performance of the system is completely at the mercy of the wind direction. In most areas of the country, the winds are not steady enough to justify designing any ventilation system for a particular wind direction. The challenge, then, is to design an exit configuration that increases airflow through the chimney regardless of wind direction.

Designs that feature a rotating member that moves to account for changes in wind direction and designs that accept wind from any direction provide possible solutions. A venturi design can be used to increase the airflow by using winds to create a low-pressure region at the exit. Turbine vents are another possibility.

A good exit can boost airflow significantly, but still not enough to justify the use of a solar chimney in most situations.

Solar Chimneys and Whole-House Ventilation

Solar chimneys are often included in conceptual drawings as part of an overall system for passive ventilation and cooling. The chimney provides the force to ventilate a building with "cool" air from the building site or from an earth contact area, such as a basement or crawl space or earth cooling tubes. While attractive in concept, such systems rarely operate successfully. Fortunately, there are far more sketches and drawings than actual buildings using the idea. Such a system will cease to function as soon as the solar chimney temperature drops to the outdoor air temperature. Stated another way, they function only when the air in the interior of the chimney is hotter than the outdoor air. This is probably an acceptable situation only on days when the building interior has been heated by solar gains and interior gains, and the ambient temperature is well below 75°F.

The solution often proposed is to utilize cool air available from a basement or a system of earth cooling tubes. Once more, the concept is attractive on the surface, but falls apart in application. The limiting factor is again the density difference between the two columns of air. The "hot" column of air must now include the earth cooling tubes or the basement. See Figure 13.12. The temperature inside the building, the solar chimney and the earth cooling tubes, averaged over the total height, must be higher than the temperature in the "cool" column of air, the outdoors. If the building is subjected to strong solar and internal heat gains, this can often be so, and the system will work to cool the building. However, once the average interior temperature falls to the outdoor temperature, the flow of air stops.

Even though the temperature in a building may be quite high, flow may not be possible due to the effect of the cool air in the cooling tubes. A particular problem can arise if the tubes are sloped toward their inlet, as is frequently suggested for water drainage. Then the cool, dense air in the cooling tubes tends to create air flow in the opposite direction than desired. In one home in northern Georgia, two cooling tubes sloped downward approximately 4 ft over their 90-ft length from the house to the tube inlet. On several occasions when the house temperature was near the outdoor temperature, the cool air column inside the tubes caused air to flow into the house and backward through the tubes, drawing hot outdoor air into the house and pushing cool air to the outdoors. Ref. 6.11.

Solar Chimney/Solar Collector Combinations

Because a solar chimney resembles an air-type solar collector, the possibility of combining the two functions is sometimes considered. This is probably the only conceivable way a solar chimney could be cost-effective in normal situations. The design must include provisions to allow the mode of operation to change from using solar heat to ventilate during the cooling season to delivering the heat directly to the house during the heating season.

Panel chimneys are most easily adaptable for such a purpose. The inlet from the house to the lower end of the chimney remains essentially unchanged from one season to another. However, the upper end of the chimney must include operable dampers or movable panels. In the ventilating mode, the damper to the outdoors is opened and the interior damper is closed. For heating, the damper positions are reversed, and air from the building is continually circulated through the chimney and back into the building. With movable dampers or panels, there is a high probability of leaks—both air leaks that, though hard to detect, reduce performance, as well as water leaks, usually easily detected.

One solar chimney/solar collector combination constructed has been plagued by both air leaks and water leaks. Another unexpected problem arose during the construction of the house, when the solar chimney was completed prior to the interior finish work. As the sheetrock was sanded, fine white dust was carried along with the air flowing through the chimney. The end result was a fine white coating over the carefully painted black absorber plate. Most of the powder was later washed away by the rain leaks.

Design Considerations

Providing design guidelines here does *not* imply that the use of solar chimneys is recommended. The design information is provided to assist a designer in optimizing the performance of a device built for experimental purposes, curiosity, or at the insistence of a stubborn client.

- Use the maximum practical cross-sectional area; maintain a fairly constant area through the entire flow path; avoid constrictions and sharp turns in the air path.
- Provide adequate inlet and exit vent areas, and account for the constricting effect of screens or dampers.
- Design the exit to take advantage of winds from all directions.
- For devices to be used as ventilators only, single-glazing is appropriate. Double-glazing is justifiable only for units that will serve as heaters during cold weather.
- Insulate the back and sides of the chimney to reduce heat losses; R values should range from 6 to 8 for ventilators and from 10 to 20 for units that will be used for heating as well.
- Seal the chimney carefully to control air leakage, and provide a positive means of closing and sealing the vent from the interior of the building to the chimney.

Overall Recommendation

Solar chimneys are ineffective in creating air speeds high enough for comfort cooling. Their construction cost is quite high, and there are many operating limitations. Even though they require no purchased energy for operation, solar chimneys are rarely justifiable as a practical ventilation measure in homes. Electric fans are a far better alternative.

7

EVAPORATIVE COOLING

The classic example of evaporative cooling used in elementary school science books is the cooling effect felt when a moistened hand is waved in the air. Everyone has felt evaporative cooling on a less localized scale when climbing out of a pool on a summer night or stepping out of a shower. The evaporative process simply removes sensible heat (cools your skin) and replaces it with latent heat (increases the moisture content of the air).

Because evaporation makes use of the phase change of water from a liquid to a vapor, it can be a powerful cooling source. But, as in all thermal processes, the amount of heat that can be transferred is only one part of the cooling problem. Temperature is the other. In most climates, evaporative cooling cannot provide cooling at temperatures low enough to be useful in general building cooling applications. Even so, in almost all climates there are specialized cases where it can be effective.

Evaporative cooling was probably one of the first mechanical cooling measures used by man. Egyptian paintings from 2500 B.C. show slaves fanning porous clay jars to provide a cooling effect. Both the American Indians of the Southwest and the ancient Persians cooled their tents with damp felt or grass mats. Leonardo da Vinci built a water-powered evaporative cooler for the bedroom of his patron's wife.

More recently, beginning about 1900, evaporative coolers came to be extensively used in textile mills, industrial plants, and homes. Textile mills were natural applications, for they needed both cooling for comfort and high humidity to keep the fibers workable. By 1953, evaporative cooling was a $30 million per year industry credited with providing people with the means to cope with the summer climate of places like Phoenix, Arizona, making development there possible. Before automobile air conditioning was available small evaporative coolers were used in the Southwest to cool cars. They were mounted in the window and used the motion of the car to create air flow.

Today evaporative coolers are commonly used in residential and commercial buildings in the arid Southwest and in limited commercial and industrial applications elsewhere. The "air conditioner" on the roof of your local laundry or cleaners may be an evaporative cooler. There are also applications of evaporative cooling in large commercial HVAC systems. Evaporative cooling can be used in combination with an economizer cycle, when outdoor moisture levels are low, to provide further "free" cooling without the use of vapor compression air conditioning. Such applications are outside the scope of this book and are not dealt with further.

THEORY

Evaporation is described as an *adiabatic process*, meaning that the total amount of heat in the thermal system remains constant. As water evaporates, the sensible heat content of the system falls, while the latent heat content increases by an equal amount. In other words, dry-bulb temperature falls, but moisture content rises. The limit of temperature reduction is the air's wet-bulb temperature at the beginning of the process. Direct evaporation cannot cool below the wet-bulb temperature. The process stops when the relative humidity reaches 100%. A simple measure of the potential for evaporative cooling at any given air condition is the wet-bulb depression, or the difference between the dry-bulb temperature and the wet-bulb temperature. It provides an upper limit of the temperature change that can be achieved by direct evaporation.

The power of evaporative cooling results from a material phase change: the evaporation of water. The amount of heat absorbed by a material as it changes from a liquid to a vapor is called the *latent heat of vaporization*. For water, the latent heat of vaporization is approximately

$$(1093 - 0.55 \times \text{water temperature in } °F) \text{ Btu/lb}$$

The initial temperature of the water being evaporated has some effect on the net heat absorbed, but for most purposes it can be assumed that each pound of water that evaporates absorbs 1050 Btu of heat, corresponding to a water temperature of 78°F in the equation above.

A perfect evaporative cooling process is illustrated in Fig. 7.1 for typical July conditions in Albuquerque, New Mexico. The outdoor conditions are represented by A on the psychrometric chart, 90°F dry-bulb temperature and 64°F wet-bulb temperature (23% RH). Air drawn from the building interior is at 78°F dry-bulb and 60.5°F wet-bulb (35% RH), plotted at C. Outside air is sent through the evaporative system and exits at saturation conditions, point B. This idealized process occurs along a line of constant enthalpy and stops at 100% RH.

The humid, cool air at B is then mixed with internal air at C. The final indoor air condition will lie somewhere along the line from B to C; its exact location depends on the relative amounts of the two air volumes. A mixture of one-half

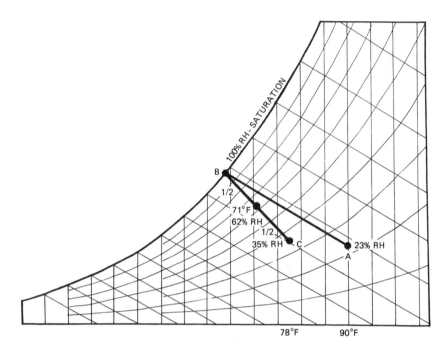

Figure 7.1. Evaporative cooling.

evaporatively cooled air and one-half interior air would provide air at 71°F and 62% RH.

REALISTIC EVAPORATIVE COOLING PROCESSES

Actual evaporative cooling systems have inherent inefficiencies and limitations that prevent them from operating as ideal processes. The idealized processes must be considered as the absolute maximum performance attainable; real systems will always provide less cooling and higher temperatures.

In an ideal evaporative cooling system, all the air sent through the system is completely saturated with moisture and leaves at 100% RH. In an actual system not all the air in the system is exposed to water for evaporation. As a result, the air is not fully saturated to 100% RH and leaves at partial saturation. The capability of an evaporative cooler to cool and humidify the air it supplies is measured by the saturation efficiency

$$Es = \frac{DBT_{in} - DBT_{out}}{WB \text{ depression}} \times 100\%$$

where

$$Es = \text{saturation efficiency, \%}$$
$$DBT_{in} = \text{dry-bulb temperature of entering air, } °F$$
$$DBT_{out} = \text{dry-bulb temperature of leaving air, } °F$$
$$\text{WB depression} = \text{wet-bulb depression for entering air, } °F$$
$$= \text{(dry-bulb temperature } - \text{ wet-bulb temperature) for entering air, } °F.$$

Commercially produced systems provide saturation efficiencies of about 80%, with some types as low as 50% and others as high as 90%.

EVAPORATIVE COOLING EQUIPMENT

Evaporative cooling equipment may use either a direct or indirect cooling process. In the direct process (Fig. 7.2), the water is evaporated directly into the air stream that flows into the conditioned space, as in the processes described above. In an indirect cooler the evaporation process is separated from the air to be delivered to the conditioned space. A heat exchanger moves heat from the conditioned air to the evaporation process. Indirect evaporative coolers are discussed later. Evaporative coolers may also be either single-stage or multistage.

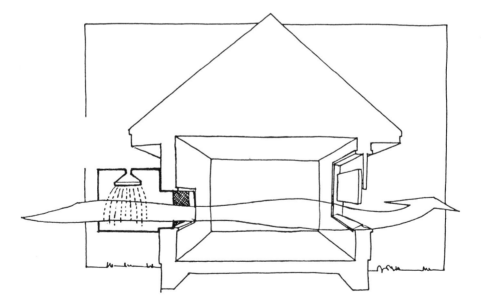

Figure 7.2. Schematic of direct evaporative cooler.

Multistage evaporative systems use two evaporation processes, with the first supplying precooled air to a second.

Direct Evaporative Coolers

In a direct evaporative cooler (Fig. 7.3), water is supplied through a float valve to a small reservoir and then flows down through fibrous pads. A fan draws large volumes of outdoor air though the pads, where it is cooled by evaporation (sensible heat reduced and latent heat increased), and then supplied to the building interior. This cool and more humid air absorbs sensible heat from the building interior. Both latent heat and sensible heat are rejected to the heat sink provided by the outdoor air.

Typical units are roughly the same size as or slightly larger than an air conditioner's condensing unit of similar cooling capacity. They are normally mounted on the roof and blow down into the building, although some units are window-mounted.

The temperature of the air delivered by an evaporative cooler may be estimated with the following equation

$$T_{\text{supply}} = TDB_{\text{out}} - (\text{WB depression} \times Es)$$

or

$$T_{\text{supply}} = TDB_{\text{out}} - (TDB_{\text{out}} - TWB_{\text{out}}) \times Es$$

Figure 7.3. Direct evaporative cooler. Courtesy of Essick Air Products.

where

T_{supply} = dry-bulb temperature of air supplied by cooler, °F
TDB_{out} = outdoor dry-bulb temperature, °F
TWB_{out} = outdoor wet-bulb temperature, °F
WBD = wet-bulb temperature depression, °F

Using the typical saturation efficiency of most coolers, this equation can be rewritten as

$$T_{supply} = 0.2 \, TDB_{out} + 0.8 \, TWB_{out}$$

This equation is useful for judging the applicability of direct evaporative coolers under different conditions. Consider the following outdoor dry-bulb and wet-bulb temperatures on a typical August day in Atlanta, Georgia, and in Albuquerque, New Mexico

	Atlanta	*Albuquerque*
Dry-bulb temperature	87°F	87°F
Wet-bulb temperature	73°F	62°F

The supply temperatures from an evaporative cooler would be

Atlanta: $T_{supply} = 0.2(87) + 0.8(73) = 75.8°F$
Albuquerque: $T_{supply} = 0.2(87) + 0.8(62) = 67.0°F$

Obviously, the direct evaporative cooler can be a useful cooling device in Albuquerque. But the higher humidity levels in the East limit its output temperature to levels too high for useful cooling in most building applications.

Where conditions do permit their use, direct evaporative coolers are a much more economical method of cooling than conventional vapor-compression air conditioners. Essentially all of the power consumption is associated with the fan, which ranges from $\frac{1}{3}$ to 1 HP in most residential units. A comparable air conditioner might consume three to four times as much electrical power. Water consumption in an evaporative cooler is not negligible. A typical evaporative cooler with a saturation efficiency of 80% requires about 1 gal of water per 1000 cfm of air flow for each 10°F of wet-bulb depression.

An evaporatively cooled building operates as an open system in which dry outdoor air is continuously drawn into the cooler, conditioned, and supplied to the building, providing a complete air change every 1 to 4 minutes.

Direct evaporative coolers humidify the air supplied to a building, so that the relative humidity indoors will always be higher than outdoors. The successful application of direct evaporative coolers depends on the existence of outdoor humidity levels well below human comfort conditions. But even in arid areas, they are sometimes considered second-class cooling systems, because they cannot provide the consistent control afforded by conventional air conditioning.

Consequently, evaporative systems are sometimes installed with conventional air conditioning systems; the conventional system serves as a backup for severe conditions.

Indirect Evaporative Cooling

Indirect evaporative coolers attempt to make use of the evaporation cooling process without increasing the amount of moisture in the air supplied to the building. Indirect coolers use a heat exchanger to separate the direct evaporation process from the air to be delivered to the building. A direct evaporation process cools air that flows across one side of the heat exchanger, removing heat, and is then exhausted to the outdoors. The air to be supplied to the building flows across the other side of the heat exchanger and is cooled without receiving moisture directly (Fig. 7.4).

Very simple indirect cooling systems using cooling towers and finned tube heat exchangers, sometimes automobile radiators, were sold in Arizona as early as 1930. Thousands of these dry-surface systems were installed in homes, banks, and stores. Few remain today; most were victims of scale and corrosion, copper shortages during World War II, and replacement by air conditioners.

In operation, cooled water from the cooling tower is circulated through the heat exchanger by a small pump (Fig. 7.5). A fan circulates interior air through the heat exchanger and supplies it to the building. The systems are quite effective in dry climates, often reducing indoor temperatures by 20 to 30°F on a hot afternoon. A simple indirect cooling process is shown on the psychrometric chart in Fig. 7.6.

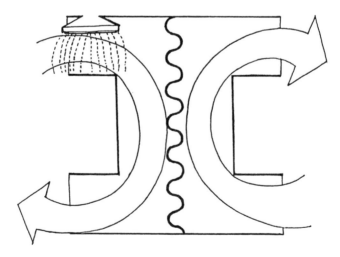

Figure 7.4. Indirect evaporative cooler schematic.

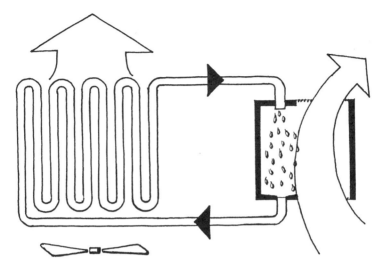

Figure 7.5. Dry surface evaporative cooling system.

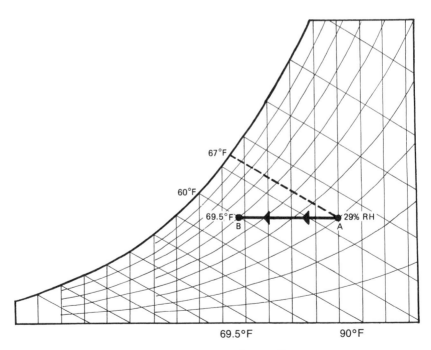

Figure 7.6. Indirect evaporative cooling process.

Outdoor air at 90°F dry-bulb and 67°F wet-bulb (29% RH) enters the cooler at point *A* and is cooled without the addition or removal of moisture along a horizontal line to point *B*, 69.5°F dry-bulb and 60°F wet-bulb (58% RH). (The actual output conditions depend on the saturation efficiency of the direct evaporation process and the effectiveness of the heat exchanger.) Both the dry-bulb and the wet-bulb temperatures of the air are reduced; the moisture content of the air is unchanged—the dewpoint temperature remains constant. In the air provided to the building, sensible cooling is achieved without an increase in latent heat. Of course the air on the other side of the heat exchanger undergoes a direct evaporative process with an increase in moisture content and latent heat. But it serves only to cool the heat exchanger and is not used inside the building.

Two-stage evaporative cooling offers significant performance improvements over indirect evaporative cooling systems. In a two-stage evaporative system, the cooled air from an indirect cooler is passed through a direct evaporative cooler for additional cooling. An example using the conditions described above (90°F dbt and 67° wbt) illustrates the results. Acting alone, a direct evaporative cooler with a saturation efficiency of 80% would deliver air to the space at 71.6°F dry-bulb and 67°F wet-bulb. Assume a saturation efficiency of 80% in the direct evaporative cooler comprising the second stage and a first stage similar to the indirect cooling example above. The second stage (direct evaporation) takes air supplied by the first stage (indirect evaporation) and yields air at 61.9°F dry-bulb and 60°F wet-bulb. The dbt of the air delivered is almost 10° lower.

One refinement used in some earlier systems was a regenerative loop that routed relatively cool air from the building interior to the exterior side of the indirect cooler. Although the difficulty of routing the ductwork limited the number of applications, such systems could cool the heat exchanger to within 4°F of the outdoor wet-bulb temperature.

Staged regenerative systems have been proposed where one cooler cools the air for the next. In theory, such a system could cool air all the way to its dewpoint temperature. But under most conditions, only 0.2 to 0.33°F of wet-bulb temperature reduction is achieved for each degree of dry-bulb temperature reduction. The practical limit of regenerative cooling is much higher than the dewpoint, probably about halfway between the dewpoint and the wet-bulb temperatures.

Plate-type indirect evaporative coolers were also developed in the 1930s. Plate-type devices have more recently been the object of research in Australia and in the United States. They consist of a series of parallel plates that form two sets of air channels. Outdoor air is circulated through one set of passages and indoor air in the other set. Water is evaporated into the outdoor air, absorbing heat through the plates from the indoor air. The two air streams do not mix; the building can be operated as a closed system. Although such systems provide some relief from extreme conditions, they seldom meet conventional standard of comfort.

GEOGRAPHIC APPLICABILITY OF EVAPORATIVE COOLING

The geographic range in which evaporative cooling is generally applicable is limited by humidity. However, there are no clear-cut boundaries defining where evaporative cooling is or is not usable; evaporative systems can provide some measure of relief from summer discomfort in any location. In many parts of the country, including most of the Southeast and the East, evaporative cooling can be ruled out as a viable cooling alternative for residences. In the very arid regions of the Southwest, it can definitely be considered as an effective alternative to air conditioning in almost any building. In other areas, a decision becomes a matter of compromise.

A rule of thumb used years ago suggested that evaporative cooling could be used wherever the average noon relative humidity during July did not exceed 40%. This encompassed most of the western states, with the exception of coastal areas, and a small portion of Texas and the Midwest. However, evaporative coolers were installed throughout a larger region, and a later guideline indicated that evaporative cooling might be satisfactory in locations where the wet-bulb temperatures usually remained at or below 75°F. A rough map of summer design wet-bulb temperatures is provided in Fig. 7.7; the wet-bulb temperatures indicated would be exceeded for no more than 100 h during the cooling season. The 40% RH figure might be used as an indication of the areas in which evaporative cooling could be considered a reasonable alternative to air conditioning. Comfort control would not be as good as with air conditioning, but would generally be satisfactory. In the larger area included by the 75°F wet-bulb guideline, evaporative cooling could be used with some greater sacrifice in comfort control. In the balance of the country, evaporative cooling is not a viable alternative for most building cooling applications. Both these rules of thumb were developed for direct evaporative coolers in typical residential applications; indirect systems are usable over a slightly broader range.

The type of building and the cooling load also affect the usefulness of evaporative cooling. The rules of thumb provided above are directed toward residences and small office buildings. In commercial, industrial, and agricultural applications, where comfort requirements are not as rigid as in residences and offices, evaporative cooling holds far more potential. Any such application where sensible heat loads are high and large volumes of ventilating air are either required or permissible is a candidate for evaporative cooling. Good examples include dry cleaning plants and buildings housing heat-producing manufacturing operations, such as foundries. In these situations, air conditioning is usually unfeasible, particularly where ventilation is required to carry away irritating or

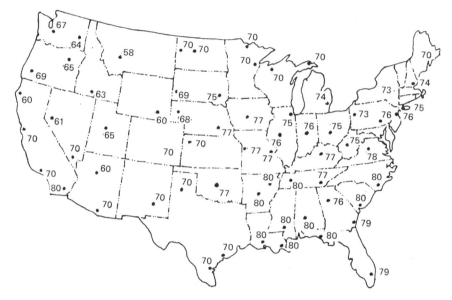

Figure 7.7. Summer design wet-bulb temperatures.

toxic fumes. Comfort standards are not as rigid, and higher temperature and humidity can be tolerated; cooling to 85°F would be welcome in many facilities.

ROOF SPRAY COOLING SYSTEMS

Roof spray cooling systems are used to reduce or eliminate heat gain through the roof of a building by spraying a fine mist of water on the roof surface. As the water evaporates, it removes large amounts of heat and lowers the roof temperature toward the ambient wet-bulb temperature. Roof spray systems do little to remove heat from the interior of the building; they are simply a method of blocking heat gains to the building.

Thus, they are most applicable to buildings that have large roof cooling loads, such as mobile homes and commercial and industrial buildings with flat roofs with little or no insulation. Roof spray systems are intended to reduce the high temperatures common on roofs in summer, not to cool air to human comfort levels. This allows a major increase in the useful range of operation over direct evaporative systems.

Roof spray systems were first used on a significant scale in southern Florida and Texas. Systems installed there during the late 1940s and early 1950s can be found still in operation. As electricity prices and air conditioning costs have risen, roof spray systems have moved farther north and are now sold throughout the country. But roof spray cooling systems are not a universal solution to high roof and ceiling heat gains. Additional roof or ceiling insulation is usually a preferred alternative, especially in locations where winter heating requirements are significant. In fact, in most residential and light commercial buildings with a well-insulated roof/ceiling, the desirability of a roof spray system is questionable.

Function

A typical system consists of water supply piping, water spray devices, and a control system. A schematic of a mobile home system is shown in Fig. 7.8. Low-cost PVC piping may be used, because temperature and pressure requirements are not high.

The control system includes a temperature sensor mounted on the roof surface. When the roof temperature reaches the setpoint of the sensor, the switch is activated and opens a solenoid valve in the main water line. This allows water to flow through the piping to the spray devices, where a fine mist is released to the roof. Pumps are not required; the water flows through the system as a result of the water pressure in the supply system.

The duration of the spray cycle is usually controlled with a timer, so that the spray continues for only a few seconds. The timer then closes the solenoid valve, so that the water sprayed on the roof evaporates before more water is added. Ideally, the spray period is adjusted to provide just enough water to completely wet the roof, but not so much that runoff occurs.

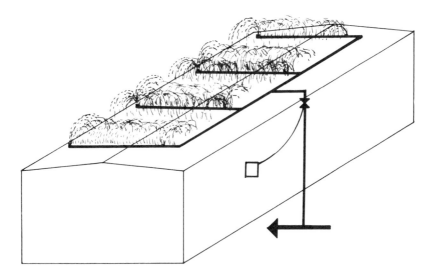

Figure 7.8. System schematic, mobile home roof spray system.

The cooling effect results primarily from the evaporation of water, not from heating the water. For instance, 1 lb of water at 65°F sprayed on a roof at 120°F removes 55 Btu of heat from the roof in being heated to 120°F. But as it evaporates, changing from a liquid to a vapor, the water removes about 1000 Btu per lb. More than 95% of the total cooling effect results from the phase change of the water. Thus the supply temperature of the water is insignificant, and any excess water supplied to the roof that does not evaporate removes very little heat.

Water consumption is minimal with a properly operating roof spray cooling system. System manufacturers cite water consumption about 0.05 to 0.15 gal per day per square foot on flat roofs.

There is no simple or straightforward method of predicting the effect of a roof spray cooling system, and great variations from one installation to another must be expected. As a very rough guide, the savings available may be estimated by assuming that the system eliminates most of the roof cooling load. Be wary of sales claims of greater savings.

Costs

Single-zone roof spray cooling systems are normally priced at $550 to $650 for installations on flat-roofed mobile homes and $700 to $800 for houses with pitched roofs. For multiple-zone systems installed on larger commercial buildings, total cost may be estimated as approximately $0.25 to $0.35 per ft^2 of roof area. The equipment alone accounts for approximately 50% of the total cost of a system.

Disadvantages and Possible Problems

The primary concerns associated with roof spray cooling systems in residences and small commercial buildings are summarized below.

Cost effectiveness—In residences and other small buildings with attics and well-insulated ceilings, roof spray cooling systems generally do not offer a good return on investment.

Appearance—On a pitched roof the exposed piping is quite visible from ground level, particularly if the piping color does not match the roof color. Systems installed on flat roofs are not as visible.

Water damage—Roof leaks might be aggravated by the use of a roof spray system. Other problems may result if the spray is allowed to fall on a chimney flue or a roof or attic vent.

Stains—The prolonged evaporation of water from the spray system can leave mineral deposits. Mildew may be encouraged by any runoff on walls.

Freeze damage—Roof spray cooling systems will freeze if not drained completely in winter. All systems must include a drain valve, and the piping should slope toward the drain to allow complete drainage.

Roof Spray or Insulation?

Roof spray systems provide benefits only during the summer. Insulation has the advantage of blocking heat flow in either direction and is valuable in both winter and summer. The value of either insulation or roof spray can be judged by the reduction in heat flow through the roof that they offer. Tables 7.1 and 7.2 provide a calculated evaluation of reduced heat flow from the addition of $R11$ insulation and the use of a roof spray system. Steady-state calculations were made, and it was assumed that the roof spray system reduces the roof temperature to 90°F.

Obviously the value of both additional insulation and roof spray depends on the existing insulation level; both have a greater effect when the existing insulation level is low. At lower initial insulation levels, both alternatives perform similarly, but at higher initial insulation levels the roof temperature reduction becomes comparatively more valuable. However, the absolute level of the reduction becomes small.

In comparing the two alternatives, it is important that roof temperatures typical of the entire day be used, rather than the peak temperature that might be

Table 7.1 Reduction in Heat Gain for Addition of $R11$ Insulation, BTU/h/ft^2.

	Initial R Value/Final R Value, h ft^2 °F/Btu				
	30/41	20/31	10/21	5/16	3.3/14.3
Assumed Roof Temperature, °F					
150	0.6	1.3	3.8	9.9	16.6
130	0.5	0.9	2.7	7.2	12.0
110	0.3	0.6	1.7	4.4	7.4

Table 7.2 Reduction in Heat Gain for Roof Surface Temperature Reduction to 90°F, BTU/h/ft^2.

	R Value, h ft^2°F/BTU				
Assumed roof temperature, °F	30	20	10	5	3.3
150	2.0	3.0	6.0	12.0	18.0
130	1.3	2.0	4.0	8.0	12.0
110	0.7	1.0	2.0	4.0	6.0

encountered. Also the cooling load that is actually produced in the building below is lower than the steady-state values of heat gain calculated in the tables. A roof temperature no greater than 110 to 120°F is probably appropriate. Comparisons should also recognize that a roof spray cooling system for a home costs about $0.50 to $0.65 per ft^2 of ceiling area, and that blown-in R11 insulation can be installed for $0.18 to $0.24 per ft^2.

Conclusions and Recommendations

The applicability and cost-effectiveness of a roof spray system for a particular building depend strongly on roof cavity or attic ventilation, the level of insulation in the ceiling and roof, the cost of adding more insulation, and the severity of the overheating problem in the building. Most residences seem to be poor candidates for roof spray cooling; insulation can be installed at equal or lower cost and provides similar cooling season savings as well as heating season benefits.

Roof spray cooling is most applicable in cases where the existing level of roof and ceiling insulation is low and the addition of more insulation is not a reasonable alternative.

8

RADIATIVE COOLING

Beyond the earth's atmosphere, the void of space is at an extremely low temperature, near absolute zero or about 460°F below zero. Cooling would be quite a straightforward matter if it was possible to use deep space as a heat sink, but the earth's atmosphere is interposed between us and this potential cooling source. Surfaces on the earth cannot radiate directly to space, but only to the sky. Even though its temperature is somewhat higher than that of deep space, the sky still provides a potential heat sink for cooling.

Radiative cooling was used by the people of North Africa to produce ice, even on nights when the air temperature remained above 40°F. A pit, insulated with straw, was dug next to a low wall. Shallow water containers were placed in the pit to cool during the night by radiating heat to the cold sky. The wall helped prevent winds over the ground from warming the water. A similar phenomenon occurs on the windshields of automobiles exposed to the cool night sky.

Over the years, various architectural forms and living practices have made use of radiative cooling effects. Exposed sleeping areas in courtyards and on rooftops make it possible to reject heat directly to the sky, simultaneously obtaining the advantages of cooler outdoor air temperatures and breezes. More recently, radiative cooling has been investigated for a variety of building cooling methods. Special roof systems, including roof ponds and radiative cooling panels, similar to flat plate collectors, are two examples.

THEORY

Radiative cooling is the rejection of heat through radiation heat transfer, a process that takes place with invisible electromagnetic waves. The process can be compared to the movement of energy as light or to the transmission of radio waves. Like other forms of heat transfer, radiation depends on the existence of a temperature differential. The rate of heat flow increases as the temperature difference increases. Because radiation travels in straight lines, the objects transferring heat must be able to "see" one another. The relative geometry of the two objects, as well as their area, has a great effect on the radiant heat transfer.

A basic radiation heat transfer equation is

$$Qr = \sigma \times F \times \epsilon \times A \times (T_1 - T_2)^4$$

where

Qr = radiation heat transfer, Btu/h
σ = Stephan-Boltzmann constant, 1.714×10^{-9}, Btu/h $-$ ft^2 $-$ $^0R^4$
F = shape factor
ϵ = emittance of radiating object
A = area of radiating object, ft^2
T_1 = temperature of radiating object, ^0R; $^0R = {}^0F + 460$
T_2 = temperature of absorbing object.

σ is a constant used in all radiation equations. F, the shape factor, accounts for how well the two objects "see" one another; it varies from 0 to 1. For many potential radiative cooling applications, the shape factor is approximately 1; a radiant panel or roof "sees" little else but the sky. The emittance also has values from 0 to 1; it compares the material being studied to a perfect radiator of heat. A theoretically perfect radiator and receiver of radiation is called a *black body* and has an emittance of 1. Many materials, including brick, concrete, wood, and glass, have emittances of 0.85 or more.

One useful concept for calculating radiative cooling rates uses the concept of sky temperature, the equivalent temperature of the clouds, water vapor, and air that make up the sky to which a surface can radiate heat. Figure 8.1 shows the relationship between sky temperature and the dry-bulb, wet-bulb, and dewpoint temperatures of the air for an average July day in Miami, Florida. This information is representative of many humid locations in the United States. In dry climates like that of the Southwest, sky temperatures are much lower, near 50°F.

The fact that the temperature of the heat sink, the sky, is so near the desired comfort temperature indicates that the potential is rather limited in humid climates. Low sky temperatures are associated with clear, dry climates where the air is more "transparent" and allows objects on earth to reject more heat directly to deep space. In such locations, the sky temperature may be more than 20°F lower than the air temperature. In humid areas, like the Southeast, sky temperatures are much higher, within 15°F of the air temperature. In most U.S. locations, the sky temperature may be estimated as the dry-bulb air temperature

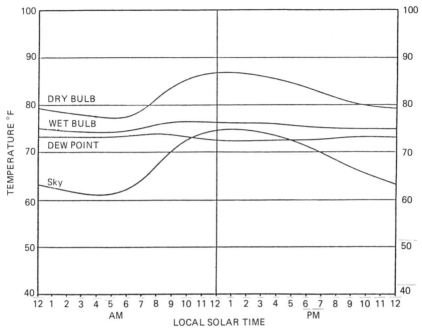

Figure 8.1. Meteorological temperature profile, average July day, Miami, Florida. 12 years average 53–64. (Source: *Passive Solar Handbook*, Lawrence Berkeley Laboratory and Florida Solar Energy Center, 1980.)

minus 15–20°F. Sky temperatures are lowest at night when building cooling needs are also low, requiring that some forms of thermal storage be provided for daytime cooling.

Sky temperatures are lowest directly overhead, along the path where the atmosphere is thinnest. This means that horizontal surfaces see the coolest portion of the sky. Surfaces facing upward also receive little radiation from warmer objects on the earth, such as trees, adjacent buildings, and hills. Thus, horizontal surfaces, such as flat roofs, are best for radiative cooling. A surface inclined at a 45° angle from horizontal is only 40 to 60% as effective as a horizontal surface.

For buildings, radiative cooling takes place when a surface emits infrared radiation, mostly in the 8–13-micron (μ) wavelength range, to the sky. This cooling effect also occurs inside a building as heat is transferred from the building or a storage system to the cooling surface. A heat balance on the surface reveals several other possible heat transfer paths that reduce overall cooling effectiveness. (Fig. 8.2). Although sky temperatures may be 20°F lower than

Figure 8.2. Heat balance on a radiative cooling surface.

the air temperature, a radiant cooling system can achieve only a portion of that temperature reduction.

A mostly unimpeded path to the sky without "shading" by other objects is desired. The radiant surface should also "see" a minimum of surfaces, because it may receive unwanted heat from them.

If radiative cooling is to be used directly in buildings, the radiant surface must reach a temperature lower than the air temperature around the building. When this occurs, the panel can also gain heat by convection from the surrounding air. This source of undesirable heat gain is a particular problem when the wind blows. For example, under typical conditions, a simple radiant panel can cool to approximately 8°F below the dry-bulb air temperature with a 3-MPH wind, but less than 5°F below the air temperature with a 10-MPH wind. For this reason, a wind screen transparent to infrared radiation may be useful in minimizing convection heat gains. Thin polyethylene sheet has been used.

Another severe limitation on radiative cooling is the formation of dew on the radiating surface or on the windscreen. Dew releases about 1050 Btu of heat to the surface upon which it condenses. Also, condensation on a windscreen reduces the radiant cooling from the panel, because it blocks the view of the sky.

Condensation will occur on any surface that is cooled to a temperature below the air's dewpoint temperature. The dew seen on grass and automobiles in the early morning is an example. Notice that it occurs only on objects with a clear view of the cool sky. A car parked under a tree or carport collects no dew.

Researchers at Trinity University (Ref. 7.1) have prepared contour maps of net July cooling rates from a dry horizontal surface at 77 sites around the country. The emittance of the surface was assumed to be 0.95, typical of several materials and finishes that might be used. Wind speeds for the weather station nearest each site were used in the calculations. The radiating surface was assumed to be held constant at three temperatures; 66, 70, and 74°F. The results are reproduced in Figs. 8.3–8.5. Of course, the amount of heat that can be rejected increases as the area of the radiating surface is increased. But once again, the amount of heat rejected is only a portion of the picture; the cooling effect must be available at a temperature low enough to be useful in a building. Although great amounts of heat could be rejected by a radiator at 90°F, the cooling effect would be of no use in cooling a building to 78°F. In using the contour maps to assess radiative cooling potential, it is suggested that either the 66 or 70°F maps be used. A radiating surface temperature of 74°F would be difficult to use in cooling a building, even to 78°F.

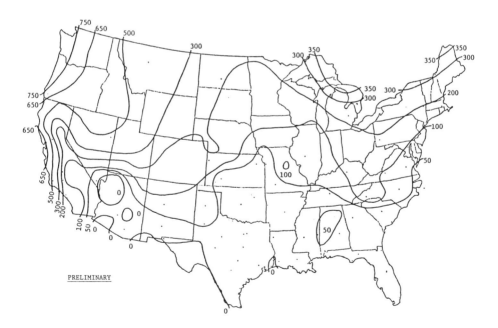

Figure 8.3. Radiative cooling potential, 66°F surface. (Source: *Passive Solar Handbook*, Lawrence Berkeley Laboratory and Florida Solar Energy Center, 1980.)

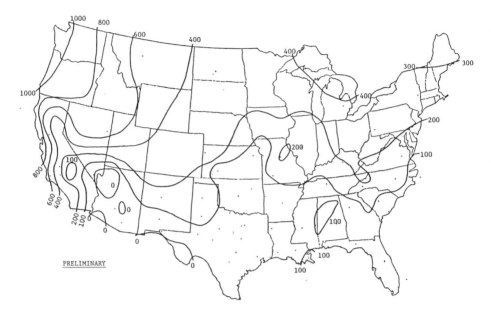

Figure 8.4. Radiative cooling potential, 70°F surface. (Source: *Passive Solar Handbook*, Lawrence Berkeley Laboratory and Florida Solar Energy Center, 1980.)

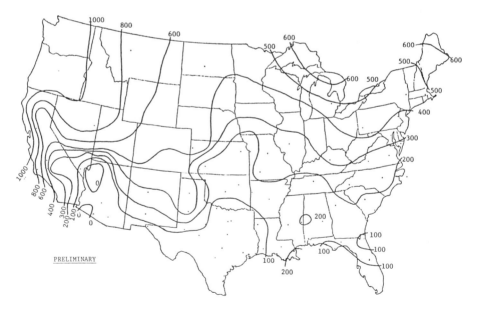

Figure 8.5. Radiative cooling potential, 74°F surface. (Source: *Passive Solar, Handbook*, Lawrence Berkeley Laboratory and Florida Solar Energy Center, 1980.)

APPLICATIONS

Applications of radiative cooling for buildings have included passive systems incorporated into the roof of the building and passive or active radiator panels similar to flat plate solar collectors. Certainly, the best known application is the roof pond concept shown schematically in Fig. 8.6. In the roof pond scheme, a flat roof collector is used to support either open water ponds or large bags of water, similar to water bed mattresses. Movable insulation panels cover the water during the day to block solar heat gains and are removed at night to allow the water to radiate heat to the night sky. With closed bags, water sprays may be used to provide further cooling through evaporation when conditions are appropriate. The mass of the water and the roof structure store cooling from the night to the following day.

Inside the building, the water-covered roof provides comfort in two ways. First, it cools the inside air by convection and by absorbing radiant heat from the furnishings, floors, and walls, which, in turn cools the air. Secondly, the cool ceiling provides a lower mean radiant temperature in the space, increasing comfort conditions directly. Roof pond houses have been successfully operated in several arid locations. The Skytherm design developed and promoted by Dr. Harold Hay is widely known, if not widely used. The roof pond may also be used to provide passive solar heating in winter.

Testing and computer simulations at Trinity University have shown that roof pond designs might be effective in meeting the entire sensible cooling load of

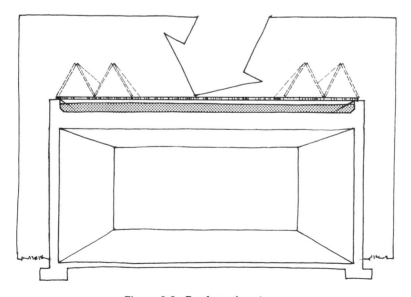

Figure 8.6. Roof pond system.

residences throughout the drier regions of the country and up to 50% of the sensible load in locations like Atlanta and Baltimore. But they cannot provide latent cooling, and there are no simple methods of passive dehumidification.

The application of roof ponds is also limited by other factors. Because the ceiling is used for distributing the cooling effect from the roof above, they are most effective in single-story buildings. The weight of the water and the need for the flat roof impose rather severe structural and architectural limitations on designs. Most have tended to resemble service stations or convenience stores.

With marginal sensible cooling capacity, no latent cooling capacity, and with a significant structural and architectural design constraints, it is unlikely that roof pond systems will be widely used in the near future.

RADIATIVE PANEL COOLING SYSTEMS

Radiative panel cooling systems have received less testing than roof ponds. Although testing has been done at several locations, actual applications to building cooling are rare. The panels are very similar to flat plate solar collectors, with a metal radiating surface inside an insulated enclosure having a cover of a material transparent to infrared radiation, such as polyethylene. Tubes through which a fluid is circulated are attached to the plate. The cooled fluid is then piped to the interior of a building to absorb heat. Like flat plate solar systems, radiative panel cooling is limited by high initial costs.

9

EFFICIENT AIR CONDITIONING

VAPOR-COMPRESSION AIR CONDITIONING

The fundamental purpose of a vapor-compression air conditioner is to remove heat from a building interior and discharge it to a heat sink, usually at a higher temperature. As the desired flow of heat is from a lower temperature zone to a higher temperature zone, it will not occur naturally. Additional energy, normally electricity, is required to make the process take place, to "pump" heat "uphill" on the temperature scale.

Air conditioners operate using the vapor-compression refrigeration cycle. Figure 9.1 is a schematic diagram of a simple vapor-compression device. Cooling is achieved by circulating a refrigerant, normally a fluorocarbon compound such as freon, inside the system, which continuously absorbs heat in the building and discharges heat to the outdoors. The cycle depends on the phase-change energy of the refrigerant. Heat is absorbed indoors when the refrigerant evaporates from a liquid to a gas and released outdoors when the refrigerant condenses to a liquid again.

A refrigeration cycle machine includes the following components

Refrigerant—A fluid that transports heat through the system, using evaporation and condensation to absorb and reject large amounts of heat. The refrigerant commonly used in air conditioners is R-22.

Evaporator—the indoor heat exchanger where the refrigerant absorbs heat and evaporates it from a liquid to a vapor.

Condenser—the outdoor heat exchanger where the refrigerant condenses from a vapor to a liquid and rejects heat.

Compressor—a "pump" that moves the refrigerant through the system and provides a pressure difference that allows the refrigerant to evaporate and condense.

Expansion device—a flow-control device that regulates the flow of the refrigerant and maintains the pressure differential in the system.

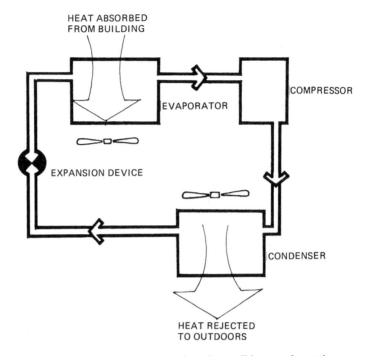

Figure 9.1. Vapor compression air conditioner schematic.

A more complete explanation of the refrigeration cycle and the function of these components is provided below. Because the process is a continuous closed loop of events, it is necessary to arbitrarily choose a location to begin tracing the cycle. The evaporator provides the cooling effect to the building, so the explanation begins there.

The evaporator consists of a set of tubes into which the liquid refrigerant flows. Because the compressor draws refrigerant from the evaporator, the pressure in the evaporator is low. As the liquid refrigerant enters the evaporator (point *A* in Fig. 9.1), it absorbs heat from the building and evaporates. Fins are attached to the tubes to increase the area for heat transfer from the air to the tubes. A fan moves the air over the evaporator.

After evaporating completely (*B*), the refrigerant is pulled from the evaporator through the suction line and into the compressor (*C*). Even after evaporating, the refrigerant may absorb additional heat. The compressor compresses the low-pressure refrigerant vapor to a high-pressure vapor. Just as a bicycle tire pump heats up when used, the temperature of the refrigerant vapor increases. The refrigerant is discharged from the compressor as a high-temperature, high-pressure gas (*D*). It then flows through the hot gas line to the condenser, another heat exchanger located outside the building.

The refrigerant gives up its heat to the condenser tubing, which, in turn, transfers it to the outdoor air. As in the evaporator, fins on the tubing and a fan assist the process. As the refrigerant condenses, its pressure remains essentially constant at the higher level created by the compressor. At the downstream end of the condenser, the refrigerant is a liquid (*E*). After condensing, the liquid refrigerant may be cooled further. The refrigerant then flows through an expansion valve (*F*). The expansion valve performs two functions: it controls the flow of refrigerant through the system and maintains the pressure difference in the system. In small air conditioners, including window units, the expansion valve is a section of capillary tubing, a thin tube with a very small inside diameter. The portion of the refrigerant circuit between the expansion valve and the compressor, including the condenser, is called the *high side*, because the refrigerant pressure is high. The low-pressure side that includes the evaporator is called the *low side*.

As the liquid refrigerant passes through the expansion valve, it enters the low-pressure evaporator, begins to absorb heat and again changes to a vapor. This process is continuous. The refrigeration cycle is a thermal system, with energy flowing into it from the building through the evaporator and from the electrical circuit supplying the compressor and the fans. Energy flows out of the system through the condenser to the outdoor air. Energy storage is insignificant.

Dehumidification can be provided by a vapor-compression machine if the evaporator temperature is below the dewpoint temperature of the indoor air. As the air passes over the evaporator, moisture condenses on the cool surfaces and is drained away. Thus the air conditioner provides both sensible cooling (reduced temperature) and latent cooling (dehumidification or reduced moisture content). In most residential and commercial systems, 70 to 80% of the total cooling capacity is sensible capacity. This ratio has some very important implications and will be discussed further in this chapter.

A useful feature of the vapor-compression cycle is that the amount of heat energy absorbed in the evaporator—the cooling effect—is greater than the electrical energy used to power the cycle. The ratio of the total cooling effect to the power consumed is the coefficient of performance, or COP. (Another measure of efficiency, the EER, is discussed later.)

$$COP = \text{cooling effect/power consumed}$$

For most systems the COP is between 1.75 and 3.5, meaning that for each Btu of electrical energy used to run the system, 1.75 to 3.5 Btu of heat is removed from the building. The actual efficiency of a vapor compression refrigeration machine is determined by the design and application of the unit. Viewing the machine as a thermal system and examining the heat flow processes is helpful in improving performance.

Improving the Efficiency of the Refrigeration Cycle

Several kinds of modifications may be made to the basic refrigeration cycle to improve the efficiency of a real machine. Usually, they involve increasing the rate of heat flow through the system. In examining these modifications, it is convenient to use a graphic representation of the thermodynamic properties of the refrigerant. A plot may be made of the relationship between the pressure and enthalpy of any refrigerant. The pressure of the refrigerant is shown on the vertical axis and the enthalpy, or total energy, is plotted on the horizontal axis; see Fig. 9.2.

The pressure-enthalpy chart (P-H chart) includes two lines that form a dome in the center of the chart. The left side of the dome is a line describing the refrigerant as a saturated liquid at various pressures, and the right side represents the pressure and enthalpy of the refrigerant as a saturated vapor. The area to the left of the dome represents subcooled liquid, or refrigerant that has condensed and then cooled below its condensation temperature. Similarly, the area to the right of the dome is the superheated vapor region, where the refrigerant has been vaporized and then heated further. Under the dome, there are points describing conditions where the refrigerant exists as a mixture of liquid and vapor. In this region, temperature and pressure are directly related, and constant temperature lines, as well as constant pressure lines, are horizontal.

A typical refrigeration cycle is plotted on the P-H diagram of Fig. 9.3. The reference points correspond to those in the earlier discussion. The line from A to B represents the evaporation of the refrigerant in the evaporator; pressure is constant and enthalpy increases as heat is absorbed. At B the refrigerant has been fully evaporated, but it continues to absorb additional heat in the evapo-

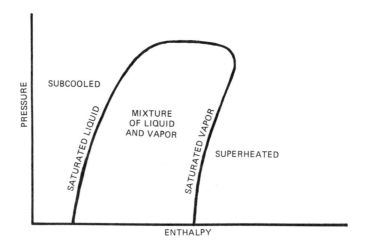

Figure 9.2. Pressure-enthalpy diagram.

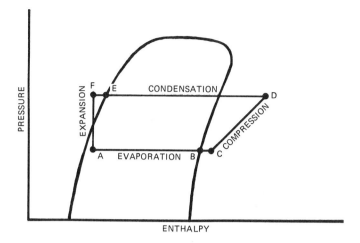

Figure 9.3. Refrigeration cycle on P-H diagram.

rator and the connecting tubing, becoming superheated, point C. The compression process is shown by the line from C to D, indicating an increase in pressure. The electrical energy input to the compressor is reflected in the increase in enthalpy.

Condensation occurs from D to E, again at constant pressure. As heat is given off by the condenser, the enthalpy of the refrigerant decreases. Leaving the condenser, at E, the refrigerant is a saturated liquid. As additional heat is removed, the liquid refrigerant is subcooled to point F. The expansion process takes place from F to A, at constant enthalpy, completing the process. The cooling effect provided by the cycle is shown by the enthalpy change in the evaporator from A to C. The energy input by the compressor is the enthalpy change from C to D. The heat rejected by the compressor is shown by the enthalpy change from D to F and is equal to the evaporator heat gain and the compressor heat input.

The theoretical COP of the cycle is the cooling effect divided by the compressor input, or

$$\text{COP} = \frac{\text{Enthalpy change from } A \text{ to } C}{\text{Enthalpy change from } C \text{ to } D} = \frac{ha - hc}{hc - hd}$$

The actual operating COP will be somewhat lower due to friction and thermal losses in the refrigerant system and inefficiencies in the compression and expansion processes. The power consumed by the fans and the electrical inefficiencies of the compressor also lower the overall COP of a real machine.

To increase the cooling effect and the COP, the energy flow representing the heat absorbed in the evaporator must be increased. The electrical energy that flows into the system is an operating cost that is to be reduced. Anything that facilitates the flow of heat into the evaporator or out of the condenser increases the overall efficiency.

Heat transfer through the system (the cooling effect) may be improved by providing larger heat transfer surfaces in the evaporator and condenser, by increasing airflow over the heat exchangers, and by preventing the accumulation of dust, dirt, or debris on the surfaces. Such changes also reduce the resistance to airflow through the evaporator and condenser and reduce the power used by the fans. Efficiency improvements may also be made directly by substituting more efficient motors in the compressor and the evaporator and condenser fans.

Eliminating heat flows that represent unwanted losses from the system is also beneficial. Leaks in duct systems and equipment cabinets are good examples. Modifications and adjustments to the refrigerant system that boost the rate of heat transfer through the system are discussed in a later section.

Great progress has been made in providing more efficient air conditioning units to the market. For instance, though most of the air source heat pumps manufactured in the United States have cooling EERs of 6.0 to 9.0 at the standard rating conditions, some available units have EERs of 14.0. The selection of a system type and specific model must be viewed as a major decision in the overall design process.

As the COP equation shows, increases in the cycle efficiency may be obtained by increasing the enthalpy change through the evaporator, $ha - hc$, and decreasing the enthalpy change through the compressor, $hc - hd$. This can be accomplished by either increasing the evaporator temperature or decreasing the condenser temperature. Figures 9.4 and 9.5 show the effect of either action on the cycle.

Such changes have been used by manufacturers to boost the efficiency of production air conditioners. For example, an energy-efficient room air conditioner might use a condensing temperature of 120°F, whereas an older standard model used 130°F. Similarly, evaporating temperatures have been increased. Larger evaporators and condensers compensate for the reduced temperature differential and allow cooling capacity to be maintained.

Similarly, anything that reduces evaporator temperature or increases condenser temperature will degrade the efficiency and output of the cooling system. Operating factors that can have this effect include

- reductions in heat transfer from the accumulation of dust and dirt on the evaporator and condenser
- reduced airflow over the evaporator and condenser caused by dirty filters, damaged heat-transfer fins, undersized ducts, trash, shrubs, or inadequate clearances
- solar heat gain and high air temperatures around the condenser

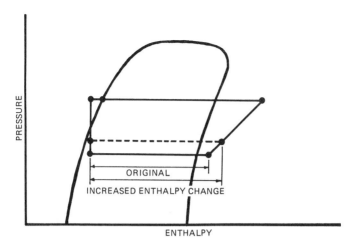

Figure 9.4. Effect of evaporator temperature increase.

Other methods of improving refrigeration system performance involve removing additional heat from the refrigerant just before it enters the condenser or evaporator. These processes are called *desuperheating* and *subcooling*, respectively. They do not involve a phase change in the liquid, only heat transfer from the superheated vapor or from the saturated liquid. The effects of desuperheating and subcooling on the evaporating and condensing processes are shown in Figs. 9.6 and 9.7. In both cases, the enthalpy change from point A to point C across the evaporator, the cooling effect, is increased.

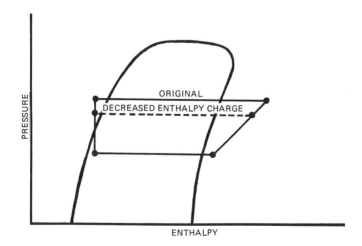

Figure 9.5. Effect of condenser temperature increase.

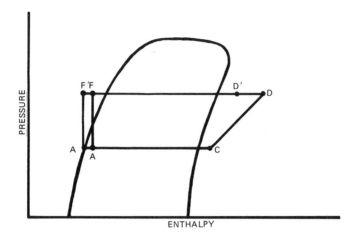

Figure 9.6. Desuperheating on P-H diagram.

Heat-reclaim devices are manufactured for use on air conditioners and heat pumps that make use of the heat from the compressor to heat domestic water. Not only do they reduce energy consumption for water heating, they improve the efficiency of the air conditioner or the heat pump (cooling mode only) by increasing the heat rejection capacity of the cooling system. During the cooling season, excess heat removed from the building, which would otherwise be discharged to the outdoors by the condenser, is used to heat water.

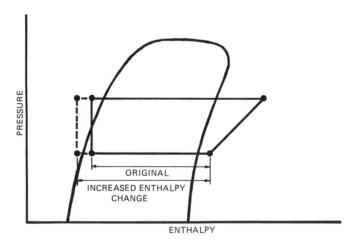

Figure 9.7. Subcooling on P-H diagram.

Selecting an Air Conditioner

Selecting an efficient unit appropriate to the building is a major step in reducing cooling energy costs. The concerns in selecting an air conditioner for low-cost cooling and comfort are

- proper sizing
- efficiency
- balance of latent and sensible capacity
- match of system to building and building use

Proper sizing and efficiency are generally the most important factors, but in houses that are well insulated and well protected from the sun, latent loads may become a much larger portion of the load. Then, the balance between sensible and latent cooling capacity becomes an important consideration. Finally, matching the system to the building and the cooling load can yield additional savings. By considering these four factors when selecting an air conditioner, one can reduce the cost of air conditioning as much as 40%. Selection of the proper unit also assures that the air conditioning system will be capable of providing a comfortable building interior during peak cooling load conditions.

Proper Sizing

The traditional methods of sizing residential air conditioning systems have included the "front door rule," the "bigger-is-better theory," and the "meanest-dog-on-the-block syndrome." The "front door rule" calls for the installation of the largest unit that will fit through the front door of the house. It usually results in higher profits for the contractor and completely eliminates any possibility of an owner complaint of inadequate cooling capacity. The "bigger-is-better theory" is applied after a load calculation indicates a reasonably sized unit and calls for adding another ton or so of capacity "just to be safe." Finally, the "meanest-dog-on-the-block syndrome" calls for an air conditioner just as large as or, preferably, bigger than the current largest unit in the neighborhood.

A slightly better rule-of-thumb design method is based on the floor area of the house. Typcially, it has been suggested that 1 t of cooling capacity be provided for each 500 ft^2 of house. Of all these design methods, only the "square foot method" is at all reasonable. However, it should be modified to 1 t per 700 to 1000 ft^2 for most well-designed and quality-built homes and then used *only* for estimating purposes. Most rules of thumb are based largely on experience with the poorly insulated and leaky houses of the past and are almost certain to lead to excess system capacity and higher costs for the homeowner.

Rather than relying on rules of thumb or guesses, one should use rational calculations to size an air conditioning system. Cooling loads are influenced by the building design; type of construction; climatic conditions; interior operating conditions; and internal loads from occupants, lighting, and equipment. Most equipment suppliers and utility companies offer cooling load estimates as a no-cost service.

Oversizing also occurs in the commercial sector, often as a result of the use of unreasonable design safety factors or some false sense of economy in reducing design costs by making approximate calculations rather than more exact ones. The economic and comfort consequences of oversizing are as severe for commercial buildings as for residences.

In both residential and commercial buildings, intentional oversizing is usually unjustified and usually creates comfort problems rather than solving them. Oversizing will certainly lead to excess equipment and duct costs. In addition, the excess capacity of an oversized unit causes the run time for the system to decrease, so that the blower has less opportunity to mix the inside air. This leads to hot spots in heat-producing areas, such as kitchens or rooms with large windows exposed to the sun.

An even more severe consequence of oversizing is the reduction of the dehumidification capacity of the system. An air conditioner removes humidity by passing the air inside the building over the cold evaporator coil where moisture condenses. Because an oversized unit runs less, it moves less air over the evaporator and less humidity is removed. The sensible building load is easily met, but humidity often rises to unpleasant levels. The occupants can either have the temperature they want and tolerate excess humidity or they can overcool the space to control humidity. Neither is very comfortable. With simple residential and small commercial systems, the correct design solution to cope with high moisture loads is normally to undersize the unit slightly, about 10%.

In commercial buildings, reheat is sometimes used to provide more effective control of humidity. The air conditioner cools the supply air to a lower than normal temperature to remove more humidity. To avoid overcooling the interior spaces in the building, the supply air is reheated to a comfortable temperature at the point of use. Control of comfort conditions is good, but energy consumption is high. Reheat systems were fairly common in years past, but they should be avoided unless precise control of humidity is required, as in a laboratory.

A common argument for oversizing is the idea that the unit will last longer if it is oversized and does not have to "work so hard." The main source of wear in bearings in electric motors and compressors is the start and stop periods when the bearing surfaces are touching one another rather than floating on an oil film. An oversized unit cycles more frequently and increases the most severe wear on its moving parts.

Finally, an oversized unit will consume more power than a properly sized unit to provide the same cooling effect. An air conditioner uses more power when it first starts than when it is running steadily. When the run cycle is over, the pressure differential created in the system and the cool refrigerant in the evaporator may be "wasted." As a unit cycles on and off more frequently, it goes through more high-power start periods and encounters more end-of-cycle losses. Efficiency is reduced, and operating cost is increased. In buildings subject to charges for peak electric power demand, an oversized system leads to further cost increases as a result of its higher power demand and lower load factor. In Atlanta, each ton of excess air conditioning capacity can result in additional demand costs of more than $150 per year. Demand charges in other areas are even higher.

Further cost increases arise from higher initial equipment and installation costs, higher maintenance costs, and increased property taxes. For most residences and commercial buildings, the comfort benefits of oversizing are undetectable or negative. Unless quick temperature pulldown or rigid interior temperature control are absolutely essential, intentional oversizing of an air conditioning system should be avoided. Where cooling loads vary considerably, a two-speed air conditioning unit should be considered.

Air Conditioner Sizing Methods

Reliable methods of calculating building cooling loads were discussed in Chapter 5. The calculated load is adjusted to compensate for duct heat gain and temperature control limit requirements, yielding the design load. The design load is expressed either in Btu/h or tons of cooling capacity. It is the recommended capacity for the cooling system to be installed. In most cases, additional safety factors and allowances are unwarranted and will lead to oversizing. All the assumptions used in the process should be considered carefully to ensure that they do not include hidden safety factors. Design temperatures were discussed in Chapter 5.

The use of the $2\frac{1}{2}\%$ design temperature does not mean that the building will be uncomfortable for $2\frac{1}{2}\%$ of the season. When loads are calculated with reasonable accuracy, the $2\frac{1}{2}\%$ design figure provides adequate capacity to keep the building comfortable throughout the entire cooling season. The actual peak individual cooling loads encountered in a building seldom occur simultaneously, particularly in residences. The various *internal* loads in a building seldom coincide with one another or with the peak *external* loads due to solar inputs and outdoor temperatures. In addition the mass of the building provides "thermal inertia" and absorbs heat as temperatures inside the building begin to rise, allowing the building to "coast" through most hot periods without excessive temperature increases. Even if a cooling system is somewhat undersized, high cooling loads resulting from greater than normal occupancy (parties in residences) or extreme weather conditions can be dealt with by anticipating their occurrence and precooling the building by lowering the thermostat setpoint.

Air Conditioner Efficiency

The efficiency of an air conditioner has a very straightforward effect on the power consumption. High efficiency means low power consumption, and low efficiency means high power consumption. Efficiency is defined as useful output divided by input. For automobiles, the EPA mileage ratings describe the efficiency of fuel usage. For air conditioners, efficiency is expressed by either the coefficient of performance (COP) or the energy efficiency ratio (EER). The EER is simply another way of expressing the COP that compares cooling output in Btu/h to the power requirements in watts. The higher the EER, the greater the efficiency of the air conditioner and the greater the amount of heat removed for each watt of power consumed

$$\text{EER} = \frac{\text{Cooling capacity (Btu/h)}}{\text{Power consumption (W)}}$$

The EER may be calculated from the COP by multiplying by 3.413 Btu/W h

$$\text{EER} = 3.413 \text{ Btu/W h} \times \text{COP}$$

In the United States, air conditioners are tested according to the Air-Conditioning and Refrigeration Institute (ARI) standards to establish standard EER ratings. ARI specifies conditions of 80°F dry bulb and 67°F wet bulb (50% RH) for the air entering the evaporator and outdoor air conditions of 95%F dry bulb. The ARI standard specifies that any production unit tested must perform to a level of at least 95% of the rated figures for that model. For conservatism, it is probably wise to use an EER of 0.95 times the rated EER in all calculations.

A variation of the EER provides a convenient way of evaluating the efficiency of an air conditioner over an entire cooling season. The SEER, or seasonal energy efficiency ratio, is calculated for a standard typical cooling season using EER data considering the efficiency of the unit under changing weather and part load conditions. In this chapter, SEER or EER may be used interchangeably in the equations and discussion, although the SEER provides the more accurate measure of actual seasonal efficiency. Table 9.1 provides information on SEERs for units manufactured in 1984.

As might be expected, the initial cost of air conditioning units, as well as the operating costs, is related to the EER. In general, the higher the EER, the higher the cost. Selecting an air conditioner based on efficiency is a process of trading off higher first cost for lower operating costs. The higher initial cost of purchasing a more efficient unit may be viewed as an investment that pays dividends when the unit operates.

Table 9.1. Split System Air Conditioner SEER Ratings.

Manufacturer	Capacity, MBtuh	SEER Btuh/W
Amana	17.0–25.0	5.85–8.5
	25.0–35.0	5.9–10.2
	36.6–58.0	8.6–10.55
Bryant	14.7–24.4	8.0–10.5
	26.4–35.4	7.7–10.65
	39.5–59.5	7.5–10.6
Carrier	12.9–24.0	7.35–10.8
	28.0–35.4	7.45–10.9
	36.0–58.0	7.45–10.95
Coleman	18.0–24.0	8.0–13.3
	27.0–35.0	8.8–13.2
	40.5–59.0	8.5–10.2
Lennox	12.3–24.0	7.5–11.1
	24.2–36.0	7.85–11.5
	36.2–61.5	7.7–12.7
Trane	18.7–24.0	6.85–12.05
	24.6–36.0	6.55–11.9
	36.6–59.5	6.8–10.7
York	12.2–24.0	8.2–9.6
	29.8–36.0	8.1–9.8
	36.6–62.0	7.9–10.0

The challenge is to select the combination of first cost and operating cost that provides the minimum life cycle cost. Because equipment costs and energy costs vary greatly, exact guidelines are difficult to provide, but most suggest a minimum EER of 8.0 for residential units.

The most difficult aspect in estimating the annual cost of operating an air conditioner is estimating the number of hours per year that the unit will operate. For central air conditioning systems, Table 9.2 provides estimates for properly sized equipment in several locations. The tabulated figure is the estimated equivalent number of hours that the cooling system would run at full capacity during a normal cooling season with an indoor temperature of 75°F. The lower end of the range is more representative of residences, and the upper end is appropriate for light commercial buildings. Obviously, weather and operating practices have a great effect, and these values are only approximate. The local electric utility can often provide better estimates of full-load operating hours for particular locations.

For room air conditioners, the number of operating hours varies more widely, according to how the units are used. The hours of use might be 300 h or fewer for a unit used only to cool a bedroom in the evening or more than 1800 h if

Table 9.2. Approximate Full-Load Hours of Operation for Air Conditioning Equipment.

Albuquerque, N.M.	800–2200	Indianapolis, Ind.	600–1600
Atlantic City, N.J.	500–800	Little Rock, Ark.	1400–2400
Birmingham, Ala.	1200–2200	Minneapolis, Minn.	400–800
Boston, Mass.	400–1200	New Orleans, La.	1400–2800
Burlington, Vt.	200–600	New York, N.Y.	500–1000
Charlotte, N.C.	700–1100	Newark, N.J.	400–900
Chicago, Ill.	500–1000	Oklahoma, City, Okla.	1100–2000
Cleveland, Ohio	400–800	Pittsburgh, Pa.	900–1200
Cincinnati, Ohio	1000–1500	Rapid City, S.D.	800–1000
Columbia, B.C.	1200–1400	St. Joseph, Md.	1000–1600
Corpus Christi, Tex.	2000–2500	St. Petersburg, Fla.	1500–2700
Dallas, Tex.	1200–1600	San Diego, Calif.	800–1700
Denver, Colo.	400–800	Savannah, Ga.	1200–1400
Des Moines, Iowa	600–1000	Seattle, Wash.	400–1200
Detroit, Mich.	700–1000	Syracuse, N.Y.	200–1000
Duluth, Minn.	300–500	Trenton, N.J.	800–1000
El Paso, Tex.	1000–1400	Tulsa, Okla.	1500–2200
Honolulu, Hawaii	1500–3500	Washington, D.C.	700–1200

(Adapted with permission from *ASHRAE Handbook—1985 Fundamentals.*)

the building is completely conditioned for the entire season with room air conditioners. In most cases, a figure near 1000 h could be used for initial comparison purposes.

Operating costs are calculated using the equation

$$\text{Operating cost} = \frac{\text{cooling capacity (Btu/h)} \times \text{power cost (\$/kWh)}}{\text{EER} \times 1000}$$

For example, consider a unit with a capacity of 5800 Btu/h and an EER of 6.4 operated for 1350 h. If the power cost is \$0.068/kWh, the cost of operating the unit is

$$\frac{5800 \text{ Btu/h} \times 0.068 \text{ \$/kWh}}{6.4 \times 1000} = 0.062 \text{ \$/h}$$

or

$$0.062 \text{ \$/h} \times 1350 \text{ h} = \$83$$

Alternatively, if the operating power requirement of the unit is known, the hourly cost of operation may be calculated as

$$\text{Operating cost} = \text{operating power (kW)} \times \text{power cost (\$/kWh)}$$

When specific information on a particular air conditioning system is not available, Table 9.3 gives approximate information from ASHRAE that can be used.

Table 9.3. Approximate Power Input of Air Conditioning Equipment.

System Type	Power Consumption, kW/t
Window units	1.78
Through-wall units	1.94
Dwelling unit, central air-cooled	1.63
Central, group, or building cooling plants	
3–25	1.40
25–100 t air-cooled	1.39
25–100 t water-cooled	1.11
Over 100 t water-cooled	0.99

(Adapted with permission from *ASHRAE Handbook—1985 Fundamentals.*)

The figures include power for both the compressor and auxiliary equipment, such as fans.

Air Conditioner Specification Sheets

Much more detailed and extensive performance information is available in the specification sheets provided by air conditioner manufacturers. A portion of a typical rating sheet is shown in Table 9.4. The table provides values of cooling capacity and sensible heat ratio at a range of indoor and outdoor conditions. The units described are split-system air conditioners with cooling capacities from 1.5 to 2.5 t. The condenser and evaporator units are listed in the first two columns; any of several evaporator units may be used with a particular condenser and compressor. The various evaporator units represent various sizes of evaporator coils and configurations, such as horizontal or vertical air flow. The airflow rate through the evaporator in cubic feet per minute is shown in column 3. Evaporator airflow is normally about 400 cfm per t of cooling capacity. The fourth column contains the diameters and lengths of the liquid and vapor lines connecting the evaporator and the condenser units.

The balance of the table consists of capacity ratings. Four outdoor dry-bulb temperatures are normally considered: 85°F, 95°F, 105°F, and 115°F. The air flowing over the evaporator, the return air from the room, is assumed to be at 80°F dry-bulb in all cases. Performance data for return air wet-bulb temperatures of 57, 62, 67, and 72°F are given; these correspond to indoor relative humidities of 38, 66, 70, and 89%, respectively. Outdoor conditions are described in terms of dry-bulb temperature only, because a wide variety of conditions are possible, and performance is comparatively insensitive to outdoor humidity.

The performance information tabulated usually consists of total cooling capacity in Btu/h and sensible heat ratio (SHR), the ratio of sensible cooling ca-

Table 9.4. Split-System Air Conditioner, Net Cooling Performance.

			Outside Air Temperature Entering Condenser										
			85								95		
			Wet Bulb Temperature Entering Evaporator										
			68/57		74/62		80/67		86/72		68/57		74/62	
Condensing Unit	Evaporator Unit	Rated Cfm	CAP	SHR	CAP	SHR	CAP	SHR	CAP	SHR	CAP	SHR	CAP	SHR
	E-1	700	20	.79	22	.75	24	.71	26	.66	18	.82	20	.77
C-1	E-2	700	20	.79	22	.75	24	.71	26	.66	18	.82	20	.77
	E-3	1000	24	.84	26	.79	29	.75	31	.71	22	.85	25	.81
C-2	E-4	1000	24	.84	26	.80	29	.76	31	.71	27	.85	25	.81
	E-5	1200	30	.83	32	.78	36	.74	39	.70	28	.84	31	.80
C-3	E-6	1200	30	.83	33	.78	36	.75	39	.70	28	.84	31	.80

NOTES
1. Net cooling capacity based on rated cfm shown. If other than rated air quantities are used, apply capacity correction factor.
2. Shaded capacities at 95 F outside air, 80 67 air entering evaporator. Rated in accordance with ARI Standard 210-79.

pacity to the total cooling capacity

$$SHR = \frac{\text{Sensible cooling capacity}}{\text{Total cooling capacity}}$$

The SHR provides a measure of the dehumidification capacity of the unit; lower SHR figures indicate greater dehumidification capacity or latent capacity. In this example, the SHR is expressed as a percentage, such as 73%. Often, it is listed as a decimal fraction, such as 0.73. Sometimes the latent cooling capacity is listed directly in the table, rather than the SHR. Otherwise, it is calculated as

Latent cooling capacity = (total cooling capacity) − (sensible cooling capacity)
Latent cooling capacity = (1 − SHR) × (total capacity)

The ARI standard rating conditions of 95°F outdoors, 80°F dry-bulb, and 67°F wet-bulb are identified by the shaded column at the center of the table. For instance, the rated capacity of a C-1 condenser unit installed with an E-2 evaporator unit is 27,000 Btu/h. The SHR is 77% or 0.77, so that

Sensible capacity = 0.77 × 27,000 Btu/h

= 20,790 Btu/h

Latent capacity = (1.0 − 0.77) × (27,000 Btu/h)

= 6210 Btu/h

Table 9.4. Continued.

95				105								115							
80/67		86/72		68/57		74/62		80/67		86/72		68/57		74/62		80/67		86/72	
CAP	SHR	CAP	SHR	CAP	SHR	CAP	SHR	CAP	SHR	CAP	SHR	CAP	SHR	CAP	SHR	CAP	SHR	CAP	SHR
22	.73	24	.68	17	.83	19	.78	21	.74	23	.69	16	.84	18	.81	20	.76	21	.71
22	.73	25	.68	17	.83	19	.78	21	.75	23	.70	16	.85	18	.81	20	.76	22	.71
27	.77	30	.72	21	.86	23	.83	26	.79	28	.74	20	.88	22	.84	24	.81	26	.76
27	.77	30	.72	21	.86	23	.83	26	.79	28	.74	20	.88	22	.84	24	.81	26	.76
34	.76	38	.71	26	.85	29	.81	32	.77	35	.72	24	.87	27	.83	30	.80	33	.75
34	.76	38	.71	26	.85	29	.81	32	.78	35	.73	24	.87	27	.83	30	.80	33	.75

EERs at ARI standard test conditions are usually presented in a separate table, such as Table 9.5, for the same units. Some manufacturers include power consumption in watts at various conditions in addition to the ARI values in their capacity tables. Then the EER may be estimated as (cooling capacity)/(input watts) for any specific set of conditions listed. It may be necessary to subtract the heat gain from the evaporator fan motor from the cooling capacity figures.

Note that the airflow over the evaporator and the voltage of the electrical service and the liquid and vapor lines used to connect the system all have an

Table 9.5. EER Data.

Condensing Unit	Evaporator Unit	Capacity (MBh)	Efficiency (SEER)
C-1	E-1	22.2	12.05
	E-2	22.4	12.40
C-2	E-3	27.4	11.90
	E-4	27.4	12.05
C-3	E-5	34.2	10.45
	E-6	34.2	10.50

influence on the output and power consumption of the unit. These and other factors may be described in the notes provided with the performance data.

Table 9.4 provides correction factors for adjusting the total and sensible capacity of the example units according to variations in evaporator airflow from the ARI conditions. For the example unit, consider what happens if the rated airflow of 875 cfm changes to 788 cfm. Using the multipliers from the table, we reduce the total cooling capacity to 0.98 times its ARI rated capacity, or $0.98 \times 28,000 = 27,440$ Btu. The sensible heat ratio is also reduced, but by a larger amount. The multiplier is 0.95, making the new SHR $0.95 \times 0.74 = 0.70$.

Total cooling capacity drops when airflow is reduced, because the heat transfer from the air to the evaporator is reduced as the air speed drops. But, because the air moves more slowly, it reaches a lower temperature. This increases the amount of condensation that takes place, increases the latent capacity, and reduces the sensible capacity.

The effects of evaporator airflow on total capacity and sensible heat fraction are summarized for the example units in Figs. 9.8 and 9.9.

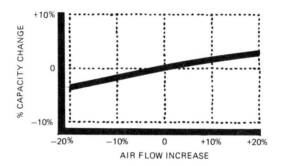

Figure 9.8. Total cooling capacity vs. air flow.

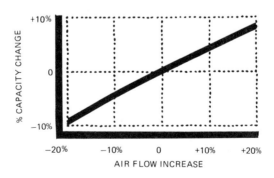

Figure 9.9. SHR vs. air flow.

Manufacturers' rating sheets provide a wealth of information on the performance of several different units for comparison. In addition, the information provides valuable insights into the effects of indoor and outdoor conditions on performance.

Air Conditioning Control and Operation

The manner in which an air conditioning system is controlled and operated has a major influence on its energy consumption and cost of operation. Unfortunately, many people have developed the notion that the most efficient operating mode for air conditioning is to turn it on in the spring and leave it on until the cooling season is over. It is assumed that thermostat setup, switching the unit off and using outdoor air for cooling during mild periods, and system shutdown when the building is unoccupied increase energy consumption and equipment wear. On the contrary, efficient operations can easily trim one-fourth to one-third of the cost of cooling in most residences and small buildings and improve the air conditioning system's reliability and life. Several effective control options for reducing air conditioner operating costs are discussed in the following section.

Alternating between Air Conditioning and Ventilation

During the air conditioning season, the outdoor temperature frequently falls below the interior thermostat setpoint. Should the building remain closed with the air conditioner operating or should the air conditioner be turned off and the building opened for ventilation? If humidity were not a question, the answer would be straightforward—ventilate. However, during the summer, cooler outdoor air usually contains much more moisture than the air inside an air conditioned building, and the decision is not always clear.

A concern that is often expressed is that the more humid outdoor air will "saturate" the interior of the building and its furnishings with moisture and increase the air conditioning load when the system is turned back on, outweighing any possible savings during the ventilation period. An added argument is that, because the outdoor temperature is low, the heat gain to the building is small, and the energy consumed by the air conditioning system is negligible.

In realistic situations such concerns are almost always overstated. The increased load resulting from moisture gain is usually small compared with the savings. Secondly, the air conditioning load on the building may still be significant, even though the temperature difference is small. Internal heat gain, both sensible and latent, still occurs and solar loads may add large amounts of heat.

There is a breakeven point, however, when outdoor humidity is very high and the temperature is only slightly below the interior temperature. Unfortunately the matter is quite complex, involving several factors that have not been well researched. The process of moisture transfer through a building and the rates at which furnishings and building materials absorb moisture are not well understood. Also, most of the variables in the problem are not simple constants. Analytical solutions are not easy, and field research has been very limited. Nevertheless, some simple guidelines and observations help to establish an effective air conditioning/ventilating operating strategy.

The air conditioning systems in most residences and small commercial buildings do not have any means of directly sensing or controlling relative humidity and moisture levels and respond only to dry-bulb temperature. Thus relative humidity often varies within a range of 40 to 85%, depending on weather conditions, thermostat settings, and changes in internal loads. Occupants are usually unaware of these variations, although very high humidity levels are compensated for by simply lowering the thermostat setpoint. But indoor humidity has no direct role in causing the air conditioning system to operate.

One simple way to judge the advisability of ventilating is to examine the indoor and outdoor air conditions on the psychrometric chart. The advantage of ventilating is simply a question of whether it is desirable to replace the air inside the house with air from the outdoors. The psychrometric chart in Fig. 9.10 shows an operating point representing the upper limits of the ASHRAE

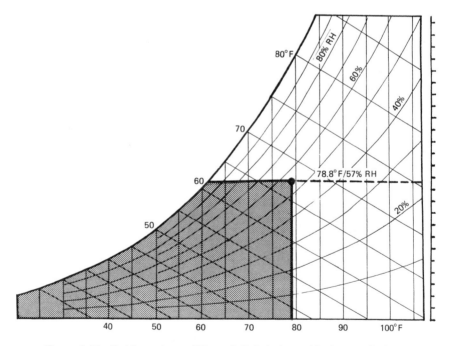

Figure 9.10. Outdoor air conditions definitely favorable for ventilation.

summer comfort region, 78.8°F and approximately 57% RH. Similar information can be easily developed for other interior operating conditions.

A line drawn horizontally to the left of the chart from the 78.8°F/57% RH point represents conditions where the outside air has a moisture content equal to that of the building interior. If the outdoor condition is within the shaded region to the left of the 78.8°F and 57% RH point and below the constant moisture line, it is both cooler and drier than the interior air. That is, both its sensible heat and latent heat contents are lower. Ventilation would be highly desirable, because comfort conditions would be improved, and there is no possibility of undesirable moisture gain.

Figure 9.11 illustrates a line of constant enthalpy drawn from the point representing indoor air. Whenever the point representing outdoor air lies on or below that line, the *total* heat content of the outdoor air is lower than that of the indoor air. A total thermal benefit would be obtained by replacing indoor air with outdoor air. But, though a total heat benefit might be obtained, the moisture content of the house could rise. For example, consider what happens when the air at 78.8°F and 57% RH inside a 1500-ft^2 house is replaced with outdoor air at 70°F and 80% RH (63.5°F dewpoint temperature). The air originally inside the house had an enthalpy of approximately 32.1 Btu/lb and a moisture content of 83 grains/lb. The outdoor air has a lower enthalpy, 30.6

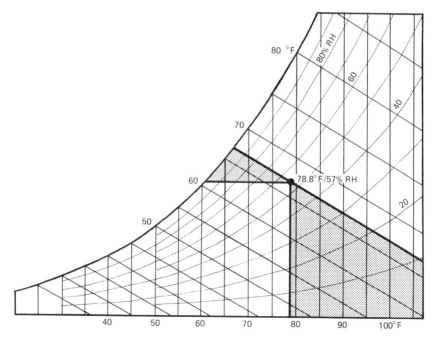

Figure 9.11. Outdoor air conditions generally favorable for ventilation.

Btu/lb, but a higher moisture content, 88 grains/lb. Completely changing the air inside the house results in an enthalpy reduction of 1300 Btu, but a net moisture gain of 4380 grains or 0.63 lb. A sensible cooling effect of 2000 Btu is partially offset by a latent heat gain of 700 Btu, still yielding a 1300-Btu cooling effect.

If the house were then closed and experienced sensible heat gain from the sun, conduction, and internal sources, the air would eventually reach its former temperature of 78.8°F. But, as a result of the addition of moisture, its relative humidity would be slightly higher, approximately 59%. The total latent heat gain is rather small and ventilation is still desirable.

Two other things occur to complicate the situation: heat and moisture storage in the building interior. A typical residence has an innate thermal storage capacity of 3 to 6 Btu of heat per degree F of temperature change for each square foot of floor area. The mass associated with passive solar heating systems increases this figure. If we assume a normal storage capacity value of 4 Btu/°F/ ft^2, a total storage capacity of 6000 Btu/°F is available in the example's interior building mass and furnishings. If the building is thoroughly ventilated for several hours, the temperature of the mass might be reduced by half of the difference between its initial temperature and the outdoor air temperature, or (78.8 − 70)/2 = 4.4°F.

Thus 6000 Btu/°F × 4.4°F = 26,400 Btu of "coolth" might be stored equivalent to slightly more than 1 h of operation for a 2-ton air conditioner. This storage effect tends to increase the value of ventilation with cooler air. Note that ceiling fans and whole house fans increase the rate at which the mass is cooled by the ventilating air, because they reduce the insulating effect of the air film at the surfaces.

Unfortunately, moisture may also be stored inside the building when it is ventilated with outdoor air. When moist outdoor air is used for ventilation, the concentration of moisture in the air is increased (higher dewpoint temperature), and the materials inside gradually absorb more moisture. When air conditioning is used again, the moisture must be removed, requiring the use of additional energy. The rate of moisture absorption and the total amount of moisture stored are not easily calculated. But the negative effects are small when the outdoor air has a lower enthalpy than the indoor air. When outdoor conditions are within the range shown by the shaded area in Fig. 9.11, it is suggested that ventilation be used whenever the outdoor conditions feel comfortable or cool and when the air conditioner will remain off for at least 4 to 6 hours.

Although it is unlikely that anyone would want to ventilate with warmer outdoor air (the region to the right of the indoor air point), a reduction in total heat would be achieved.

A third ventilation possibility exists when the outdoor air is within the set of conditions shown in Fig. 9.12. The enthalpy of the outdoor air is higher, but sensible cooling is still possible. Here, analysis and recommendations are not

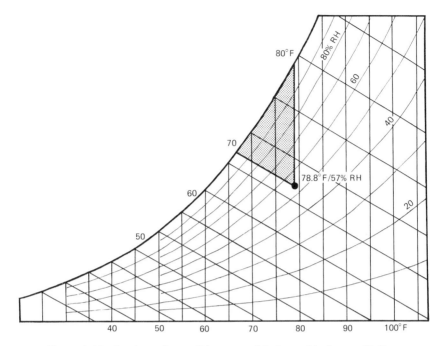

Figure 9.12. Outdoor air conditions possibly favorable for ventilation.

as straightforward, and such variables as thermal storage mass, acceptable comfort limits, and sensitivity to humidity become more important. Ventilation is suggested when the outdoor conditions feel comfortable or cool and the air conditioning can be turned off for at least 12 h. Some temporary high-humidity problems may be experienced when the building is closed and air conditioning is turned on again.

Thermostat Setpoint

Perhaps the simplest method of reducing the cost of air conditioning is to increase the thermostat setpoint. An increased setpoint reduces the temperature difference between the building interior and the outdoor air and consequently reduces the heat gain from conduction and infiltration. When the outdoor air is at 95°F, a thermostat setpoint change from 74 to 78°F reduces the temperature difference from 21 to 17°F. This results in a direct reduction in sensible heat gain from conduction and infiltration of nearly 20%. Latent infiltration gain is also reduced, because the higher interior temperature results in less dehumidification of the air leaking in. In total, reductions in air conditioning costs of 5 to 12% per degree have been predicted and reported for thermostat setup.

Higher thermostat settings also effectively shorten the cooling season and increase the time during the season when natural ventilation can be used as a substitute for air conditioning. Figure 6.16 shows the number of hours in each month of the cooling season above various temperatures for Atlanta. The effect of choosing higher thermostat settings is apparent.

Thermostat Setup and System Shutdown during Unoccupied Periods

A common belief is that leaving a building closed and turning the air conditioning system off or increasing the thermostat setpoint to a very high setting will result in a buildup of heat that causes increased energy consumption and increased wear on the system. The reasoning is that the temperature of the building interior and furnishings rises during the off period and the air conditioner has to work so much harder when it is switched back on that the savings are lost. This is not true.

The only situation where a problem may develop is thermostat setback on heat pumps in the heating mode. If a heat pump thermostat is set back too far at night and then set up in one step in the morning, heating energy consumption can be increased. The problem arises in the way the control system operates. If the output of the heat pump is not adequate to meet the load (indicated by the difference in the thermostat setpoint and the indoor air temperature), then the electric resistance heat is turned on. Because the heat pump can operate at a COP of 3.0 or more, and the resistance heat operates at a COP of 1.0, significant increases in energy consumption can result.

It is not possible for a similar situation to occur with an air conditioner or a heat pump in the cooling mode. There is no cooling component analogous to the resistance heat, there is only the compressor and the refrigerant system. The air conditioner and the heat pump in the cooling mode are either on or off.

To understand the concept of a buildup of heat inside the building, it is useful to examine the heat gain process in a building. Consider the thermal system of the building as the building envelope itself, with the air conditioner as a separate component (Fig. 9.13).

A large part of the cooling load on a building varies directly with the indoor/outdoor temperature differential. If an air conditioner system is switched off, the interior air temperature and the temperature of the building and furnishings rise. The temperature differential driving the flow of heat into the building is reduced, and the rate of heat gain is reduced (Fig. 9.14).

When the air conditioning system is switched back on, the air conditioner will operate continuously for a longer than normal time before it cycles off. It is not subjected to additional wear or stress. Nor does it have an overall cooling load greater than the load it would have had to meet had it been in operation for the entire period. On the contrary, the load is somewhat smaller, and a net savings results.

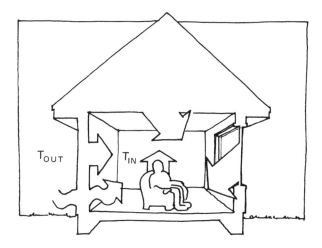

Figure 9.13. Building thermal system and system shutdown.

Whenever a building will be unoccupied for more than a few hours, the thermostat should be set up. A setting of 82°F is suggested if the unoccupied period is to be less than 4 h; 85°F is appropriate for longer periods. If the building will be unoccupied overnight or for one or more days, it may be possible to turn the air conditioning system off completely or to set the thermostat to a very high temperature. The alternative selected should avoid excessively uncomfortable cooldown periods when the occupants return. Systems switched off in

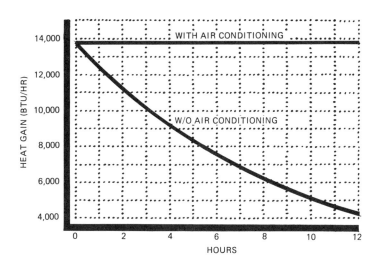

Figure 9.14. Heat gain with and without A/C.

commercial buildings should be restarted in time for the building to become reasonably comfortable before people arrive. High outdoor temperature and humidity call for smaller increases in settings and earlier restarts; milder conditions allow higher settings and later restarts. Adjust the control strategy to suit the conditions; time clock settings should not be considered to be constants.

Three sets of circumstances may limit the use of thermostat setups and system shutdown. First, if the building is subject to electrical demand charges, care should be taken not to create a peak condition when the air conditioning is switched on. This is more likely to be a problem in buildings that have multiple air conditioning systems or multiple compressors, particularly if the systems are oversized. In buildings with single systems a significant increase is almost impossible. In small multiple-system buildings a higher demand peak is unlikely because all the units would probably already be running simultaneously.

Second, time-of-day billing structures may also pose a minor difficulty; it may be desirable to allow the cooling system to run during off-peak hours to precool the building and reduce more costly on-peak power costs. Such opportunities are usually confined to larger buildings and are unusual in residences. Few utilities use time-of-day billing schedules at present.

Finally, if cooling capacity is marginal or inadequate, system shutdowns and large thermostat setups may lead to comfort problems when the building is first occupied on days with extreme weather conditions. Precooling may be necessary to meet the cooling load.

Guidelines for Efficient Air Conditioning Operation Applicable to Air Conditioners and Heat Pumps

- Use the minimum required quantity of outdoor air. In commercial buildings with an outdoor air supply, adjust dampers to the minimum permissible opening, and investigate automatic controls that keep dampers completely closed during unoccupied hours and morning startup. In systems without an outdoor air supply, control the air quantity by controlling infiltration into the building. With room air conditioners, use the outside air setting only when absolutely necessary to remove odors.
- Change or clean filters as required to maintain good airflow and good heat transfer from the evaporator, as often as once a month in dusty conditions.
- Set the air conditioner thermostat to a higher setting, 78 to 85°F, and use internal fans to provide comfort equivalent to a lower setting.
- Check thermostats for proper operation using a reliable thermometer, not the thermometer in the thermostat. Thermostat thermometers are notoriously inaccurate, often by more than 5°F, and can create problems if they are used by uninformed occupants to judge comfort. Verify that thermostats are sensing the true room air temperature and not being biased by

heat from lamps, televisions, office equipment, solar exposure, or heat transferred through an outside wall.

- Observe the cycling pattern of the air conditioner; on cycles should be at least 5 min long. Short cycling leads to poor performance and high wear. Short cycling may be caused by an improperly adjusted thermostat or by cool air from a diffuser blowing directly on the thermostat, or a grossly oversized system.
- Eliminate air leaks. Seal leaks in ductwork, diffuser connections, filter racks, and the evaporator and blower cabinet. Humidifiers, electrostatic filters, and other add on equipment are also likely leak points. Duct leaks are particularly important to control if the ducts are in a hot unconditioned space, such as an attic. Minor duct leaks to the building interior are not a problem; route ducts inside the conditioned space wherever possible. Remember that leaks on the return side of the system pull air *into* the system and are difficult to detect.
- Room air conditioners can leak like sieves if not properly installed. Follow instructions and use tape and foam pads generously to seal the unit to the window casing. In double-hung windows, be certain that the gap between the two sliders is sealed with a foam pad. If you are qualified, you may want to open the air conditioner and seal small leaks in the barrier between the indoor and outdoor side of the unit. Be *very* careful not to block the condensate drain path from the evaporator to the outdoors.
- If a multiple-speed fan is installed, set the fan speed in accordance with the latent heat load in the building. If latent gain is small and humidity is low, operate the fan on high speed for maximum total heat transfer from the evaporator. If interior humidity is excessive, set the fan to a lower speed temporarily to allow greater moisture removal.
- Control hot spots in the building. To control temperatures in a single overheated location, it may be necessary to overcool the entire zone. Instead, reduce heat gain in the overheated area, or use a small portable fan to circulate the air from cooler areas and increase comfort.
- Turn air conditioners *off* whenever possible. If the outside conditions are not comfortable, leave the building closed; if they are, ventilate. Turning the unit off will always save energy, even though the unit may have to run continuously for a period when it is turned back on. In buildings used only during the day, delay starting the air conditioner until soon before the building opens. Turn it off before the occupants leave and let the building coast. Modify operating schedules as the weather changes.
- Cool only the occupied portion of the building, close down unused rooms.
- Keep drapes, blinds, and shades closed to block solar gain. Focus on east windows during the morning, south windows from midmorning to midafternoon, and west windows during the afternoon.

10

HEAT PUMPS

A heat pump is a refrigeration machine, much like an air conditioner, that has the capability to move heat in either of two directions. A heat pump used in a residence or small commercial building looks very much like a normal air conditioner. The major difference is that the flow of refrigerant through the two heat exchangers, the evaporator and the condenser, can be reversed. This allows them to swap roles, permitting the system to be used as either a heating or a cooling device. During the winter, it extracts heat from the outside air and delivers it to the interior of a building. In summer, the refrigerant system is reversed, and heat is removed from the building and discharged outdoors.

The use of heat pumps dates back to 1926, when T. G. N. Haldane built a 17,000-Btu/h unit in Scotland that extracted heat from water and air. The commercial application of heat pumps in residences and commercial buildings began in the 1930s, but did not reach significant volumes until the 1950s. Sales of heat pumps grew rapidly, but soon declined as a result of reliability problems that arose from inadequate product design and development. Reversing valve and compressor failures and evaporator icing were the main problems. Today, a wide variety of efficient, dependable heat pumps are available from a number of reputable manufacturers. Recent studies have shown that the median life of a residential heat pump can exceed 20 years. Rising electricity prices and the promotional efforts of utilities have caused heat pumps to become synonomous with energy conservation and efficient building operation in much of the country.

In the cooling mode, a heat pump and a conventional air conditioner perform similarly. During the cooling season there are no inherent advantages of a heat pump over other air conditioners. The energy-saving recommendations in the previous chapter for air conditioners also apply to heat pumps in the cooling mode. The energy efficiency ratio (EER) and seasonal energy efficiency ratio (SEER) are used for heat pumps as for air conditioners.

The heat pump is preferable to other heating systems because it operates more economically in the heating mode and it combines both heating and cooling functions in a single system that uses a single energy source. The major disadvantage is that its first cost is normally higher than that of other systems, 10 to 25% more than the combination of a gas furnace and conventional air conditioner. Even so, in areas with both heating loads and cooling loads, the heat pump is usually a very attractive choice. Some utilities offer incentives for the use of heat pumps rather than conventional air conditioning and separate heating systems.

The name *heat pump* is very descriptive; the units literally pump heat from one location to another. While a pump moving water uphill works against gravity, a heat pump works against a temperature difference. Both in the cooling mode and the heating mode, the heat pump moves heat from a low-temperature region to a high-temperature region. As the second law of thermodynamics points out, this can be done only if energy is consumed in making the process happen. The electric energy consumed by the compressor and fans is used to move a much greater quantity of energy as heat against the temperature difference. As with air conditioners, the ratio of the amount of heat moved (the heating or cooling capacity) to the amount of energy used by the heat pump is the coefficient of performance, the COP. COPs for heat pumps range from slightly more than 1.0 under extremely unfavorable heating conditions to more than 4.0 during favorable conditions.

HEAT PUMP OPERATION

Most heat pumps use air or water as a sink to accept heat during the summer and as a source to supply heat during the winter. For convenience, an air-source heat pump is used as an example in this discussion; the same principles apply to water-source heat pumps.

In the cooling mode, a heat pump operates like the air conditioner described in the preceding chapter. All the same components are involved except for a refrigerant-reversing valve. The heat pump's reversing valve is installed in the refrigerant system between the compressor and the heat exchange coils. It allows the flow of refrigerant to be reversed in the system, so that the indoor heat exchanger (the evaporator in the cooling mode) can become the condenser in the heating mode. Similarly, the outdoor heat exchanger (the condenser in the air conditioning mode) becomes the evaporator in the heating mode (Fig. 10.1).

Because heat moves from the evaporator to the condenser, the heat pump can either heat or cool a building. The operation of the heat pump in the heating mode is similar to that in the cooling mode; the flow of the refrigerant and the role of the two heat exchangers are simply reversed. Heat is collected from the exterior air and rejected to the air inside the building. It is as if a room air conditioner were simply turned around in a window.

The amount of heat that a heat pump can move and its COP are direct func-

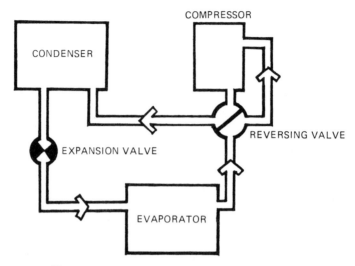

Figure 10.1. Schematic diagram of a heat pump.

tions of the temperature of the heat sink/source and the building temperature. In the heating mode, as the outdoor temperature drops, the heat pump capacity and efficiency drop off proportionally. In summer, higher outdoor temperatures mean reduced performance. The effects of outdoor air temperature on operation and efficiency are more pronounced in winter than in summer, as the variation in temperature is greater. Electrical resistance elements are usually installed to provide additional heating capacity at low outdoor temperatures.

TYPES OF HEAT PUMPS

Heat pumps are categorized by the type of sink/source they use; there are water-source heat pumps, air-source heat pumps, and ground-source heat pumps. The predisposition toward heating issues has been responsible for eliminating the consideration of the heat "sink" from the terminology. We really should refer to a heat pump as an air-sink/source type, rather than as an air-source type. Heat sources/sinks are discussed later in this chapter. The primary difference between heat pumps that use air as a sink/source and those that use water is the type of heat exchanger used with the sink/source. Air units usually have a fin and tube heat exchanger, similar to an automobile radiator, and water units use a coil-type heat exchanger. The design of the refrigerant circuit in a water source unit is also somewhat different, simpler in some respects. Water-source systems do not have to tolerate the large changes in temperature that an air-sink/source system does.

Because not all heat pumps are used for heating air directly, another set of categories is required. It refers to both the type of sink/source and the medium used to move the cooling or heating effect that is produced. Thus, a heat pump may be an air-to-air type, if it uses air as a sink/source and provides heating and cooling to a building through a forced-air system, or an air-to-water type, if it is used for heating water or as part of a loop system in a commercial building. Air-to-air heat pumps are by far the most prevalent type used in small buildings, both residential and commercial. Water-to-air heat pumps are also used, but their applicability is more limited, and they are not as common. Water may be the primary heat sink/source, as from a well or lake, or it may be simply the medium used to transfer heat from the earth by a set of buried pipes.

Water-to-air heat pumps are sometimes used in large commercial buildings that have uneven heating and cooling loads. They might be used to collect heat from the overheated west side of a building during a fall afternoon and distribute it to the other perimeter zones of the building that require heating. Or the excess heat produced by a computer center might be used to offset a heating load elsewhere. Such systems can be very economical when a load imbalance occurs, with part of a facility requiring heating while another part requires cooling.

Air-to-water heat pumps are being used to heat water for use in homes and in restaurants and motels. Their possible use for supplying "waste" cooling to a building interior is discussed in a later chapter. Rather than using gas or electricity to heat water directly, the heat pump collects heat from the air.

Heat Sources and Heat Sinks

The ideal heat sink/source would have infinite heat capacity and a convenient temperature. The temperature of the sink should either increase in winter and decrease in summer or remain as constant as possible during the year. As sinks/sources that change their temperature from cool in summer to warm in winter are extremely rare, a nearly constant temperature sink/source would be the most reasonable expectation. In all but the extreme northern portions of the country, the ambient air is an adequate year-round heat sink/source. Deep wells and deep earth sink/sources are very desirable, because their temperature fluctuates only a few degrees during the year and the temperature is close to the desired building temperature. For most purposes, the two most practical heat sinks are the atmosphere and ground water from wells. Earth coils and pipe fields are also being investigated and applied with good results.

Air-Source Heat Pumps

Air-source heat pumps are available in capacities ranging from less than $\frac{1}{2}$ t to systems large enough for large commercial buildings. Most are split systems, (indoor unit and outdoor unit), but unitary equipment (all components in a single housing) is available in smaller models.

Air-source heat pumps are rated in terms of high-temperature (47°F) and low-temperature (17°F) heating performance, with efficiency and capacity figures provided for both. The indoor temperature is the same for both rating points, 70°F dry-bulb. The exact testing and rating methods are specified by ARI standards.

At 17°F, a typical unit might have a heating COP of 1.9 to 2.0. The range of performance includes COPs of 1.9 to 2.0 for lower cost models up to 2.3 for higher cost, more efficient units. At 47°F, the COP of a typical unit might vary from 2.7 to 3.1, though some models would rate from 2.2 to 3.3. Cooling capacity and COP or EER are reported at 95°F outdoors and 80°F dry-bulb and 67°F wet-bulb, indoors, the equivalent of 50% RH. Rated cooling SEERs range from 5.8 to 14, with most units in the range of 7.5 to 9.0. For most models, the cooling capacity at 95°F is roughly equivalent to the heating capacity at 47°F.

As is done for air conditioners, an SEER is used to indicate the performance of a heat pump over the entire cooling season. A similar concept is used for the heating performance. The seasonal performance factor, SPF, expresses the ratio of heating energy (in Btus) provided by the heat pump to the amount of energy it consumes (in watt-hours). The heat output and power consumption of the electrical resistance heat elements installed with the heat pump are also included in the figures. The SPF is also called the HSPF, or heating season performance factor. Typical heat pump SPF figures are shown in Fig. 10.2 (Ref. 10.1). Most

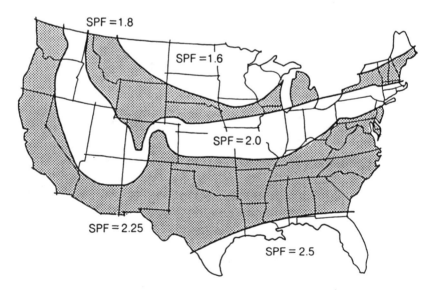

Figure 10.2. Typical heat pump seasonal performance factors.
Reprinted from HEAT PUMPS (1981) by Dermot McGuigan, page 34, and is used by permission of Storey Communications, Inc./Garden Way Publishing.

energy conservation programs recommend an SPF and SEER of at least 7.5 to 8.0. The economics should be calculated to determine the attractiveness of using units with even higher performance.

Applications

Where heat pumps are used as a replacement for a conventional heating system, there is sometimes a problem with the flow capacity of the duct system. If the old system did not include air conditioning, the duct system may be too small to handle the higher airflow required by a heat pump. In the heating mode, a heat pump requires more air flow than a combustion furnace or electric furnace of equal heating capacity. As a general guideline, the duct system should be capable of flow volumes of about 450 cfm for each ton (12,000 Btu/h) of cooling capacity at standard ARI rating conditions.

The heating capacity of an air-source heat pump declines as the outdoor temperature falls. While the heat pump capacity falls at lower temperatures, the heating load on a building increases. A typical unit with a heating capacity of 38,000 Btu/h at 47°F has a capacity of only 20,600 Btuh at 17°F. Figure 10.3 illustrates the change in heat pump capacity and building load for the energy-conserving house example used earlier and a typical heat pump.

For this example, note that, at an outdoor temperature of 35°F, the heat pump capacity and the building load are equal. This temperature is referred to as the system's *balance point*. At temperatures above the balance point, the heat pump will have excess capacity, and at temperatures below the balance point, the

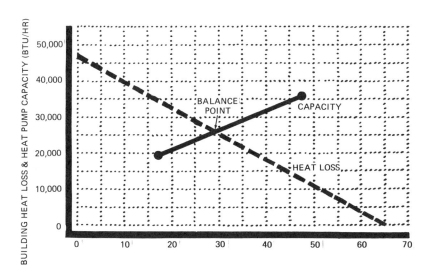

Figure 10.3. Heat pump heating capacity and building heating load.

heating capacity of the heat pump will fall short of the requirements of the house. The difference in capacity and load at low temperatures is normally made up with electric-resistance heat elements installed in the duct.

Only in rare instances will the design heating load and the design cooling load of a building each be equal to the heating and cooling capacities of a heat pump. A mismatch on either cooling or heating is to be expected, with the heating load greater than the cooling load in most locations. Normal system sizing procedures call for sizing and selecting a heat pump for the cooling condition and then adding electric-resistance heat to bring the heating capacity at design conditions up to the required level. In cooler regions, where heating loads are much greater than cooling loads, some oversizing of the cooling capacity is permissible, perhaps 20%.

In warmer, more humid areas, sizing to heating loads and oversizing cooling capacity should be done cautiously, because it can cause a reduction of dehumidification capacity and uncomfortable interior conditions. The savings achieved in the winter by avoiding the use of resistance heat at lower outdoor temperatures may be offset by the inefficiency of the unit during the cooling season and the decrease in summer comfort. In locations where the design cooling load exceeds the design heating load, the heat pump capacity should be chosen to closely match the cooling load. Excess heating capacity in the winter poses no significant problems.

Where locally specific sizing guidelines are available, they should be considered. Such information is sometimes supplied by the local electric utility or a state energy office.

Air-Source Heat Pump Manufacturers

Several manufacturers of unitary, air-source heat pumps are listed in Table 10.1. Included in the listing are the model numbers of the most efficient unit manufactured by each company in each of four approximate cooling capacities: 18,000 and 36,000 Btu/h. The information was developed from the June 30, 1984 edition of the *Directory of Certified Applied Air-Source Heat Pumps* from the Air-Conditioning and Refrigeration Institute.

Water-Source Heat Pumps

In general, water-source heat pumps offer higher cooling and heating efficiencies than air-source heat pumps, because they may be designed for a more stable and favorable sink/source temperature (Fig. 10.4). This allows the manufacturer to optimize the refrigerant circuit for a more specific set of operating conditions, thus improving the efficiency of the unit. Another operating advantage is the elimination of energy consumption for defrosting the outdoor coil during the heating season. With air-source heat pumps in the heating mode, it is nec-

Table 10.1. High-Efficiency Air-Source Heat Pumps.

Manufacturer	18,000 Btu/h SEER	Model No.	36,000 Btu/h SEER	Model No.
Carrier Air Conditioning	14.00	Outdoor 38SQ961(2) + 385Q002430 Indoor 28VH002+40FS075	13.20	Outdoor 38SQ961(2) + 38SQ03630 Indoor 28VH004+40FS120
Lennox Industries, Inc.	9.40	Outdoor HP16-211V-1P Indoor CPS12-26-1+ES1202	10.45	Outdoor HP14-261/411V-1P Indoor CP12-41-1
Rheem Air Conditioning Div.	11.20	Outdoor RPGA-018JA Indoor RHQA-11+RCQB-A018	10.50	Outdoor RPGA-036JA Indoor RHQA-13+RCQB-A036
Rudd Air Conditioning Div.	11.20	Outdoor UPGA-018JA Indoor UHQA-11+RCQB-A018	10.50	Outdoor UPGA-036JA Indoor UHQA-13+RCQB-A036
The Coleman Co., Inc.	11.00	Outdoor 3418A830 Indoor 3418A030	9.45	6036-901
Trane Dealer Products Group	10.20	Outdoor BWX724A-B Indoor BXF724P	10.55	Outdoor BWX736B Indoor BXV739P
Bryant Air Conditioning	10.10	Outdoor 545CJ024 Indoor 506B036	10.00	Outdoor 545CJ036 Indoor 510B048
Day & Night Air Conditioning	10.10	Outdoor 545CJ024 Indoor 5068036	10.00	Outdoor 545CJ036 Indoor 5108048
The Williamson Co.	9.75	Outdoor 7320-02-2020 Indoor 7324-25-2009	9.35	Outdoor 7320-03-2020 Indoor 7324-03-2009
Payne Air Conditioning	9.40	Outdoor 545CJ1024 Indoor 517EN024	10.00	Outdoor 545CJ036 Indoor 510B048
Trane Commercial Systems	9.90	SPHE-B201	9.55	RPUBB302-A
Whirlpool Heating and Cooling Products	9.65	Outdoor NCHAA18AK Indoor NEAGA24AB	9.15	Outdoor NCHAA35AK Indoor NEAGA35AB
Hail-Quaker Corp.	9.65	Outdoor NCHAA18AK Indoor NEAGA24AB	9.15	Outdoor NCHAA35AK Indoor NESCO35AO
Sears, Roebuck & Co., Inc.	9.65	Outdoor B67.821910 Indoor 867.824040	9.15	Outdoor B67.821940 Indoor 867.821131
Climate Control	9.25	Outdoor H-R811018-2T 25, 2C Indoor H811018	9.25	Outdoor H-R811036-25 2C, 2T

(Excerpted by permission from *Directory of Certified Applied Air-Source Heat Pumps*, June 30, 1984, Air-Conditioning and Refrigeration Institute.)

Table 10.1. (Continued)

Manufacturer	10,000 Btuh SEER	Model No.	36,000 Btuh SEER	Model No.
Amana Refrigeration, Inc.	9.10	Outdoor ERHQ18-W018 Indoor EBCH1805M	8.30	Indoor H-V, H814042 EPHO3600-1E
York Heating and Air Conditioning	8.60	Outdoor E2CP018A06A Indoor G111S018AA	9.00	Outdoor E4CP060A06 Indoor N2AHD14A06 + G1HCO36A
Arco Comfort Products Co.	8.55	Outdoor RYB017GAA Indoor B311+T1, HB11024	8.60	Outdoor RYB0356AA Indoor 8345+T1, H814042
Southwest Manufacturing	8.50	PH-241	8.30	PH-361
Bard Manufacturing Co.	8.25	Outdoor 18HPQ2 Indoor H24Q51	8.60	36WH2
Addison Products Co.	8.75	PH018P-1	8.35	PH038R-1
Century by Heat Controller	8.25	Outdoor QH848-1D Indoor QHA48C	8.10	PH060-1
Heat Controller, Inc.	8.25	Outdoor QH848-1D Indoor QHA48C	8.10	PH860-1
Goettl Air-Conditioning, Inc.	8.60	GBHP-481A	7.60	GAHP-633
Magic Chef Air Conditioning Div.	8.55	Outdoor PE48P-1, S-1 Indoor H2A48P, S	8.55	Outdoor PE60P-1, S-1 Indoor H2A60P, S
Patco, Inc.	7.50	Outdoor APB48P-7, S-7 Indoor HC5-481P, S		
Fraser & Johnston	7.80	Outdoor E0HP-F048A Indoor GAHH-048A	8.10	BBHT-F060A
Luxaire Heating and Air Conditioning	7.80	Outdoor EBHP-F048A Indoor GAHH-048A	8.10	BBHT-F060A
Moncrief Heating and Air Conditioning	7.80	Outdoor EBHP-F048A Indoor GAMC-048A	8.10	BBHT-F060A
Airtron, Inc.	8.30	Outdoor ASH8481CA Indoor CYB047AA		
Marvair Co.	7.90	Outdoor 48HP-XXX-A# Indoor 48HPH, HPV-XXX-A#	7.60	Outdoor 60HP-XXX-H# Indoor 60HPH, HPV XXX n#

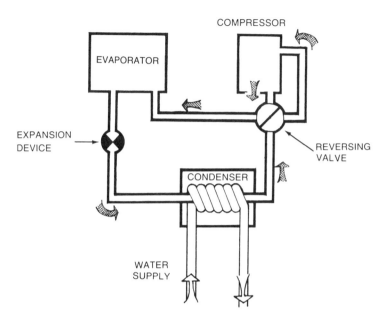

Figure 10.4. Schematic diagram of a water-source heat pump system, cooling mode.

essary to periodically melt any ice that may form on the evaporator coil. Water-source heat pumps can have heating COPs of 4 and EERs near 19. Because the temperature of the sink/source varies greatly from one water source to another, such performance figures as SPF and SEER are not reported for water-source heat pumps. Instead, the heating COP and the cooling EER are reported for specific supply water temperatures. The designer should take care to use realistic water temperatures.

In comparing water-source and air-source heat pumps, the energy consumed by the pump used to supply water to the heat pump must be considered. For example, with a 3-t heat pump, a cooling EER of 12.0 is reduced to an effective EER of 9.95 if a $\frac{1}{2}$-HP pump (60% electrical efficiency) is used to supply water to the heat pump. A heating COP of 3.0 would be reduced to 2.55 under the same circumstances. A $\frac{1}{8}$ HP pump (35% efficiency) would result in an effective EER of 11.0 and a COP of 2.79. For other cases, the following may be used to estimate the effective EERs and COPs of the heat pump and pump combination

$$\text{Effective EER} = \frac{\text{HPCC}}{\text{HPCC/EER} + (\text{HP}/n) \times 746}$$

$$\text{Effective COP} = \frac{\text{HPHC}}{\text{HPHC/COP} + (\text{HP}/n) \times 746 \times 3.41}$$

where

$HPCC$ = heat pump cooling capacity, Btu/h
$HPHC$ = heat pump heating capacity, Btu/h
EER = heat pump energy efficiency ratio, cooling Btu/h/W
COP = heat pump coefficient of performance, heating
HP = pump motor horsepower
n = pump motor efficiency, approximately 60% for fractional horse-power motors; it varies from 0.35 for $\frac{1}{6}$-HP and smaller motors to 0.85 for 10-HP motors
746 = W/HP
3.413 = Btu/W-h

Ratings for water-source heat pumps may or may not include the power consumed by the water circulation pumps. One ARI rating standard adds 60 W of power consumption for each gallon per minute of water required, or about 10 W per 1000 Btu/h of capacity. This implies a rule of thumb suggesting that the efficiency figures for water-source heat pumps rated *without* pump energy considered should be reduced about 10% to account for pumping energy consumption. When comparing equipment, examine specifications carefully to ensure that all equipment ratings are consistent.

Water-source heat pumps are usually rated by the manufacturer at three sink/source water temperatures or at three exiting water temperatures. ARI cooling performance figures are based on an 85°F entering water temperature and an exit water temperature of 95°F. Room air is 80°F dry-bulb and 67°F wet-bulb (50% RH). The actual water flow rate through the unit varies and, for rating purposes, is set to provide the specified water temperatures. Heating performance is tested at the same water flow rate used in the cooling tests with a 70°F room air temperature to the unit. The water temperature entering the unit is 70°F. Caution should be used in comparing performance data with different water temperatures and different flow rates.

Water-Source Heat Pump Manufacturers

Table 10.2 lists several manufacturers of water-source heat pumps. Included are the model numbers of the most efficient unit manufactured by each company in each of four approximate cooling capacities, 18,000 and 36,000 Btu/h. The information was developed from the June 30, 1984 edition of the *Directory of Certified Applied Air Conditioning Products* from the Air-Conditioning and Refrigeration Institute.

Water Sources

The water used as a sink/source by a heat pump is often referred to as *condenser water*. Here, we finally have a bias toward cooling: the coil through which the

Table 10.2. High-Efficiency Water-Source Heat Pumps.

Manufacturer	18,000 Btu/h SEER	Model No.	36,000 Btu/h SEER	Model No.
York Div., Borg-Warner, Corp.	11.9	CLHP-16CL0, CRB	8.8	CLHP-33V, H
Lear Siegler, Inc.	10.5	D, E019HHC, D019HSC	11.8	D035V
American Air Filter	11.4	DHW, VW-19	11.0	DHW, VW-36
Friedrich Air-Conditioning & Refrigeration Co.	11.3	801-19B	10.6	803-036, -E, -F, -G, -H
Command-Aire Corp.	11.0	SWP191ED, 197ED	11.0	SWP351ED, 353ED, 354ED
FHP Manufacturing Div. Leigh Products, Inc.	10.2	EMH23-1, -1	11.2	HEH34-1, -2, -3, -4
Solar Oriented Environmental Systems, Inc.	10.2	PSH200	11.2	PSH300
The Trans Co.	10.7	WPRA19HXXB	10.8	WPHA/VA33HB, C, DXB
Climate Control, Commercial Products Div.	10.7	VF200F/G3, 5, 7	10.8	VF330F/63, 5, 7
Bard Manufacturing Co.	–		10.7	HWPD36
Carrier-Air-Conditioning	9.0	50BQ01931, 41	8.8	50HQ, VQ0334
McQuay Group (McQuay Perfax, Inc.)	10.1	HPH/HPV-019A, B	10.6	HPH/HPV-041A, 8
Heat Exchangers, Inc.	9.3	5K19CMH, HT	10.1	5K33CMH, HT
Marvair Co.	10.4	WHP, V360-02-AX-XXX-11	10.2	H, V360-02-AX-XXX-11
California Heat Pump Co.	9.0	CHP-19CLB, CRB	8.8	CPH-33V, H

(Excerpted by permission from *Directory of Certified Applied Air Conditioning Products*, June 30, 1984, Air-Conditioning and Refrigeration Institute.)

water flows is acting as the condenser in the cooling mode. In the heating mode, the roles are reversed, and the water provides heat to the evaporator.

The vast majority of water-source heat pump installations rely on ground-water supplied by wells as condenser water. A growing number of systems circulate water through buried pipe fields in a closed loop. A much smaller number of water-source units use surface water, either a river, lake, pond, bay, lagoon, or the ocean. The major disadvantage of using surface water is the much larger variation in temperatures over the year. Except at significant depths, sur-face water temperatures tend to follow air temperatures during the year. Water depths of less than 20 ft should certainly not be considered for heating appli-cations except in extreme southern areas. Secondary problems arise in locating the heat exchanger or pump intake pipe in the water and routing connecting piping; few buildings are located adjacent to bodies of water. Other concerns include physical damage to the equipment by debris or boaters, fouling of the piping by algae, scale, and sediment, and blockage of the inlet.

Water-source heat pumps should never be connected to municipal water sys-tems, even if a fixed monthly rate is charged. Not only does this practice rep-resent a gross misuse of a valuable resource, it is usually illegal.

A variety of water sinks/sources have been proposed for use with heat pumps, from swimming pools to abandoned septic tanks. Combinations with solar or woodburning systems are also considered. Approach such concepts with caution and a firm grasp of the laws of thermodynamics.

Wells as a Water Source

In almost all cases, wells are the best source of water for heat pump applica-tions. More than 40,000 heat pumps using wells as a water source have been installed in Florida alone. A typical heat pump and well system includes two wells: a supply well and a recharge, or return, well. Water is drawn from the supply well, used in the heat pump, and returned to the ground in the recharge well. The supply well may also be used as the building's domestic water source. A single-well heat pump application is discussed in the ground-source heat pump section. Much of the information that follows was developed with the aid of publications from the National Water Well Association. Several excellent ref-erences provide additional details. (Ref. 10.2)

Wells normally used for residences and small commercial buildings are 6 in. in diameter and are drilled. A casing of either PVC or steel pipe, installed in the upper portion of the well, penetrates soft or unstable soils. The cased section of the well is usually bored to a diameter of 9 in. When rock or stable soils are reached, the diameter is reduced to 6 in. Increasing the diameter of the well beyond 6 in. does little to increase the available water flow. For example, dou-bling the diameter of a normal well increases the flow rate by only about 20%. Hand-dug wells are rarely suitable for heat pump applications.

If multiple supply wells are used to increase the amount of water available, they should be adequately spaced. The addition of a second well within 10 ft of an existing well will provide an increase in total water flow capacity of only about 30%. A separation distance of at least 30 ft should be used under most conditions. Of course, there is a considerable degree of variation in the nature of water-bearing formations.

The cost of a drilled water well can be estimated as approximately $7.00 per ft of depth for a well with PVC casing to approximately $9.00 per ft for metal casing. PVC casing is usually adequate. The required depth of a well varies widely from location to location, even on a local basis, and is difficult to predict. In many areas the depth to a producing water formation may vary 100 ft or more within a horizontal distance of only a few yards. Average well depths range from less than 40 ft in locations where the water table is quite high, such as coastal regions, to well over 300 ft.

Water temperature is seldom a concern, because most wells draw water from a depth where there is little seasonal variation in the temperature of the supply water. The normal temperature of water from wells at a depth of 30 to 60 ft is given in Fig. 10.5. (Ref. 10.2.) The temperature of well water at 30 to 60 ft can be estimated by adding 2 to 3°F to the mean annual air temperature, available from local weather stations. At depths greater than 30 to 60 ft, the temperature of well water usually begins to increase. For each 64 ft of additional depth, a temperature increase of 1° may be assumed. However, this increase is really significant only in very deep wells. For most wells, the water temperature may be estimated as the mean annual air temperature without any adjustment.

The use of a recharge well to return the water used by the heat pump to the subsurface aquifer is recommended. Some areas of Florida have been subjected to severe surface settling and salt water intrusion into aquifers as a result of excessive extraction of water from wells for irrigation and municipal use. Discharging water from the heat pump to the surface into a sewer, pond, or drain is not a good idea. A septic tank and field cannot be used to dispose of the volume of water a heat pump uses, and there is not sufficient pressure available from a well pump to discharge the water through lawn sprinklers. Recharge wells are needed.

The recharge well is similar to the supply well. Its diameter and depth must be at least as large as the supply well. The return pipe should extend into the well and below the static water level. A rule of thumb for the location of the recharge well states that it should be at least 50 ft from the supply well. The water level in the recharge well will be much higher than in the supply well. Under certain circumstances, it is possible that the recharge well might overflow. Provisions should be made to prevent damage if an overflow occurs.

The local laws and regulations regarding the use of a well should be examined carefully before starting a water-source heat pump project. Except in rural areas a permit is often required. As a result of fears of contaminating aquifers, some

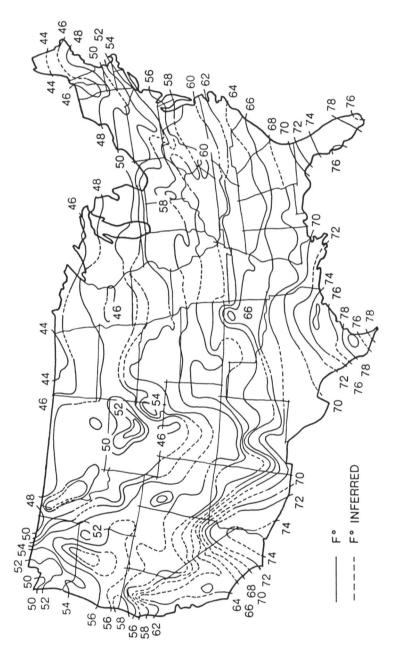

Ground water temperatures. Map courtesy of National Water Well Association.

Figure 10.5. Deep well water temperatures.

areas have restrictions on the use of groundwater with heat pump systems. If a heat pump system is designed and operated properly, there is no real danger of groundwater contamination. However, an improperly designed or constructed system can allow surface water to enter the well and flow into the aquifer. Surface contaminants, including sewerage and runoff containing dissolved fertilizers, pesticides, and other chemicals, can flow into the well. For that reason, it is advisable to use a concrete cap along the casing to positively preclude surface water entry. In some locations a cap is required. Groundwater is a precious and delicate resource; wells should not be used recklessly. The same care and precaution applied to drinking water wells should be applied to heat pump wells. Contact the National Water Well Association for the names of qualified firms in your area.

If surface water penetration is prevented, the use of well water in a heat pump and the subsequent return of the water to the aquifer does not constitute a hazard. The water is not contaminated in any way; the only effect is a small temperature change.

There is some risk, in drilling a water well, that an adequate supply of water will not be available at a reasonable depth. Every well driller has stories of drilling wells to 500 ft or more and encountering flow rates of less than 1 gal per min. Talk to local drillers, extension agents, and well owners in your area for specific information for typical wells.

Applications

As a rule of thumb, the amount of water to be circulated can be estimated as 3 gal per min for each ton of capacity. This assumes a temperature change of 10°F in the water as it flows through the heat pump. The water flow rate can be decreased by increasing the temperature differential through the heat pump, but only at the price of reduced efficiency.

Changes in the flow rate and temperature differential may be evaluated with the following equation

$$Q = M \times C_p \times \Delta T$$

where

Q = heating or cooling capacity, Btu/h
M = mass flow rate of water through the heat pump, lb/h
C_p = specific heat of water = 1.0 Btu/lb°F
ΔT = temperature difference through the heat pump, °F

The temperature of the water delivered to the heat pump must be held within reasonable tolerances for proper operation of the heat pump. For heating, a minimum supply water temperature of approximately 50 to 60°F is required for standard units. Low-temperature models or adapter kits are available that allow the use of water at inlet temperatures as low as 45°F. The major concerns with low water temperatures are reduced heating capacity and the possibility of forming ice in the water discharge line. For operation in the cooling mode, an inlet water temperature of approximately 95°F is usually specified as a maximum and 55°F as a minimum. High water temperatures in the cooling mode lead to reduced cooling capacity and excessive refrigerant system pressures. Manufacturers' literature should be consulted for specific information.

In the cooling mode, the efficiency and capacity of a water-source heat pump increase as the water temperature decreases. In the heating mode, higher efficiency and heating capacity are obtained with higher water temperatures. Table 10.3 contains performance data at several operating conditions for water-source heat pumps manufactured by Mammoth, A Nortech Company. (Ref. 10.4.) The water temperature in the table is the temperature of the water entering the heat pump.

The smallest pump that will supply the required water flow rate should be selected to avoid excess power consumption and the resulting decrease in system efficiency and increase in operating costs. The water flow requirements of the heat pump should be determined from the manufacturer's literature. If the well also supplies domestic water, an additional 5 gal/min of flow capacity should be provided. Be sure to account for any drawdown in the water level that may occur when the pump is operating.

In addition to lifting water from the well, the pump must have enough capacity to overcome the frictional losses that occur in the piping, valves, filters, and the heat pump itself. Where the water level is unusually high and the pumping depth is less than 22 ft, a self-priming end-suction-type pump may be mounted at the surface. At greater depths a submersible pump located in the bottom of the well or a jet pump must be used.

The water piping should be designed so that the flow velocity of the water is no more than 6 to 7 ft per second for PVC pipe and no greater than 4 ft per second for copper. If an end-suction pump is used, the suction line between the water source and the heat pump should be sized for a velocity of 3 to 4 ft per second. Heat pump manufacturers often specify maximum flow velocities through the unit, usually no more than 8 to 10 ft per second.

A pressure tank is required to maintain a minimum water pressure in the system and to prevent short cycling of the pump. The tank contains an air bladder that is compressed to maintain an operating pressure of 15 to 25 lb per in.^{2} in the system and deliver water. Manufacturers' literature should be consulted for tank size selection; be careful not to undersize the pressure tank.

Water flow requirements are normally greater in the heating mode than in the cooling mode. To avoid excessive pumping energy consumption and costs during the summer, controls may be used to reduce the flow rate. If the supply water contains sand or other particulates, a filter may be required.

Some heat pumps offer a heat recovery coil for domestic water heating, either

Table 10.3. Mammoth heat pump data.

CAPACITY AND EFFICIENCY RATINGS

MODEL 054

ENTERING WATER TEMP. 6	GPM	WATER PRESSURE DROP (PSI)	NOM. CFM 3	HEATING 1				COOLING 2			
				MBH	WATTS 4	COP	ADJ. 5 COP	MBH	WATTS 4	EER	ADJ. 5 EER
45	6.8	0.77	2080	44.9	4260	3.09	2.82	64.1	4330	14.80	13.53
	9.0	1.27		46.9	4330	3.17	2.82	64.7	4140	15.63	13.82
	12.0	2.10		48.5	4390	3.24	2.78	65.0	4010	16.21	13.74
50	6.8	0.77	2080	48.1	4370	3.22	2.95	63.5	4470	14.09	12.92
	9.0	1.27		50.4	4430	3.33	2.97	63.5	4260	14.91	13.23
	12.0	2.10		52.2	4490	3.41	2.94	63.8	4120	15.49	13.18
55	6.8	0.77	2080	51.5	4490	3.36	3.08	61.8	4610	13.41	12.32
	9.0	1.27		53.9	4540	3.48	3.11	62.3	4380	14.22	12.66
	12.0	2.10		55.8	4600	3.55	3.07	62.7	4220	14.86	12.69
60	6.8	0.77	2080	54.7	4610	3.48	3.19	60.3	4740	12.72	11.71
	9.0	1.27		57.3	4660	3.60	3.23	60.8	4490	13.54	12.09
	12.0	2.10		59.4	4720	3.69	3.20	61.2	4330	14.13	12.12
65	6.8	0.77	2080	57.9	4740	3.58	3.30	58.9	4880	12.07	11.14
	9.0	1.27		60.7	4790	3.71	3.34	59.3	4610	12.86	11.51
	12.0	2.10		63.1	4840	3.82	3.33	59.5	4430	13.43	11.55
70	6.8	0.77	2080	61.2	4890	3.67	3.38	57.1	5010	11.40	10.54
	9.0	1.27		64.3	4930	3.82	3.44	57.4	4730	12.14	10.89
	12.0	2.10		66.8	4970	3.94	3.44	57.7	4530	12.74	10.99

MODEL 027

ENTERING WATER TEMP. 6	GPM	WATER PRESSURE DROP (PSI)	NOM. CFM 3	HEATING 1				COOLING 2			
				MBH	WATTS 4	COP	ADJ. 5 COP	MBH	WATTS 4	EER	ADJ. 5 EER
45	4.0	.72	1105	23.5	2190	3.14	2.83	32.9	2270	14.49	13.11
	5.0	1.10		24.2	2250	3.15	2.78	33.3	2210	15.07	13.27
	6.0	1.50		25.0	2290	3.20	2.76	33.5	2150	15.58	13.47
50	4.0	.72	1105	25.0	2250	3.26	2.94	32.3	2330	13.86	12.57
	5.0	1.10		25.8	2310	3.27	2.90	32.7	2270	14.41	12.72
	6.0	1.50		26.6	2350	3.32	2.88	32.9	2210	14.89	12.80
55	4.0	.72	1105	26.3	2320	3.32	3.01	31.6	2390	13.22	12.02
	5.0	1.10		27.3	2370	3.38	3.00	32.2	2330	13.82	12.24
	6.0	1.50		28.2	2410	3.43	2.98	32.4	2270	14.27	12.32
60	4.0	.72	1105	27.9	2390	3.42	3.11	30.9	2450	12.61	11.49
	5.0	1.10		29.0	2430	3.50	3.11	31.2	2390	13.05	11.60
	6.0	1.50		30.0	2470	3.56	3.11	31.6	2330	13.56	11.75
65	40	.72	1105	29.4	2470	3.49	3.17	30.1	2510	11.99	10.95
	50	1.10		30.3	2500	3.55	3.17	30.4	2450	12.41	11.05
	60	1.50		31.5	2520	3.66	3.20	30.8	2390	12.89	11.20
70	4.0	.72	1105	30.9	2550	3.55	3.25	29.3	2570	11.40	10.43
	5.0	1.10		31.9	2570	3.64	3.26	29.6	2510	11.79	10.53
	6.0	1.50		33.2	2590	3.76	3.30	29.9	2450	12.20	10.64

Table 10.3. (Continued)

MODEL 035

ENTERING WATER TEMP. 6	GPM	WATER PRESSURE DROP (PSI)	NOM. CFM 3	HEATING 1					COOLING 2			
				MBH	WATTS 4	COP	ADJ. 5 COP	MBH	WATTS 4	EER	ADJ. 5 EER	
45	5.0	1.03	1435	28.4	2560	3.25	2.91	46.7	2740	17.04	15.36	
	6.0	1.42		30.0	2680	3.28	2.89	48.3	2620	18.44	16.21	
	7.5	2.15		31.4	2800	3.29	2.83	48.7	2520	19.33	16.40	
50	5.0	1.03	1435	31.1	2750	3.31	2.99	45.6	2800	16.29	14.71	
	6.0	1.42		32.6	2830	3.38	2.99	46.7	2700	17.30	15.26	
	7.5	2.15		34.1	2890	3.57	2.99	47.5	2610	18.20	15.52	
55	5.0	1.03	1435	33.7	2860	3.45	3.12	44.6	2880	15.49	14.03	
	6.0	1.42		35.2	2930	3.52	3.13	45.6	2780	16.40	14.52	
	7.5	2.15		36.7	2990	3.60	3.13	46.4	2700	17.19	14.73	
60	5.0	1.03	1435	36.3	2970	3.58	3.25	43.4	2970	14.61	13.27	
	6.0	1.42		37.8	3040	3.64	3.26	44.4	2870	15.47	13.75	
	7.5	2.15		39.3	3090	3.73	3.25	45.1	2790	16.16	13.92	
65	5.0	1.03	1435	38.9	3080	3.70	3.37	42.1	3060	13.80	12.57	
	6.0	1.42		40.4	3140	3.77	3.38	43.0	2970	14.48	12.91	
	7.5	2.15		41.9	3190	3.85	3.37	43.8	2880	15.21	13.15	
70	5.0	1.03	1435	41.5	3200	3.80	3.47	40.7	3140	12.96	11.83	
	6.0	1.42		42.9	3250	3.87	3.48	41.7	3060	13.63	12.19	
	7.5	2.15		44.6	3290	3.97	3.49	42.4	2870	14.28	12.40	

MODEL 064

ENTERING WATER TEMP. 6	GPM	WATER PRESSURE DROP (PSI)	NOM. CFM 3	HEATING 1					COOLING 2			
				MBH	WATTS 4	COP	ADJ. 5 COP	MBH	WATTS 4	EER	ADJ. 5 EER	
45	7.5	0.63	2080	48.5	4610	3.08	2.81	72.4	4820	15.02	13.74	
	10.5	1.13		53.6	4770	3.29	2.91	73.2	4570	16.02	14.08	
	14.0	1.85		55.6	4920	3.31	2.83	73.8	4340	17.00	14.25	
50	7.5	0.63	2080	54.8	4780	3.36	2.97	71.4	4930	14.48	13.27	
	10.5	1.13		58.1	4930	3.45	3.06	72.3*	4710	15.35	13.54	
	14.0	1.85		60.5	5060	3.50	3.00	72.9	4540	16.06	13.55	
55	7.5	0.63	2080	59.1	4950	3.60	3.21	70.2	5040	13.93	12.79	
	10.5	1.13		62.7	5100	3.60	3.21	71.0	4850	14.64	12.96	
	14.0	1.85		65.4	5220	3.67	3.16	71.7	4710	15.22	12.92	
60	7.5	0.63	2080	63.3	5130	3.62	3.32	68.9	5150	13.38	12.30	
	10.5	1.13		67.3	5270	3.74	3.34	69.7	4990	13.97	12.40	
	14.0	1.85		69.8	5390	3.79	3.28	70.3	4870	14.44	12.31	
65	7.5	0.63	2080	67.6	5310	3.73	3.44	67.3	5260	12.79	11.79	
	10.5	1.13		71.9	5450	3.87	3.46	68.1	5120	13.30	11.84	
	14.0	1.85		75.2	5570	3.96	3.44	68.6	5020	13.67	11.71	
70	7.5	0.63	2080	71.9	5500	3.83	3.54	65.6	5360	12.24	11.29	
	10.5	1.13		76.5	5640	3.97	3.57	66.5	5250	12.67	11.31	
	14.0	1.85		80.1	5740	4.09	3.57	66.9	5160	12.97	11.15	

MODEL 045

ENTERING WATER TEMP. 6	GPM	WATER PRESSURE DROP (PSI)	NOM. CFM 3	HEATING 1				COOLING 2			
				MBH	WATTS 4	COP	ADJ. 5 COP	MBH	WATTS 4	EER	ADJ. 5 EER
45	6.0	0.75	1715	34.9	3190	3.21	2.88	54.1	3220	16.80	15.11
	7.5	1.10		36.5	3270	3.27	2.87	54.9	3110	17.65	15.42
	9.0	1.50		37.5	3350	3.28	2.82	55.6	3070	18.11	15.40
50	6.0	0.75	1715	37.7	3320	3.33	3.00	53.4	3330	16.04	14.47
	7.5	1.10		39.3	3370	3.42	3.01	54.3	3220	16.86	14.80
	9.0	1.50		40.4	3420	3.46	2.99	54.9	3100	17.71	15.08
55	6.0	0.75	1715	40.4	3440	3.44	3.12	52.5	3440	15.26	13.82
	7.5	1.10		42.2	3480	3.55	3.15	53.3	3340	15.96	14.06
	9.0	1.50		43.4	3510	3.62	3.14	54.0	3210	16.82	14.40
60	6.0	0.75	1715	43.2	3640	3.58	3.25	51.6	3550	14.54	13.20
	7.5	1.10		45.0	3680	3.68	3.27	52.3	3450	15.16	13.41
	9.0	1.50		46.4	3610	3.77	3.28	52.9	3320	15.93	13.70
65	6.0	0.75	1715	46.0	3650	3.69	3.36	50.4	3670	13.73	12.51
	7.5	1.10		47.9	3680	3.81	3.40	51.2	3560	14.38	12.77
	9.0	1.50		49.4	3720	3.89	3.40	51.7	3440	15.03	12.99
70	6.0	0.75	1715	48.7	3760	3.79	3.46	49.0	3780	12.96	11.84
	7.5	1.10		50.7	3790	3.92	3.50	49.7	3680	13.51	12.03
	9.0	1.50		52.3	3820	4.01	3.51	50.3	3540	14.21	12.33

1 Rated at 70°F Entering Air Temperature.
2 Rated at 80°F db/67°F wb Entering Air Temperature.
3 Rated per ARI 325-82.
4 Rated at 230V, 60HZ, single phase.
5 Includes well pump requirement of 60 watts per gpm per ARI standard 325-82.
6 For entering water temperatures below 45°F, the water flow rate should be increased to maintain a leaving water temperature of at least 38°F.

as a standard feature or an option. The coil not only assists with heating domestic water, but improves the cooling performance of the heat pump by removing some of the heat from the conditioned space and reducing the heat rejection load on the condenser. The coil supplies heat for water heating, using heat from the water source and providing the COP benefits of the heat pump.

Additional information on the use of water wells with water-source heat pumps is available from the National Water Well Association. Many manufacturers of water-source heat pumps offer detailed application and installation manuals for their products.

Earth-Coupled Heat Pumps

Where groundwater is unavailable or the necessary wells too costly, an earth-coupled heat pump may be considered. An earth-coupled heat pump system relies on the ground as a heat sink/source. As a heat sink/source, the ground has the advantage of smaller temperature fluctuations during the year than the air. The disadvantage is that some form of heat exchanger is necessary to make the ground available as a sink/source to the heat pump. The ground has an effectively infinite heat capacity; the difficulty lies in transferring heat between the ground and the heat pump.

The normal methods of earth-coupling use a closed loop of coils or banks of pipes buried in the earth to reject heat to the ground during the cooling season and to absorb heat from the ground during the heating season. Water is recirculated in the piping system between the heat pump and the buried pipes. A small circulator pump and an expansion tank to allow the water to expand and contract without damaging the heat pump or the piping complete the system.

Two types of earth heat exchanger systems are used: the horizontal loop and the vertical loop. The horizontal loop consists of a field of pipe usually buried 3 to 8 ft below the surface of the ground, Fig. 10.6. The vertical loop consists

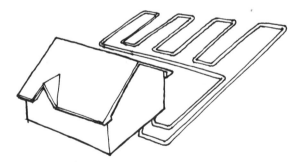

Figure 10.6. Horizontal pipe field configuration.

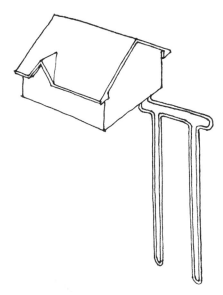

Figure 10.7. Vertical pipe loop configuration.

of a loop of piping inserted into a deep well or hole (Fig. 10.7). More than one vertical loop may be linked together to obtain the required heat exchange area.

Horizontal loops can be used only on sites that have adequate ground surface area for the field and are best suited to relatively flat sites. They occupy a large area and may conflict with landscaping and built areas. Soil conditions that favor the use of trenching machinery are desirable; rocky soils make excavation more difficult and increase the likelihood of tube punctures.

The depth of burial is a key concern with horizontal pipe loops; the pipe must be buried to a depth that adequately protects it from the extremes of air temperature that occur during the year. Winter is usually the more severe condition, because the differential between the required loop temperature and the ground temperature is smaller. In the South, however, shallow pipe fields and an unprotected surface may lead to high temperatures in the loop and condenser pressure problems with the heat pump during the cooling season. The necessary depth varies somewhat with surface conditions and location, but a minimum of 4 ft is suggested.

The pipe may be routed with both the line to the heat pump and the line from the heat pump in the same trench. The two pipes should be separated at least 2 ft vertically, the line from the heat pump being deeper. The upper pipe, the line to the heat pump, must be at least 4 ft below the surface.

The diameter of the pipe is normally $1\frac{1}{2}$ to 2 in., with high-density schedule

Table 10.4. Guidelines for Horizontal Earth Coils.

Average Well Water Temperature, °F	Minimum Depth, ft	Minimum Pipe Length, Lineal ft/t
80	4	500
75	4	475
70	4	450
65	4	425
60	4	400
55	5	450
50	6	500
45	NA	NA
40	NA	NA

(Courtesy of Mammoth, a Nortek Company.)

40 SDR-15 polybutylene being the preferred material. Table 10.4 suggests pipe lengths based on the average annual well water temperature.

The landscaping and conditions of the ground surface above the horizontal heat exchanger are quite important in avoiding excessive summer ground temperatures. Refer to the section on earth cooling tubes for additional information. Buildings and landscaping over the pipe field should be considered carefully. Leaks in buried pipes are very difficult to locate and repair.

Vertical loops are preferred if the site is small, the ground is rocky, the surface is rough, of if disturbing large areas of the surface is undesirable. They also provide more stable water temperatures than horizontal fields, because the average depth of the pipe below the surface is much greater. For economy, $4\frac{3}{4}$-in.-diameter holes may be bored into the ground without casing and the tubing inserted into the hole. Sand or small gravel is backfilled into the hole, and a concrete plug is poured at the top to prevent groundwater intrusion (Fig. 10.8).

The preferred pipe materials for vertical pipe fields are the same as for horizontal fields. Normally, $1\frac{1}{2}$-in.-diameter pipe is used. The bore holes should be at least 15 ft apart to reduce heat flow interference. Table 10.5 provides guidelines for sizing vertical heat exchanger fields. Again the suggested tube length is based on water temperature and expressed in lineal feet per ton of capacity.

Another type of earth-coupled heat exchanger consists of a single drilled well used to supply water to the heat pump and to accept the return water. A schematic of such a system, sometimes called a *dedicated well*, is shown in Fig. 10.9. In the event that an attempt to drill a conventional supply well yields inadequate water flow, the dedicated well may provide a good "bailout" alternative.

The dedicated well is normally a 6-in.-diameter hole drilled and cased to rock like a conventional well. A submersible pump is set in the well just below the water level to supply water to the heat pump. The return line from the heat

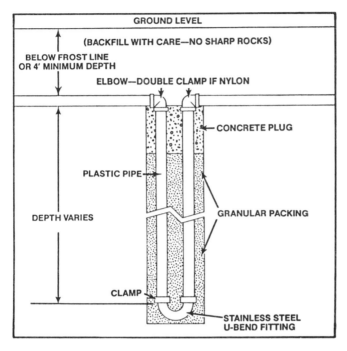

Figure 10.8.   Typical vertical pipe layout. (Courtesy of Mammoth, a Nortek Company)

pump is routed into the hole to within 3 to 4 ft of the bottom. The water is not removed from the well, but is continuously recycled. Where water flow is adequate, a dedicated well may also be used to supply water for domestic use.

The depth of the well must be adequate to allow the water in the hole to

Table 10.5.   Guidelines for Vertical Earth Coils.

Average Well Water Temperature, °F	Minimum Wetted Pipe Length, Lineal ft/t
80	190
75	180
70	170
65	160
60	150
55	170
50	190
45	220
40	260

(Courtesy of Mammoth, a Nortek Company.)

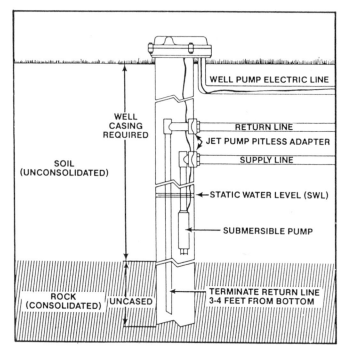

Figure 10.9. Schematic of a dedicated well. (Courtesy of Mammoth, a Nortek Company)

exchange heat with the earth before being recycled to the heat pump. A rule of thumb is to provide 150 ft of wetted well depth per ton of heat pump capacity.

There have been a few attempts to use buried tanks as heat exchangers; they are generally not totally successful. The problem lies in the surface area of the tank available for heat transfer and the mass of the earth in contact with the tank. Although there is a very large volume of water available in the tank, there is a relatively small contact area through which heat can be transferred to the earth. Only if the tank is extremely large will there be adequate heat transfer capacity. It is certainly not economical to consider the use of a tank in place of a closed piping loop.

Exact design procedures for earth heat exchangers are not available. Part of the problem is the variation in soil properties and moisture levels from location to location. The conductivity, density, and diffusivity of soil and its moisture content affect the heat storage capacity and the rate of heat transfer through the ground. These properties, and consequently the performance of an earth heat exchanger, vary with the type of soil and the conditions at a given location. The rule of thumb in use today should provide adequate performance in most cases, but by no means always provide optimum cost solutions.

Current research and application work is in progress on horizontal and vertical loops at the University of Oklahoma. A design manual that describes findings to date is available (Ref 10.3).

Seasonal Heat Storage

Seasonal heat storage is an interesting concept that may improve the efficiency of groundwater heat exchange systems. The idea is to reject heat into the ground during the summer while cooling a building and then take advantage of that stored heat during the winter heating season. The reverse effect provides storage of "coolth" in the ground during the latter part of the winter for use during the following summer. The annual cycle of storing and removing heat effectively changes the temperature of the ground so that the heat pump sees more favorable temperatures throughout the year. The concept has not yet been developed to the point that it is ready for general use. Some research has been conducted on the use of a dual well system in northern U.S. and Canadian climates. It is likely that such systems will be most applicable to large building complexes with high heating and cooling loads.

Where a supply well and a recharge well are used with a heat pump system, they may be piped to allow reversing the flow of the system. This provides some seasonal storage benefits and assures that the water level at the site is more effectively replenished.

11

HUMIDITY CONTROL

It's not the heat, it's the humidity!

Everyone is aware of the negative effect of humidity on comfort, particularly those who live in the Southeast or in coastal areas. Houston, New Orleans, and Mobile are famous for their muggy summer weather when high humidity causes discomfort even if temperatures are reasonable. Houston could never have grown as it has during the last two decades without air conditioning to control the humidity.

Water vapor gets into a building in two ways: it leaks and diffuses in from the outdoors, and it is produced on the interior of the building. Procedures for estimating latent cooling loads are provided in Chapter 5. Reducing interior humidity calls for: reducing moisture migration from the exterior, eliminating or controlling interior sources, and removing moisture.

The first two processes are the most desirable from an energy standpoint; the third is expensive. Practical passive dehumidification systems have not yet been developed.

HUMIDITY AND MILDEW

In most of the country, humidity seems to be the all around villain in the cooling problem: it reduces comfort conditions directly, limits the usefulness of passive cooling systems, and as a final blow, it promotes the growth of a variety of unsavory organisms such as mildew. Mildew can spring to life quickly, needing only a relative humidity of 70% or more maintained for about 12 h. If mildew damage were restricted to an occasional blue-green growth on a pair of shoes tucked into a dark closet corner, it would be more tolerable. But mildew and other humidity-loving microorganisms can cause severe damage to the structure of a building and its furnishings.

A few basic measures in the design of a building can help control mildew and other interior humidity problems. The keys are control of the sources of moisture and good ventilation to prevent local moisture concentrations. Excess humidity and mildew are particular concerns in southern coastal areas and in houses without air conditioning.

- Vent all moisture-producing appliances and equipment, including ovens, ranges, laundry equipment, and bathrooms.
- Use louvered doors on closets and storage areas to encourage air circulation.
- Use vapor barriers properly; install a polyethylene barrier in all walls, as well as the ceiling and floor if possible. Do not rely solely on the vapor barrier on a fiberglass batt. Except in southern Florida and southern Texas, vapor barriers should be installed near the interior surface of the building. If in doubt, contact a local homebuilders' association.
- Install a polyethylene vapor barrier on the ground below crawlspace floors.
- Locate supply ducts and returns to provide good airflow throughout the building; avoid stagnant areas.
- Ventilate attics well. The HUD Minimum Property Standards require at least 1 ft^2 of free vent area per 300 ft^2 of attic floor area if a vapor barrier is properly installed.

For the most part, humidity control in residences and small buildings has been a secondary consideration in designing and installing cooling systems. This is partly a result of the difficulty in analyzing latent cooling loads and partly a result of the lack of effective humidity control methods. The general move toward better insulated buildings with better solar gain control only makes the humidity problem worse. As latent loads become a larger fraction of total cooling loads, higher indoor humidity and greater discomfort will result.

DEHUMIDIFICATION WITH AIR CONDITIONERS

In well-designed, commercial air conditioning systems, the latent cooling load on the building is considered separately in load and system sizing calculations. The balance between sensible and latent loads varies considerably from one type of building to another, and system designs must respond accordingly. An office building with computer facilities usually has a relatively large sensible load and a small latent load. The sensible heat fraction for the building (called the *room sensible heat fraction*, or RSHF) might be above 0.85, indicating that 85% of the total cooling load is a sensible heat load. A restaurant, however, where large numbers of people and cooking equipment contribute to the load, has a larger latent load. In extreme cases, the cooling load resulting from moisture gains in a building can equal the sensible cooling load, producing an RSHF as low as 0.50.

In the past, residential cooling loads have been strongly dominated by the sensible load component. The sensible heat gains from conduction through the building skin, solar gains, infiltration of hot outdoor air, and lights and appliances outweighed the latent gains from people, cooking, and moisture gains by air infiltration and diffusion through the building skin. Most houses had RSHFs of approximately 0.70 in humid areas and 0.80 in drier areas.

Load calculations and cooling system design for residences have dealt with latent capacity in a very simplistic manner. The usual procedure is to predict the sensible cooling load and then add 20 to 30% to account for the latent load. In general, this method has yielded satisfactory results; latent cooling capacity is adequate in most air conditioned homes. In others the occupants compensate by lowering the thermostat setting or if the problem is severe, by modifying the the air conditioner. The usual action is to reduce the evaporator fan speed to allow the air passing over the cool coils to reach a lower temperature and condense more moisture. The use of mechanical dehumidifiers should be reserved for those cases where humidity is so high that mildew is present and damage to furnishings and the building itself is possible. The energy cost of dehumidification with a mechanical dehumidifier is high.

The trend toward better insulation, double- or triple-glazing, improved solar gain protection, and glazing location for reduced solar gains creates a potential latent load problem. Most of the normal conservation steps taken in building design are effective only in reducing the sensible heat gain into the building. Insulation, shading, and reduced lighting wattage do nothing to reduce latent heat gains. Infiltration control measures are the only typical energy conservation or passive solar measures that reduce latent heat gains as well as sensible heat gains.

The consequence is that energy-conserving and passive solar buildings usually have a much lower RSHF (higher latent load fraction) than conventional buildings. Their sensible heat gains are dramatically reduced, though their latent gains are dropped only slightly. Extreme cases exist in highly insulated earth-sheltered buildings with high interior mass and well-protected glazing. Such buildings are sometimes capable of maintaining interior dry-bulb temperatures only slightly above the comfort zone, 80 to 82°F, by passive means, but can do nothing to control the interior humidity. The same problem occurs to a lesser degree in any well-insulated building with good solar gain control.

When an air conditioner is used in such a building, the results can be disappointing. The air conditioning system in almost all residences and small commercial buildings is controlled only on the dry-bulb temperature of the interior air. The thermostat and the air conditioner know nothing about the humidity inside the building. The air conditioner runs only until the interior dry-bulb temperature reaches the thermostat setpoint and then stops, regardless of the humidity. The result can be a cool clammy building, with the comfort benefit of lower temperature reduced by the high humidity. Unless moisture is removed in proportional amounts, the relative humidity is increased as the temperature falls.

At present there are no simple, low-cost solutions to control humidity. There is little flexibility in the latent capacity of air conditioners available for residences. Modifications to improve latent capacity can be made, but are not generally practical. Dehumidifiers are quite expensive to operate.

HOW DOES AN AIR CONDITIONER DEHUMIDIFY?

Dehumidification occurs when humid air is cooled to its dewpoint. Air conditioners dehumidify by moving air from inside the building over the cool evaporator coils and allowing condensation to occur. Sensible cooling is achieved as the air is cooled. The lower the evaporator temperature, the greater the heat transfer from the air to the evaporator and the greater the amount of dehumidification.

A typical set of conditions for indoor air being returned to an air conditioning system might be 80°F with a humidity ratio of 70 grains (0.0097 lb) of moisture per pound of dry air. Moist air at these conditions has a dewpoint of about 56.5°F, so that condensation and dehumidification will begin when the air is cooled to 56.5°F.

To cool the building interior to 75°F and a humidity ratio of 65 grains (0.0093 lb) of moisture per pound of dry air (50% RH), the air supplied from the air conditioner must be at a lower temperature and have a lower moisture content, say 55°F and a humidity ratio of 50 grains (0.0072 lb) of moisture per pound of dry air (79% RH). These conditions are plotted on the psychrometric chart in Fig. 11.1. They represent a building cooling load with an RSHF of approximately 0.7. The line between the supply air point, the room air point, and the return air point is parallel to a 0.7 sensible heat fraction line drawn on the chart. This process is possible with a normal air conditioner, for the evaporator coils typically run at approximately 50 to 55°F.

While buildings are moving toward lower RSHFs and greater latent cooling loads, air conditioning equipment is moving in the opposite direction. The trend with equipment is toward higher SHRs and reduced latent capacity, compounding the humidity control problem. Many design changes made to improve efficiency also reduce the latent cooling capacity.

High latent cooling capacity or dehumidification requires low evaporator temperatures and low evaporator airflow rates to allow the air to be cooled to a temperature sufficiently low for condensation to occur. Unfortunately, lower evaporator temperatures and lower airflow rates reduce the total cooling capacity of an air conditioner. As manufacturers have attempted to improve the EERs of their units, refrigerant systems have been redesigned to raise the evaporator temperatures, and evaporator airflow rates have been increased.

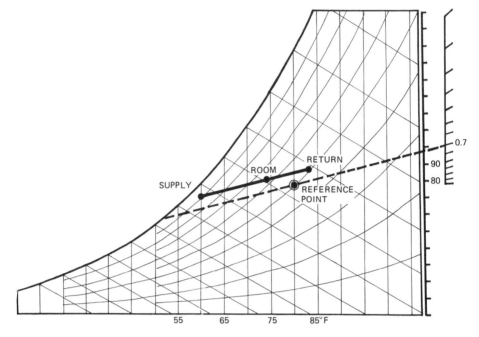

Figure 11.1. Air conditioning operation and dehumidification.

Although these steps are effective in increasing total cooling capacity and EER, they also result in reduced latent cooling capacities. As a result, the SHR of some new high-efficiency air conditioners is greater than 0.80. It is paradoxical that efforts to make buildings and air conditioning equipment more efficient have created problems with humidity control and comfort.

One alternative for better latent cooling performance offered by some air conditioning system manufacturers is a latent load discriminator and fan speed control option. A sensor responds to excessive humidity in the room by slowing the evaporator fan. Usually only two speeds are provided. The reduced fan speed reduces overall capacity, but increases latent capacity. When humidity is lower, the fan is operated on the higher speed for greater overall efficiency.

In selecting an air conditioner, the SHR as well as the EER must be considered. If the unit has too high an SHR, it may not provide adequate dehumidification capacity. It may be desirable to sacrifice total efficiency (EER) slightly to obtain better dehumidification performance (lower SHR). One method of making tradeoffs between units might be to estimate a latent cooling EER by multiplying the latent heat ratio by the EER

$$\text{Latent heat ratio (LHR)} = 1.0 - \text{SHR}$$
$$\text{Latent cooling EER (LCEER)} = \text{LHR} \times \text{EER}$$

Using the latent cooling EER as a basis of comparison will allow selection of the unit with the best dehumidification efficiency. The figure indicates the amount of dehumidification effect obtained (in Btu) per watt of input power. In the example below, unit C is significantly more efficient than unit A in dehumidifying

	Unit A	Unit B	Unit C
SHR	0.80	0.70	0.68
EER	10.45	8.30	9.10
LCEER	2.09	2.49	2.91

The latent cooling EER should not be used alone in comparing air conditioners; the latent load is only a portion of the total cooling load.

In the absence of better information, Table 11.1 provides guidelines for estimating the RSHF. Air conditioners with SHRs as low as 0.6 and as high as 0.9 are available. However, for a particular type of unit and for an approximate EER value, a fairly limited range of SHRs may be expected. The range of products to be available in the near future should include air conditioners with low SHRs and high EERs.

VAPOR-COMPRESSION DEHUMIDIFIERS

Most dehumidifiers used in homes and small buildings are vapor-compression dehumidifiers. They are essentially small air conditioners that are designed for a very low sensible heat ratio; the majority of the cooling effect is used to remove moisture from the air rather than cool it. In size and construction, vapor-compression dehumidifiers are very similar to room air conditioners. A typical dehumidifier (Fig. 11.2) has the same major components as a room air conditioner.

The compressor circulates refrigerant through a circuit that includes an evaporator and a condenser mounted adjacent to one another. Room air is first cooled

Table 11.1. Approximate RSHF Values for Homes.

Energy-conserving house	
Drier climate	0.75
Humid climate	0.60
Typical house	
Drier climate	0.83
Humid climate	0.73
Superinsulated house	0.50–0.65
Earth-sheltered or superinsulated house with excellent sun protection, cooling seldom required, primarily for dehumidification	0.40–0.50

Figure 11.2. Dehumidifier.

and dehumidified as it flows over the evaporator and then reheated by the condenser and fan motor. Moisture condensing on the evaporator drips into a container or may be drained away through a hose. The unit is controlled by a humidistat that senses room air humidity.

Dehumidifiers are rated by their moisture removal capacity, expressed in pints (pt) per day. Typical units have capacities ranging from 15 to 40 pt per day. Airflow capacities range from 180 to 260 cfm. Because standard dehumidifier tests are conducted at 60% RH and 80°F, most models are designed to provide optimum performance at these conditions.

Unlike an air conditioner, the dehumidifier places both the evaporator and the condenser in the interior of the building. A dehumidifier's evaporator removes energy as both latent and sensible heat from the air, but the condenser discharges that energy back into the building as sensible heat. In addition, all the electricity used to power the compressor, fans, and controls is also released to the building.

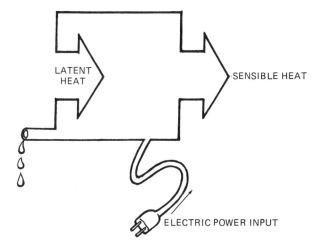

Figure 11.3. Dehumidifier as a thermal system.

A dehumidifier is not a cooling device. It is more like an evaporative cooler operating in reverse. To see the net effect, examine the dehumidifier as a thermal system (Fig. 11.3). The energy flow into the dehumidifier (from the cooling and dehumidification process and from the electric power supply) is equal to the energy flow from the dehumidifier to the building interior (the sensible heat output). The sensible heat contained in the condensed water is small and may be ignored.

As an example, consider a standard dehumidifier model with the following characteristics

> Dehumidification capacity = 25 pt/day
> Power consumption = 460 W
> Airflow = 260 cfm

For each hour of operation, the unit removes 25/24 or 1.04 pt of water. This is equivalent to a latent cooling capacity of

$$\frac{1.04 \text{ pt/h} \times 8.34 \text{ lb/gal} \times 1050 \text{ Btu/lb}}{8 \text{ pt/gal}} = 1140 \text{ Btu/h}$$

Because the heat released as the moisture condenses flows directly into the building, the dehumidifier does not remove heat, it merely converts it from latent heat to sensible heat.

In addition to the 1140 Btu/h of sensible heating resulting from moisture condensation, the electricity consumed by the dehumidifier is also converted to

Table 11.2. Dehumidifier Sizing Guidelines.

Conditions without Dehumidification	Required Dehumidification, pt/24 h Area, ft²			
	500	1000	1500	2000
Moderately damp— space feels damp and has musty odor only in humid weather	10	14	18	22
Very damp—space always feels damp and has musty odor; damp spots show on floor and walls	12	17	22	27
Wet—space feels and smells wet; walls or floor sweat or seepage is present.	14	20	26	32

heat and added to the building. In the example this amounts to 460 W × 3.413 Btu/W, or 1570 Btu per h. In total, the dehumidifier removes 1.04 pints of water per hour and adds 2710 Btu of sensible heat per hour.

Dehumidifiers are sometimes thought to be a simple solution to high humidity problems. It is assumed that a dehumidifier can be used to meet the latent cooling load in conjunction with passive cooling and load reduction measures that take care of the sensible load. In fact, dehumidifiers are more applicable for use with oversized conventional air conditioners than with weaker passive cooling systems. In climates where dehumidification is desirable, passive cooling usually cannot provide adequate sensible cooling capacity to carry the additional sensible load created by a dehumidifier.

Dehumidifiers are an effective means to cope with excessive humidity levels that might lead to mildew or materials damage. However, because of their high power consumption, they are normally not a part of a low-energy cooling approach and should be used only when there is a strong need. The sizing guidelines in Table 11.2 are taken from the Association of Home Appliance Manufacturers.

OPERATING A DEHUMIDIFIER WITH AN AIR CONDITIONER

The simultaneous use of a dehumidifier with an air conditioner is one method of increasing the rate of moisture removal and lowering interior humidity. However, the energy cost is quite high. Though an air conditioner rejects the heat of condensation to the exterior of the building, a dehumidifier releases both the heat of condensation and the heat of its own operation to the interior. The air conditioner must then remove the heat load produced by the dehumidifier.

The combined effect may be quantified by calculating a modified EER (EER') for the combination of the air conditioner and the dehumidifier. The latent capacity of the dehumidifier, represented by the rate of moisture removal, and its power consumption are added to the total capacity of the air conditioner

$$EER' = \frac{\text{A/C capacity} - \text{dehumidifier heat input (Btu/h)}}{\text{A/C power} + \text{dehumidifier power (W)}}$$

For a dehumidifier located entirely inside the conditioned space, its net effect on total heat is a heat gain to the space equal to its power consumption.

Example: Calculate the effective EER' of a 30,000-Btu/h air conditioner with an EER of 9.5 (power consumption = 3160 W) operating with dehumidifier having a moisture removal capacity of 25 pt/24 h and a power consumption of 460 W

$$EER' = \frac{30,000 \text{ Btu/h} - 460 \text{ W} \times 3.413 \text{ Btu/h per W}}{3160 \text{ W} + 460 \text{ W}}$$

$$= \frac{7.9 \text{ Btu/h}}{\text{Watt}}$$

Obviously, the effective cooling efficiency of the air conditioner and dehumidifier combination is somewhat less than that of the air conditioner alone. Dehumidifiers should be used only when the additional latent cooling capacity is absolutely necessary to remedy a high humidity problem. They are not an efficient cooling device.

RUN-AROUND CYCLE

An effective means of swapping sensible cooling capacity in an air conditioning system for latent cooling capacity is provided by the run-around cycle illustrated schematically in Figure 11.4. Two water-to-air heat exchangers are located in the ductwork on either side of the cooling coil or evaporator. The two heat exchangers, usually finned tube coils, are connected by a piping loop through which water or a water and antifreeze mixture is pumped.

As cool air from the evaporator passes over the downstream, or reheat, coil, it cools the water in the coil. This chilled water is then circulated to the upstream, or precooling, coil, where it cools the entering air. The heat extracted by the precooling coil is transferred through the piping loop to the reheat coil and rejected into the air leaving the system. The temperature of the entering air is lowered in the precooling coil, so that it may be more effectively dehumidi-

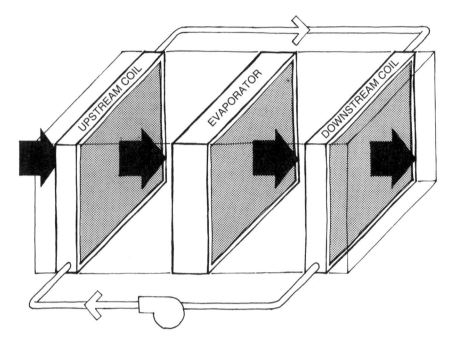

Figure 11.4. Run-Around Cycle.

fied by the evaporator. In some cases there may even be condensation at the precooling coil itself. The temperature of the exiting air is increased, but the moisture content is reduced. In essence, the run-around cycle acts as a reheater, with the reheat energy supplied by the building itself. The sensible cooling capacity is reduced, and the latent cooling capacity is increased; the SHR of the system is reduced.

To date, run-around coils have been applied most frequently in large commercial buildings and laboratories and industrial environments, where temperature and humidity control are critical. Residential applications are more difficult, because the system design is somewhat less flexible and components of appropriate capacity are difficult to obtain.

In both new systems and retrofits, run-around coils can be useful when high latent loads drive the sensible heat ratio down below the SHR of the air conditioning equipment. Because two additional coils are added to the air distribution system, the pressure drop will increase and fan capacity must be carefully considered. But the added fan power and initial cost may be justified if there is an imbalance between the latent cooling load in the building and the latent capacity of the air conditioning system. It is likely that manufacturers of package air conditioning systems will begin to incorporate run-around cycles into their products in the future.

12

LANDSCAPING FOR PASSIVE COOLING

LANDSCAPING FOR LOW-ENERGY COOLING

The use of landscaping elements to protect southern homes from summer heat has a long history. Shaded building sites have always commanded a premium. Today, landscaping can provide significant savings in air conditioning costs as well as greater aesthetic value.

Landscaping offers three kinds of cooling benefits: site temperature reductions, wind channeling, and sun control. The overall air temperature at a site may be reduced several degrees as a result of the presence of plants, but such benefits are difficult to plan for on a single small site. Wind channeling, although often discussed in energy-conscious design literature, has little application for most building projects. Variable wind directions and the limited size of most sites impose severe limitations. For almost all buildings, sun control is by far the most important energy application of landscaping.

Site Cooling by Landscaping

Trees, shrubs, and other plants provide a site with natural protection from hot summer sun. The leaves of plants intercept solar radiation before it strikes the surface of the ground and dissipate the heat into the atmosphere, leaving the ground and the air underneath the plants cooler. The temperature of asphalt surfaces without shading have been observed to reach 128°F, while the ambient air temperature was 98°F. With shading from plants, the temperature of the same surface would be 30 to 40°F cooler. Site temperature reductions of up to 10° have been attributed to landscaping. Midday summer air temperatures are often 5° lower under large trees than in exposed areas. On sunny summer days, the temperature over grassy areas is 10 to 14°F cooler than over bare soil.

Comfort conditions in a building and on the site are directly improved by the temperature reduction provided by plants and by the protection from solar ra-

diation. And because less heat is stored in the ground and in paving and buildings on the site, the temperature of the site drops more rapidly at night as air
temperatures fall. Trees and shrubs also act as natural evaporative coolers. They
extract nutrients from the ground in which they grow by absorbing water through
their root system. The nutrients are dissolved in the water and move upward
through the plant in the sap, driven by the evaporation of water through the
stoma, or openings, in the leaves. This process is known as evapotranspiration,
or productive evaporation.

The solution of dissolved nutrients taken from the soil is very dilute, so the
plant must absorb and evaporate large quantities of water. Each pound of water
evaporated by a plant provides more than 1000 Btu of cooling for the air around
the plant. A large oak tree can evaporate more than 100 lb of water in a single
summer day, providing a cooling effect of more than 100,000 Btu. It is thought
that up to half of the total solar radiation that arrives at a site during the spring
and summer is dissipated by evapotranspiration.

Soil temperatures are also strongly affected by the presence of plants. Maximum upper-level soil temperatures under a grass cover have been determined
to be as much as 35° cooler than in soil with a bare surface. The temperature
increase due to solar exposure extends well below the surface and can significantly increase the temperature of the soil below an unshaded surface to a depth
of at least 10 ft. The implications for earth sheltered buildings and mechanical
systems using the earth as a heat sink are obvious.

Obviously, it is desirable to leave as many plants as possible on a building
site. The reductions in air temperatures achieved by landscaping at a building
site can reduce the conduction and infiltration heat gain portions of a building's
cooling load by 15 to 30%. Although truly effective use of landscaping must
be done on a fairly large scale, noticeable improvements can be made even on
a single-site basis. When landscaping planning is coordinated on a larger scale,
for entire communities or developments, major improvements in site conditions
are possible.

A good example is provided by the community of Davis, California. Street
widths were limited; parking bays were built in lieu of making the entire street
wide enough to allow parking on both sides. The removal of trees from the site
was strictly limited, and numerous new trees were planted. The efforts made
during the development of the community have resulted in a much more comfortable and attractive community with noticeably reduced energy consumption.

Wind Channeling with Landscaping

Examples of the use of landscaping to channel winds for ventilative cooling in
buildings can be found in many publications. Actual successful applications of
wind channeling are considerably more difficult to find. The principles involved
are certainly sound; the direction and speed of winds reaching a building can

be greatly altered by landscaping elements. But winds for ventilation are only one of many concerns in a building, and plantings for channeling winds may conflict with other energy and design goals, most notably sun control. Perhaps most limiting is the fact that a single building site usually does not encompass adequate area to allow wind channeling to be applied. On typically sized residential sites, effective wind channeling plantings would have to be located on neighboring lots, Fig. 12.1.

The practicality of channeling winds is further limited in most areas of the country by the extreme variations in wind speed and direction. Design for the prevailing wind direction is not a viable concept; there is often no real prevailing wind direction. Because natural ventilation is normally not the primary design cooling strategy, the desirability and potential benefits of wind channeling

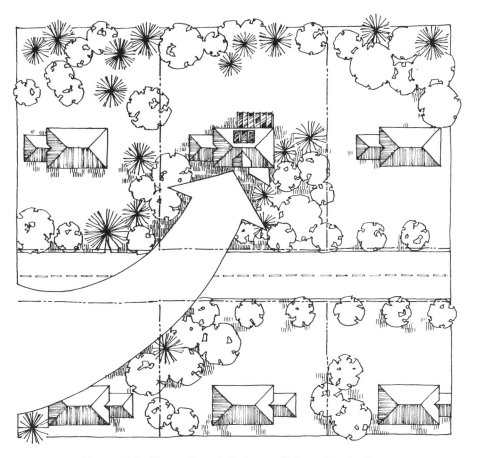

Figure 12.1. Channeling winds for ventilation with plantings.

are not significant. In most building projects, there is little opportunity to successfully channel winds and little justification for attempting to do so.

Sun Control for Buildings by Landscaping

Vegetation is a natural sun control device. In the same way that plants protect a site from solar radiation, they can be used to protect a building. The potential for reductions in building energy consumption is significant. A study at the University of Georgia found that the temperature of a west-facing exterior frame wall surface could be reduced by as much as 40°F by protecting the wall with vines planted on a trellis. A difference of more than 250 Btu/h in the peak steady-state heat gain through 100 ft^2 of $R15$ wall surface would result.

Deciduous plants offer a further benefit with their natural coordination of leaf growth with shading requirements. Plants are generally much more closely co-

SOUTH

Figure 12.2. Compromise landscaping design for heating and cooling.

ordinated with building heating and cooling needs than sun angles. Although the sun's position is identical in September and March, the cooling and heating needs of buildings are dramatically different. Cooling is often required in September and heating is required in March. Deciduous plants can provide a more effective dynamic response than fixed shading devices, because they shed and regrow their leaves in coordination with air temperature.

However, even deciduous plants should not be used indiscriminately for shading passive solar systems. A plant's bare branches and twigs still provide noticeable shading, blocking as much as 40% of the solar radiation passing through the branch pattern of trees. Removable or adjustable shading devices are more appropriate for south-facing glazing used for passive solar heating. But for west- and east-facing glazing, vegetation is ideal.

The compromise between landscaping to allow useful winter solar heat gains and landscaping to block undesirable summer solar heat gains is not as severe as it might seem (Fig. 12.2). Essentially all of the useful winter gains reach a building through a zone that extends about 45° to the east and west from the south corners of the building. During the summer the sun's path is such that the solar radiation received on a south-facing surface is quite small. Leaving the zone to the south of the building relatively unobstructed can allow the ma-

Figure 12.3. Wisteria vine for shading.

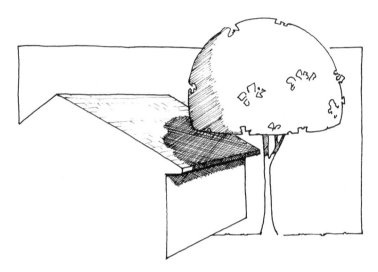

Figure 12.4. Roof shading with trees requires overhang.

jority of the useful winter heat to reach the building, but does not create a severe summer heat gain problem. The east and west sides are the most important concern for shading during summer.

Glazed areas are first priority for shading by landscaping. Solar gains of more than 200 Btu/h per ft^2 may occur through glazed areas; solar gains through an opaque insulated wall are an order of magnitude lower. The highest priorities are east- and west-facing surfaces and inclined or horizontal surfaces; the next priority is glazing that faces other directions, and then the west and east opaque walls and the roof. Less dramatic but still significant benefits are available from shading other building surfaces and the building site in general. Examples of the use of trees, shrubs, vines, and other vegetation are provided in Figs. 12.3 and 12.4.

One measure that has been used successfully for years is the planting of annual vines on temporary trellises or frames in front of windows exposed to intense solar gains. Rural homes often have simple trellises made by extending strings from a planter or stakes in the ground to the eaves of the house. Fast-growing plants like morning glory or pole beans are allowed to climb the strings and shade the windows. Although such shading schemes do require a certain amount of work, they provide benefits other than just energy savings.

Design Recommendtions

- Concentrate on the use of landscaping elements for such control at the building; west- and east-facing glazing are the highest priority. Shading opaque building surfaces is also beneficial, particularly on the west side of the building.

- Retain as much vegetation on the site as possible to provide site cooling; when adding plantings, consider their potential value for shading.
- Maximize the use of ground covers; minimize hard surfaces and bare areas. Choose tall and dense species of plants that require little maintenance.
- As attractive as kudzu may seem, its bad qualities make it questionable for use in landscaping. Consider Kentucky Wonder pole beans. They grow as fast as kudzu and die completely in the fall.

13

EARTH COOLING

This chapter will first examine the earth as a potential cooling resource and then proceed to several possible applications for effective earth sheltering and building cooling. The concept of using the earth to assist in heating and cooling a building is an old one that has received enormous attention in recent years. Underground construction, earth sheltering, berming, and earth cooling tubes are ideas familiar to almost everyone involved in building design and construction. But even though the basic thermodynamic and heat transfer relationships involved in earth contact are well known, and unquestionably successful applications may be found in the far North, little is known about applications in climates where both heating and cooling loads are significant. Optimistic designers and building owners have attempted to extrapolate the successes with underground buildings in Minnesota and Michigan to other vastly different climates with mixed results.

The temperature of the earth at a site is always more moderate than the air temperature and follows a different pattern of variation, creating several opportunities for reducing energy consumption in buildings. These opportunities include not only earth sheltering to reduce heating and cooling loads, but also the application of mechanical systems that rely on the earth as a heat sink or source.

Consider the use of the earth in directly controlling building heat losses and gains by reducing the thermal stress on the building envelope. This is often described as *earth sheltering, earth contact*, or *earth coupling*, and it involves placing large areas of the building envelope in direct contact with the earth. The most dramatic effects are possible in areas where the above-surface climate is extreme and the difference between air temperatures and earth temperatures is great. In the United States, such areas include such northern states as Minnesota and Michigan, with strong winds and very cold winter conditions with as many as 12,000 heating degree-days per year. In comparison with the area's average December air temperatures of 10 to 25°F, an earth temperature of 50°F is quite moderate.

During the cooling season the earth can also provide shelter from extremely high air temperatures and intense sun. Traditional dwellings in the desert areas of the American Southwest, where summer temperatures can reach 120°F and solar radiation is intense, reflect such applications. Other examples of earth cooling exist in the burrows and dens of numerous animal species. However, earth sheltering is more a way to avoid solar radiation and higher air temperatures than a way to remove heat from a building. With summer earth temperatures around buildings no lower than about 65°F, the earth/building temperature difference and the potential for useful cooling are rather small.

THE EARTH AS A COOLING RESOURCE

The value of using the earth to reduce heating and cooling loads in less severe climates is not yet well understood. Even more vague is the proper mix of heating and cooling design strategies. It is certain that expectations of the value of earth sheltering and earth cooling in the milder climates of the United States are generally too great. Earth contact is not a magic solution to building heating and cooling needs, and attempts to apply it should be approached with caution.

There are many common misconceptions about the temperature of the earth and the potential applications of the earth as a cooling and heating resource. The earth near the surface is *not* a constant-temperature heat sink. The idea that the temperature of the earth around buildings remains at an unchanging 55 to 60°F year-round is far from correct. At the depths associated with buildings there are large seasonal variations in earth temperatures, even in undisturbed soil. And buildings themselves have an effect on the temperature of the soil around them.

There are three important issues to be discussed regarding the earth as a cooling resource:

1. the average temperature of undisturbed earth
2. the periodic variations in undisturbed earth temperatures during the year and
3. the effects of surface features, soil properties, and geological factors on local ground temperatures and heat-transfer rates through the soil.

The earth does provide a good potential for blocking solar gains and reducing conduction loads, but it seldom presents an opportunity for substantial heating, cooling, or dehumidification. The major difficulty is the earth temperature. For direct use in conditioning a building, the earth temperature must be above the desired interior temperature when heating or below it for cooling. For dehumidification the critical temperature is the desired dewpoint temperature of the inside air. Unless the earth temperature meets these requirements, direct use of the earth for heating, cooling, or dehumidifying is not possible. Even where the temperature is acceptable, the temperature differential is too small for significant benefits in most cases. It is more appropriate to think of the earth as a means of blocking or reducing undesirable heat flows to a building than as a source of energy for direct use by the building.

EARTH TEMPERATURES

For *undisturbed* deep earth, the annual average earth temperature is very near the annual average air temperature. Undisturbed earth refers to earth in an area not influenced by buildings, wells, pipelines, mines, or other features and deep enough not to be affected by surface conditions—20 ft or more.

Annual average undisturbed earth temperatures range from 42°F in the extreme North to more than 77°F in southern Florida. As illustrated in Fig. 13.1, there is a strong variation in the earth temperature around the country (Ref. 13.1). The temperature isotherms were developed from mean annual air temperatures; the individual values are mean annual earth temperatures from field measurement stations. The variation in the data in the extreme North is a result of the insulating effect of deep winter snow cover.

As a rule of thumb, the annual average temperature of undisturbed earth may be estimated as the annual average air temperature plus 0 to 3°F. In the extreme northern United States and in Canada, the actual earth temperature may be 3 to

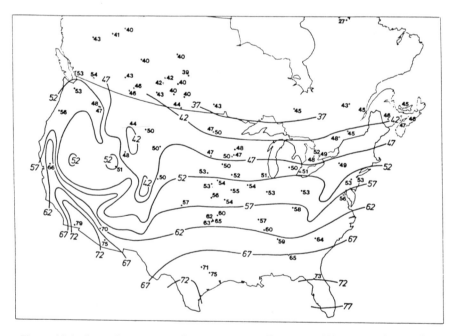

Figure 13.1. Annual average earth temperatures. (Courtesy of Kenneth Labs and Solar Age Magazine.)

7° higher, because the normal winter snow cover insulates the earth from the winter air.

The difference between the earth temperature and the temperature of the air may be used as a simple indicator of the potential usefulness of the earth for reducing building envelope thermal loads. In northern regions, this temperature difference is usually in the range of 20 to 30°F. In southern regions the difference is much smaller, about 10 to 20°F. Unfortunately, the potential for earth cooling is much higher in northern areas than in the South or Southwest where it is needed most. In southern Florida, earth temperatures at depths of 10 ft can exceed 80°F during the late summer.

Even in Atlanta, a relatively mild cooling climate in the mid-South, the earth's temperature severely limits the use of earth cooling. A maximum temperature differential of only about 78 − 64, or 14°F, is available from the deep undisturbed earth to the indoor air. Temperatures are higher at shallower depths and around buildings, usually reducing the maximum differential to less than 10°F.

PERIODIC VARIATIONS IN EARTH TEMPERATURE

The potential for earth cooling at the peak of the cooling season looks even dimmer when the normal winter to summer variation in the earth temperature is considered. At a depth of 6 ft, late summer earth temperatures are roughly 10° higher than the annual average. A normal annual pattern of undisturbed earth temperature variation at several depths is shown in Fig. 13.2.

It can be seen that there is a time lag between the annual cycle in temperatures for the earth and the air. As air temperature drops in the fall, earth temperature

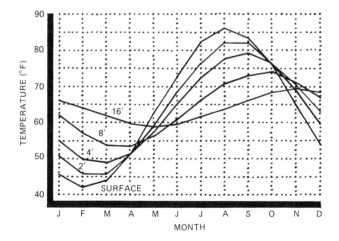

Figure 13.2. Annual pattern of undisturbed earth temperature.

continues to rise for a time. Similarly, in the summer as air temperature climbs, earth temperature lags behind. This time lag varies according to depth; the greater the depth, the greater the lag. The lag can be a positive force, as it tends to "store" cool winter and spring temperatures in the earth for cooling during the summer. But the effect is most significant only in northern areas where summer cooling loads are small.

For undisturbed soils the time lag between earth temperature and air temperature may be estimated as 5.5 days per foot of depth for wet soils to 10.5 days per foot of depth for light dry soils. For both damp, light soil and dry, heavy soil, a value of 7.5 days is appropriate. Again the presence of a building affects the time lag effect.

The variation in temperature from winter to summer is affected by depth, decreasing with greater depths. In other words, the temperature of the earth becomes more stable at greater depths. Figure 13.3 shows this effect for three soil types. The maximum and minimum earth temperatures during the year at a particular depth may be estimated by adding or subtracting the appropriate temperature variation corresponding to the depth to the annual average temperature.

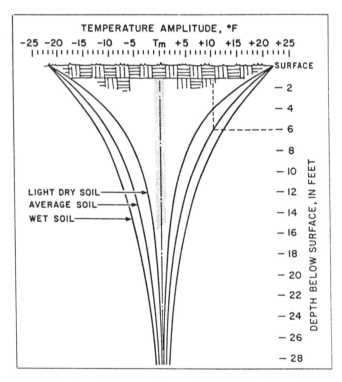

Figure 13.3. Variation in earth temperatures with depth. (Courtesy of Kenneth Labs and Solar Age Magazine.)

The significance of the annual variation in earth temperature can be observed by taking a 4-ft depth as an example. This represents an average depth for a single-story, earth-sheltered house with the floor 8 ft below grade. In Atlanta, with an annual average earth temperature of approximately 60°F, the summer temperature of *undisturbed* average soil is 60 + 15 = 75°F. Thus, a below-grade wall exposed to undisturbed soil at a depth of 4 ft is essentially thermally neutral, offering little potential for cooling a building interior at 75°F and little potential for heat gain.

INFLUENCES ON EARTH TEMPERATURES

The earth temperatures discussed above are the temperatures of *undisturbed* soil under *typical conditions*. Several factors can lead to large variations in the *actual* temperature of the earth at a building site. Almost all will increase the temperature of the soil during the cooling season.

One of the reasons that the deep earth is cooler than the summer air is that it is isolated from the warmer conditions at the surface by the upper layers of soil. The lower layers are insulated from warm summer air and, equally important, from the direct heating effects of the sun. Anything that reduces this insulating or isolating effect will tend to increase the temperature of the lower layers of earth during the summer and decrease it during winter. Such factors include high-conductivity soils, the amount of moisture in the soil, holes or pipelines, and buildings. Soils with high moisture content or high conductivity will increase the flow of heat down into the earth during summer and increase the earth temperature. Figure 13.4 compares the temperature variation at 6 ft for light, dry soil and for wet soil. For the light, dry soil, the maximum temperature

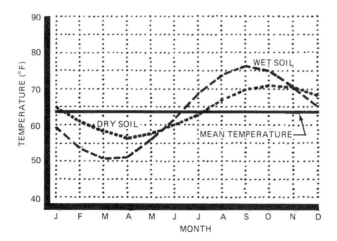

Figure 13.4. Earth temperature variations with soil properties.

variation during summer is less than 8°F above the annual average, but for the wet soil, it increases to over 12°F. Thus, soil properties can increase the peak summer ground temperature in Atlanta at a depth of 4 ft from 72 to 76°F.

Any feature or structure, including a building, that disturbs the state of the soil can act like a heat wick into the earth. However, the effects of buildings on earth temperatures are complex and not yet fully understood. In general, buildings would be expected to increase the temperature of the ground by reducing the amount of cooling done to the ground by the winter air. Instead of losing heat to the winter air, the soil around and below a conditioned building receives heat and then begins the next summer with a higher than normal temperature. The usefulness of the earth as a heat sink is further reduced by exposure of the ground surface to solar radiation. Temperatures in excess of 90°F have been measured in Georgia at a depth of 6 ft below unshaded surfaces.

APPLICATIONS OF EARTH COOLING

The temptation to extrapolate an experience with a cave or a cool basement during the summer to a house design is indeed strong. High energy prices and fertile imaginations have spawned numerous wishful earth cooling solutions. In general, the proposed methods fall into two categories: direct earth contact and isolated earth contact. The direct earth contact alternatives rely on a portion of the building envelope itself to transfer heat directly to the soil around the building. Earth berms, earth sheltering, and underground construction fall into this category. Earth cooling tubes and similar concepts make up the second category. In these systems, the building is not necessarily directly in close thermal contact with the ground, but relies on tubes or ducts to dissipate heat to the soil and provide cooling to the building. Unfortunately, most of these schemes do not recognize the innate limitations of the earth as a heat sink for practical cooling processes. The would-be, energy-saving homeowner usually overlooks the high humidity and musty odors associated with caves and basements. (This is not a condemnation of earth-sheltered or underground houses; if properly designed and built, they can be quite comfortable and energy-efficient.)

Dehumidification, the other equally important aspect of cooling, is extremely difficult to accomplish when using the earth directly as a heat sink. The dewpoint temperature of air at 78°F and 60% RH is approximately 67°F. This point represents the upper limit of the comfort range without air movement; an earth cooling system must be able to cool to at least 67°F to provide efficient dehumidification. In Atlanta the annual average undisturbed earth temperature is 60 to 64°F, and summer temperatures are well above 70°F. Earth temperatures are seldom low enough for dehumidification to comfortable conditions during summer. The temperature limits the availability of the heat sink for latent cooling even more than sensible cooling. In addition, most earth contact concepts are not compatible with dehumidification, even if the earth temperature were low enough. For instance, attempting to use earth sheltered walls and floors to dehumidify would result in wet walls and floors, damaged furnishings, and odors.

Throughout most of the country, the temperature of the earth is not low enough to provide direct use of the earth even for sensible cooling of buildings. There is simply not enough temperature difference to drive a significant amount of heat transfer. Although the capacity of the ground for accepting heat is enormous, the natural temperature differences are not adequate for cooling at temperatures of 70 to 85°F. Reasonable amounts of sensible cooling can be achieved by direct means only with extremely large surface areas for heat transfer. Latent cooling to comfortable conditions is extremely unlikely.

The picture is not totally gloomy. Far northern sites offer reasonable potential for meaningful cooling contributions, because earth temperatures are much lower, and summer cooling loads, both sensible and latent, are smaller. Throughout the country, the heat capacity and the relatively stable temperature of the ground do imply that the potential for indirect use of the earth through a heat pump system is rather good. And though below-grade walls may not cool a house, they add little or no heat and may reduce the cooling load. Rather than considering earth contact as a *cooling* method, it should be considered as a *heat gain avoidance* method. In this light, earth contact may be thought of as the ultimate form of shading.

The limitations and possible applications of earth cooling are discussed further in the following sections.

DIRECT EARTH CONTACT COOLING

Direct earth contact cooling involves placing the building envelope—the walls, floor, and possibly the ceiling—in direct contact with the earth (Fig. 13.5). These surfaces then act as heat exchangers, transferring heat from the building interior to the earth. With the surrounding earth at a low temperature, heat will flow from the warm air inside the building to the earth. The flow of heat is impeded by both the wall and the layers of earth adjacent to the wall. Though evaluating the resistance of the wall is straightforward, estimating the resistance of the soil around the building and the dynamic effects of its thermal mass on the heat transfer process is extremely difficult. If an inside wall or floor temperature is assumed, then the cooling effect of the wall or floor is easily estimated as 1.5 Btu/h per ft^2 for each degree of temperature difference between the wall and the air. Accurate calculations are difficult, and conditions vary from one location to another. In addition the effects of heat storage in the ground and seasonal earth temperature variations caused by the exchange of heat with the buildings are not clear.

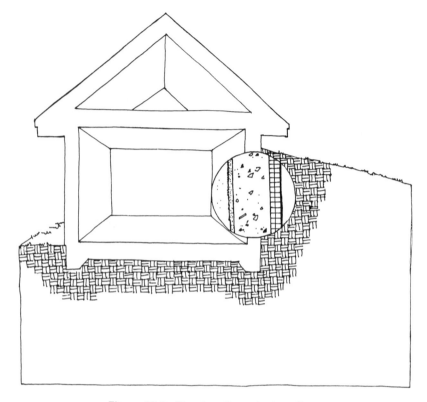

Figure 13.5. Direct earth contact cooling.

EARTH COOLING TUBES

The concept of the earth cooling tube is a simple and popular one, involving the use of a buried tube or pipe to cool air for conditioning a building. The building receives cooling from the earth, but is free of the design constraints imposed by direct earth contact. Because the tubes are separate from the building, retrofits are possible.

As shown in Fig. 13.6, the most common earth cooling tube concept simply draws outdoor air through an underground tube in contact with the earth. The air is cooled and delivered to the interior of the building, where it displaces warm air to the outside. Other schemes use earth-cooled air or water to cool the condenser of an air conditioner or heat pump. Earth-source heat pump applications are discussed in detail in Chapter 10. In this chapter *earth tubes* will refer only to systems that circulate air directly to a building, rather than to the heat pump systems.

Isolated cases of the use of earth tube cooling concepts can be traced back

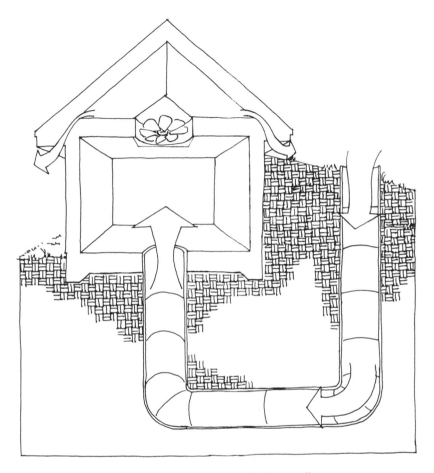

Figure 13.6. Open-loop earth tube cooling.

several centuries. Natural caves and tunnels were employed for cooling the homes of the wealthy Romans. Similar examples were found elsewhere in southern Europe, but they are rare due to the dependence on naturally occurring geological formations. Man-made systems are much more recent. It has been suggested that Thomas Jefferson's Monticello used below-grade passages for earth cooling. Isolated instances of the use of underground tunnels or rooms for cooling in 19th century homes can be found in many parts of the country, including the Hay House discussed in Chapter 1.

Modern applications include homes, small commercial buildings, chicken houses, and agricultural buildings. The recent concern over energy prices and the public's fascination with "free" energy from passive systems have sparked a high level of interest in residential systems. Although little formal research has been conducted, several hundred individuals have built earth tube systems into their homes in the past few years.

In practice earth cooling tubes seldom live up to the hopes and expectations of enthusiasts; the sensible cooling capacity is limited, and dehumidification on a reasonable level is not possible. The cost of installing an earth cooling tube system is not small and is seldom justified by the cooling capacity provided. The money could be put to better use in other conservation and cooling measures.

Generally, earth cooling tubes are not recommended for use in residences or commercial buildings. But due to the tremendous interest, they are discussed here in some detail. The following section will examine earth tube concepts, performance, analysis methods, and design. This information is provided primarily to demonstrate the limitations of earth cooling tubes and to assist in optimizing a cooling tube system being built as an experiment. Earth cooling tubes are not recommended as a viable cooling system for general use.

EARTH TUBE COOLING SYSTEMS

Earth cooling systems make use of one of two airflow configurations: the open loop or the closed loop. The distinction between the two is in the manner in which cooling air is circulated. In theory, the open-loop system, illustrated in Fig. 13.6, draws outdoor air into the tubes, cools it, and delivers it to the building interior, where the cool air forces warm air inside the building to flow to the outdoors. New outdoor air is constantly being introduced into the system and provides positive ventilation of the building.

The closed-loop system, however, recirculates air from the building rather than taking in outdoor air (Fig. 13.7). Air flows from the building interior, through the tubes, and back to the building interior. No ventilating air is introduced into the building.

The closed-loop system has obvious advantages when outdoor conditions are severe and high volumes of ventilating air are not required. Consider a day when the ambient temperature is 85°F and the relative humidity is 60%. Indoor conditions of 78°F and 60% RH or better are desired. (Recall that even though the relative humidity is the same in both cases, the warmer outdoor air contains much more moisture than the cooler indoor air.) An open-loop system must condition the air from 85°F and 60% RH to 78°F and 60% RH, requiring the removal of about 5.2 Btu of heat per pound of air.

The closed-loop system might take air from the house at a temperature and humidity level only slightly higher than the desired conditions, perhaps 83°F/ 55% RH. Less than half the energy must be removed, only 2.3 Btu/lb of air. The process of cooling from 83°F/53% RH to 78°F/60% RH represents a cooling load with a sensible fraction of 60%—40% of the load is latent heat—typical

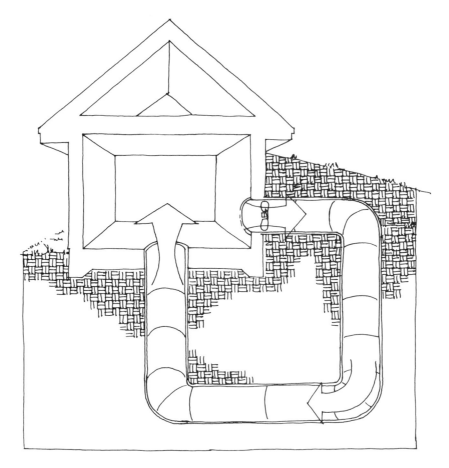

Figure 13.7. Closed-loop earth tubes cooling system.

of well-insulated residences with good solar gain control. The open-loop process of cooling outdoor air from 85°F/60% RH to 78°F/60% RH requires the removal of far more moisture. The process has a sensible fraction of only about 0.3; 70% of the load is associated with moisture removal.

The closed-loop significantly reduces the amount of cooling required and is preferred to the open-loop except where fresh ventilating air is required. Residences generally do not require positive ventilation; adequate fresh air is provided by infiltration.

In either system, the tube field may be arranged for either parallel or series flow; both are illustrated in Fig. 13.8. In the series flow configuration, all air flows through each segment of pipe, entering at one end and flowing through

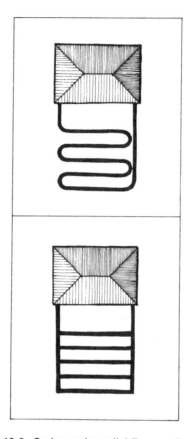

Figure 13.8. Series and parallel flow configurations.

the only path to the other end. In the parallel flow arrangement, the air is split after it enters the tube field and is distributed to one of several branch circuits. Near the end of the tube field the branches join to form a common exit tube.

There are three major reasons that parallel flow configurations are preferable for earth cooling tube systems. First, resistance to airflow increases with greater tube length, reduced tube diameter, the addition of bends and turns, and increased fluid speed. By selecting a parallel flow configuration with several small tubes instead of a single larger tube, the resistance to flow can be reduced, and less fan power is consumed. Flow resistances and fan power can be estimated by techniques commonly applied to heating and air conditioning duct design.

A second consideration is the rate of heat transfer from the air to the tube wall. As air flows through the tube, it is gradually cooled and eventually approaches a temperature near that of the tube wall. The tube wall temperature is the lowest possible air temperature that can be attained. Low air temperatures are desirable, but the rate of heat transfer decreases as the temperature difference between the air and the tube wall decreases.

With a long tube, each air molecule follows a longer path and is cooled for a longer period of time, providing lower output temperatures. With shorter tubes, the rate of heat transfer per foot of tube is kept high, because the temperature difference between the air and the tube wall is higher, but output temperatures are also higher. The proper compromise calls for a tube system that cools the air to a temperature only as low as required for the application while maintaining the highest heat-transfer rate possible.

Finally, heat-transfer-capacity requirements dictate that a certain minimum tube wall area be used. Often the solution is a parallel flow configuration where the length of each tube is adequate to allow the temperature reduction required, but not so long that heat transfer rates drop off. To meet the overall tube area requirements, additional tubes are added to the system in parallel to one another. Selecting this optimum tube length is a complex calculation process.

Although very little actual operating information on earth cooling tubes is available, design conclusions may still be made on the basis of engineering analysis. With previously written equations (Ref. 13.2), a computer program was written to examine earth cooling tube performance (Ref. 13.3). The results of numerous computer runs have been combined with field observations and testing to produce the following conclusions and recommendations.

BASIC COOLING CAPACITY

Performance Predictions

There are no simple methods for estimating earth cooling tube capacity, and, because there has been little operating experience, there are few usable rules of thumb. However, the results of computer simulations will allow a rough estimate

$$(T_{ts} - T_e) = \frac{Q'r^{(2-n)}}{2\pi^{(n/2)}k} \int_{r\eta}^{\infty} \beta^{(n-3)} e^{-\beta^2} d\beta \qquad [1]$$

where

T_{ts} = Outside tube surface temp. (°F)
T_e = Bulk earth temperature (°F)
Q' = Rate of heat flow per unit length of tube (Btu/hr-ft)
r = Tube radius (ft)
n = 2 (for a line source)
k = Thermal conductivity of soil (Btu/h-°F-ft)

$$\eta = \left(2\sqrt{\alpha t}\right)^{-1}$$

α = Thermal diffusivity of soil (ft²/h)
   = k/cp
β = Variable of integration
c = Specific heat of soil (Btu/lb °F)
ρ = Density of earth (lb/ft³)
t = Time after start (h)

The following values were used in the simulations:

Thermal conductivity of earth = 0.75 Btu/h °F ft
Thermal diffusivity of earth = 0.025 ft²/h
Time after start = 25 h
Mass flow rate = 448 lb/h
   (flow velocity = 500 ft/min)
Inlet temperature = 85°F
Earth temperature = 65°F
Tube length = 60 ft
Specific heat of air = 0.24 Btu/lb °F
Thermal conductivity of pipe = 0.08 Btu/h °F ft
Pipe wall thickness = 0.125 in.

The cooling capacity of a single tube is plotted in Fig. 13.9. Using a value for cooling capacity from this chart, we can calculate the output temperature for the pipe. These results are reasonable only for the set of conditions described above and should be considered as optimistic estimates of performance. The effects of various factors are discussed in the following pages.

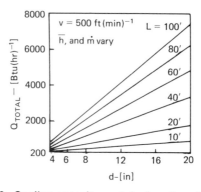

Figure 13.9. Cooling capacity vs. tube length and diameter.

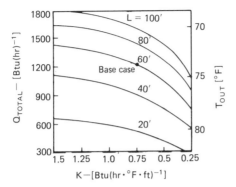

Figure 13.10. Cooling capacity vs. soil conductivity

Soil Conductivity

The thermal conductivity of the soil around the tube has a major influence on performance, as indicated in Fig. 13.10. Typical values are shown in Table 13.1.

Earth Temperature and Inlet Temperature

As the difference between the inlet temperature and the earth temperature decreases, cooling capacity also decreases. Figure 13.11 illustrates this effect. For a 6-in. diameter tube, the change in the temperature of the air as it flows through the tube is shown on the right of the figure for reference.

Tube Length and Tube Diameter

The total surface area of the buried tube, a key factor in overall cooling capacity, may be increased by two means: increasing the diameter or increasing the

Table 13.1. Typical Soil Conductivity.

Soil and Conditions	Conductivity Btu/h/ft/°F
Light, dry	0.20
Light, damp	0.50
Heavy, dry	0.50
Heavy, damp	0.90
Wet	1.40

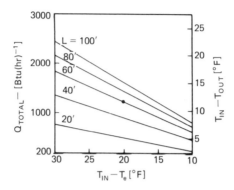

Figure 13.11. Cooling capacity vs. temperature difference

tube length. However, increased diameter reduces air speed and heat transfer, and greater length increases the pressure drop through the tube and increases fan energy. Usually, the correct design solution is a set of parallel tubes each with the proper diameter for best overall performance.

Inspection of the performance curves will reveal that *total* heat transfer and heat transfer per foot of length increases with increasing tube radius (assuming constant flow speed). But because the transfer of heat through the earth also limits the overall cooling capacity, the cooling capacity per square foot of tube wall decreases for larger tubes. A diameter should be selected that balances the thermal and economic factors for the best performance at the lowest cost. For most systems, this diameter probably lies between 4 and 8 in. The optimum is determined by the actual cost of the tube and the excavation. Excavation costs in particular vary greatly from one location and soil type to another.

For a given tube diameter, an increase in airflow rate will reduce the film coefficient and increase both total heat transfer and outlet temperature. This implies that high airflow rates are desirable for closed systems. However, for open systems, the airflow rate must be selected by consideration of both the required outlet temperature and total cooling capacity.

Tube Depth

Deeper is better. But again, sensible compromises are in order. In general, a depth of 5 to 10 ft should be used. Shallower tubes are subject to high summer temperatures, and the decrease in temperature obtained by burying tubes deeper than 10 ft is usually small. The required tube depth is strongly influenced by surface conditions. Exposed sites without trees or ground cover have much higher subsurface ground temperatures.

Several types of powered trenching devices are available, but most can dig only to a depth of 4 or 5 ft or less. Although the simplicity and reasonable cost are tempting, summer ground temperatures at 4 ft are usually too high for useful cooling. Increased tube length cannot compensate for high ground temperatures.

Extreme caution should be used while working in deep trenches, particularly in unstable soils. Cave-ins do occur.

Tube Layout

The layout of an earth cooling tube field is essentially a duct design problem. The same considerations in sizing ducts and fans for heating and cooling systems apply to earth tube systems. Avoid restrictions and sharp bends that would increase pressure drop and fan power. An air velocity between 500 and 1200 fpm is suggested. If possible, the tubes should be routed though shaded areas with ground cover and trees. If an open loop is used, the air inlet should be located in a cool, shady location. Temperatures are also usually lower in lower lying areas.

Tube Materials

In the base case, the tube has a $\frac{1}{8}$-in.-thick polypropylene wall with thermal conductivity equal to 0.08 Btu/h ft °F. Simulations indicate that metal, concrete, clay, or plastic pipes may be substituted with little impact on performance. Increasing the conductivity of the base case tube to a value corresponding to that of aluminum increased total heat transfer by less than 10%.

Limitations of Practical Applications

Direct earth tube cooling is not a practical, cost-effective cooling approach for buildings. Systems costs are high, and the cooling output is low. Several specific conclusions are discussed here.

System Cost

System costs vary widely depending on the cost of excavating the trench. Generally, the cost of an earth cooling system would be near the cost of an air conditioning system. However, the earth tube system could not meet the latent cooling load and it would not provide equivalent comfort. The cooling tube system becomes an expensive experiment that cannot replace an air conditioning system.

Dehumidification

An earth cooling tube cannot provide significant latent cooling. The temperature of the pipe walls is low enough to cause condensation only at extreme conditions. Condensation has been observed in some systems, but only with very low airflow and high ambient dewpoint temperature. Reports of water flowing continuously from systems in the operation are probably attributable to groundwater leakage into the tubes. Even if some moisture can be removed from the ambient air, it is even more difficult to dehumidify to normal interior comfort conditions.

In cooling warm, humid air, an earth tube system will always increase the relative humidity of the air. As air is cooled, its capacity to hold water is reduced. When cooled without moisture removal, air initially at 85°F and 60% RH will reach 70% RH at 80°F, 83% RH at 75°F and 98% RH at 70°F. Remember that comfort for the human body is determined by relative humidity, not absolute moisture content. The discharge of humid air, even though it is cooler, into the interior of a building can cause discomfort, as well as mildew.

Moisture Accumulation

Leaky joints or damaged tubes will allow moisture to enter the tubes. Perforated plastic pipe is used around the foundations of buildings to drain away excess moisture in the soil. If used as an earth cooling tube, perforated pipe will still collect water. Suggestions that drain tubing be used in cooling tube systems fall into the same category as cutting a hole in the bottom of a floating boat to let the water drain out. Simply sloping the tube toward one end will not eliminate moisture accumulation. The slope will prevent the accumulation of large amounts of water, but cannot remove small puddles or moisture that adheres to the tube walls. Corrugated or convoluted tubes are particular problems.

Moisture accumulation can lead to biological growth and resulting odor problems. Stale or musty odors similar to those in a damp basement have occurred in homes with cooling tubes. Closed-loop systems seem to be more susceptible to odors. No cases of disease caused by buried tubes have been discovered in the course of this work. However, the bacillus responsible for Legionnaires Disease has been isolated in soil samples around the country and can grow in cool standing water. A researcher at the Centers for Disease Control in Atlanta indicated that the probability of such a problem in an earth cooling tube is small.

Airflow

It is not practical to use natural convection or the stack effect in a building to cause air to flow through an earth cooling tube. Figure 13.12 illustrates the flaw

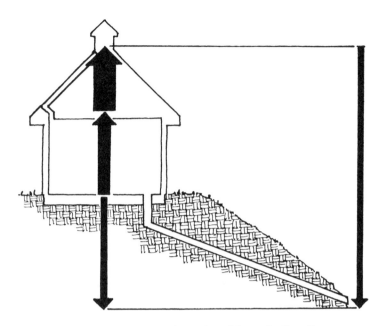

Figure 13.12. Earth cooling tube with stack effect flow.

in this popularly suggested scheme. The buoyancy force created by the temperatures shown will cause air to flow through the tubes and into the building, as intended. However, once the indoor air temperature drops to the outdoor temperature, 75°F here, the flow stops. Flow will occur only when the house is warmer than the outdoors.

When the house temperature drops below the outdoor temperature, the system will flow in reverse, drawing warm air into the house, cooling it in the house and the tube, and discharging it through the open end of the tube. Reverse airflow was observed in one earth tube system even when the house was warmer than the outdoors. The tube sloped toward the inlet, allowing the cool air inside the tubes to flow downhill and draw air from the house into the tubes.

A solar chimney, also commonly suggested for use with cooling tubes, is an only slightly better alternative. Under the right conditions a solar chimney can induce flow through a tube system and into a building. However, the column of cool air inside the house and the tubes pulls against the flow created by the chimney and can overcome it during periods of low solar gain. And of course, the solar chimney cannot function at night and cannot create flow in closed-loop tube systems.

A fan is required to circulate air in a closed-loop system, and for reasonable flow rates and reliable operation in open systems as well.

Field Test Results

Unfortunately, there have been few quantitative studies of operating earth cooling tubes systems. Most of the information available is either subjective or includes only limited thermal measurements. One rigorous performance evaluation was conducted by J. M. Akridge and C. C. Benton of the Georgia Institute of Technology on a house in northern Georgia. Ref. 6.11 and 13.4. The monitoring effort spanned both cooling and heating conditions and made use of an extensive network of thermocouples and instruments for airflow, humidity, and solar radiation measurements.

The house was a "double envelope design" that incorporated two 21-in.-diameter aluminum cooling tubes. The two tubes were each approximately 100 ft long and were arranged in a parallel open-loop configuration with the inlet end down a slope from the house in a wooded area. The other end of the tubes discharged into the crawlspace below the "inner envelope" of the house (Fig. 13.13). Although the house was designed to use a solar chimney incorporated into the greenhouse and attic to create air flow through the tubes, the owners encountered many of the problems associated with solar chimneys described in Chapter 6 and finally installed an electric fan.

The overall performance of the house during the cooling season was found to be quite good. A peak interior temperature of 80°F was measured during the test period when the outdoor temperature reached 93°F. However, the moderate interior temperatures were attributed primarily to high insulation levels, small internal heat gains, control of solar gains to the inner house, good management of ventilation, and closing the house during hot times of the day.

However, the cooling tubes did contribute a noticeable sensible cooling effect to the house. Sensible cooling capacity of as much as approximately 10,000 to 12,000 Btu/h were observed when inlet temperatures were high. Normal cooling capacity was in the range of 4000 to 5000 Btu/h. Figure 13.14 shows typical temperature performance data. The airflow velocity through the tubes was approximately 2.6 ft per second on the fan's low speed and 6.0 ft per second on high speed. The sensible cooling capacity under these conditions was approximately 2800 Btu/h at the lower flow rate and 6000 Btu/h at the higher flow rate.

As shown by the wet-bulb temperature readings in Fig. 13.14, the cooling effect provided by the system was essentially entirely sensible. The cooling tubes offered no latent cooling or dehumidification. This was verified by the performance data and by observing dust patterns in the tubes in an inspection of the entire length of both tubes. The tube wall reached the dewpoint of the air and caused light condensation only during the night when there was no flow through the tubes and the tube walls cooled somewhat.

For the plotted data, the relative humidity of the air entering the house is 95% for the low speed and 90% for the high speed. Although the tubes cooled the air, they did not remove any moisture and consequently raised the relative

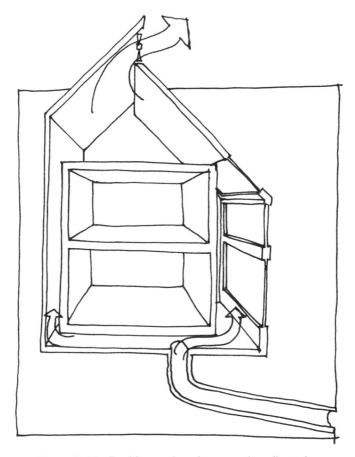

Figure 13.13. Double envelope house and cooling tube.

humidity of the air, contributing to uncomfortably high indoor humidity. There was no way to remove the moisture that entered the house from internal sources and infiltration. The open-loop configuration of the tubes introduced large volumes of humid outdoor air into the house and further aggravated the problem.

The house remained moderately comfortable during the cooling season with reasonable interior temperatures. However the high humidity levels were frequently unpleasant and led to some mildew problems. Though the cooling tubes did help reduce peak temperatures, they were unable to alleviate the humidity problem and in fact contributed to it. The use of a closed-loop configuration, recirculating air from the house, would have reduced the influx of outside moisture and improved the sensible cooling capacity somewhat. However, no significant amount of dehumidification would have been achieved.

There is some question about whether condensation in the tubes—necessary

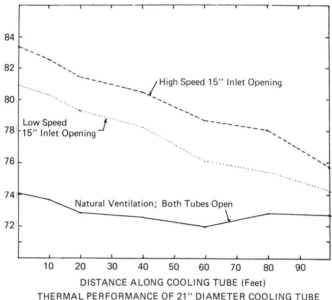

THERMAL PERFORMANCE OF 21″ DIAMETER COOLING TUBE

Figure 13.14. Typical cooling tube performance data.

for dehumidification—is desirable. The resulting moist surfaces present an ideal environment for the growth of a variety of microorganisms. Two houses in Mississippi with closed-loop cooling tubes systems were observed to have persistent musty odors during the cooling season.

A small central air conditioning system or even a window unit could have offered the same sensible cooling effect as the cooling tubes in the test house and offered some dehumidification as well. The cost of operating such a unit ($98 for an 8000-Btu/h unit with an EER of 6.5 operated 1000 h per season) should be compared with the cost of installing a cooling tube system and operating the fan. Again, earth cooling tubes are not recommended as cost-effective cooling systems.

14

OTHER LOW-ENERGY COOLING CONCEPTS: GOOD AND BAD

Over the years, the discomfort associated with high summer temperatures and humidity has spawned a variety of imaginative cooling systems. Some have been straightforward and simple, such as the use of water-filled clay pots for evaporative cooling in arid, Middle Eastern climates thousands of years ago. Others, like the ventilator shown in Fig. 14.1, have been rather complex. Many earlier ideas concentrated on increasing air motion over the body; Figs. 14.2 and 14.3 illustrate such devices.

Mechanical air conditioning systems and new technologies have dramatically expanded the number and variety of proposed solutions to the cooling problem. Some are thermally sound, cost-effective measures that can be quite useful. Others belong in the same category as perpetual motion machines. This chapter describes and discusses a number of popularly known cooling and cooling load reduction alternatives. Most of them are not recommended for general use in the United States—some are useful only in specialized buildings or climates, but most are simply not economical or even feasible. A few are sound concepts that can be used successfully to reduce cooling costs. Caveat emptor.

DOUBLE-ENVELOPE HOUSES

Double-envelope houses have attracted a very enthusiastic following of designers, builders, and owners who feel that the concept offers an effective answer to both heating and cooling requirements throughout the country. The double-envelope concept involves building a house with two insulated skins, or envelopes, that form an air gap around the living space. During the late 1970s, some designers and builders even claimed 100% passive solar heating and passive cooling in any climate. Although some of the enthusiasm has waned and the claims have been tempered by the reality of climatic limitations, double-envelope houses are still being constructed. But they are no more capable of full

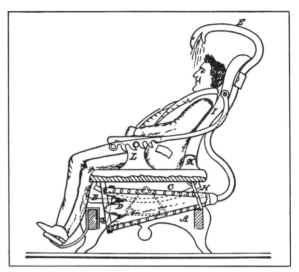

ROCKING MOTION
OPERATES BELLOWS

Figure 14.1. Chair/ventilator. (Reproduced by permission from *Principles of Air Conditioning*, Delmar Publishing, Inc., 1972.)

FAN, WHEEL,
GEAR COMBINATION

Figure 14.2. Early mechanical fan. (Reproduced by permission from *Principles of Air Conditioning*, Delmar Publishing Inc., 1972.)

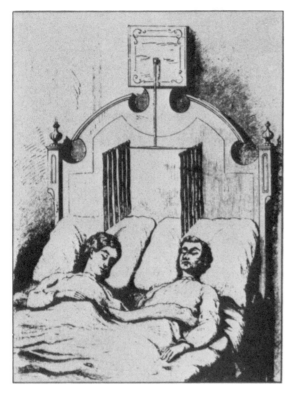

CLOCK MECHANISM
MOVES FAN DEVICE

Figure 14.3. Clock mechanism fan. (Reproduced by permission from *Principles of Air Conditioning*, Delmar Publishing, Inc., 1972.)

comfort cooling in warm, humid areas than other passive and energy-conserving designs.

The proposed theory of operation for a double-envelope house is shown in Fig. 14.4. The design includes both an outer building envelope and an inner envelope that forms the primary living space. The attic, the north wall cavity, the crawl space, and the sunspace form a continuous path between the two envelopes. The intent of the design is to allow natural air circulation to move heat inside the loop, surrounding the house with tempered air year-round and alternately storing or removing energy in the mass of the house and the ground beneath the crawl space. The air circulation in the loop is meant to be naturally driven and controlled, balancing the energy flow in accordance with the house's needs. Many variations from the basic concept have arisen, with basements, one or two floors, and other combinations of features.

Most double-envelope houses include standard passive heating features and energy conservation considerations, as well as the double wall and convection loop. High levels of insulation are used: two walls at $R12$ or more and ceiling

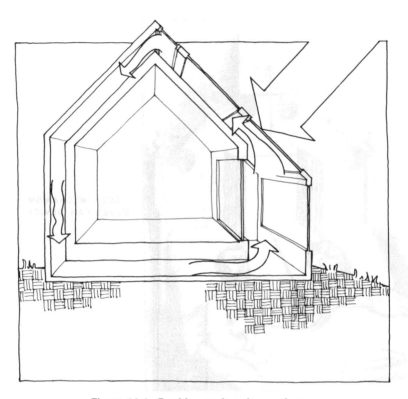

Figure 14.4. Double envelope house theory.

insulation consisting of an $R30$ layer at the ceiling and $R19$ batts in the roof. Careful caulking and sealing, double-glazed windows, careful site planning, and sensible glazing location are common. In addition, the interest, care, and commitment of the homeowners and builders ensure that the building is carefully constructed and that energy conservation is a key consideration in the operation of the house.

For the most part, double-envelope houses have performed well; with reported results as good as or better than more conventional passive solar and energy-conserving houses. Most researchers and analysts agree that the good performance is attributable to sensible design, high levels of insulation and weatherization, quality construction, and diligent operation of the house for energy efficiency. Several tests have shown that the circulation loop does not distribute enough air or move enough heat to be a major factor. Storage in the ground below the crawl space is minimal. The good performance is a result of effective, but nonradical design, construction, and operation principles. The originally postulated magic of the circulation loop is not real.

Double-envelope houses have proven to be more effective at reducing energy consumption during the heating season than during the cooling season. This is to be expected, because insulation, weatherization, and other conservation measures can dramatically reduce infiltration and heat transmission through the envelope, but have little or no effect on internal heat sources, solar gains and latent heat. Because conduction and infiltration have a reduced role in setting cooling loads in well-insulated and well-sealed buildings, reducing them has a comparatively smaller effect. The smaller summer temperature differential also reduces the proportional impact of conduction and infiltration measures on cooling.

Double-envelope designs generally do a good job of minimizing summer cooling loads, but they are certainly not the substitute for air conditioning they were once touted to be. The heat sinks used by double-envelope houses for cooling, the ambient air and the earth, cannot be effectively employed for complete cooling in warm, humid climates.

Furthermore, several of the passive cooling alternatives commonly used in conjunction with double-envelope designs are either not sound concepts or not reasonably cost-effective. The limitations of thermal chimneys, earth cooling tubes, and earth contact cooling have already been examined in other chapters, but the application of thermal chimneys to double-envelope houses warrants special consideration here.

Many double-envelope houses are two-story designs with a sunspace on the south side that opens into the attic area. Roof vents are included to provide an exit path for hot air during summer. In many cases, the south roof includes large glazed areas to increase the attic temperature and thereby increase ventilation from the thermal stack effect. The height of the air column and the high attic temperature would seem to be an ideal application of the stack effect. But actual conditions frequently preclude any ventilation from stack effects at all.

Figure 14.5 illustrates a set of conditions encountered in field-testing a house in Georgia. (Ref. 6.11.) With the sunspace maintained at habitable temperatures, it is difficult to induce any significant airflow through the building using the stack effect. High flow rates demand high temperature differences, and temperatures high enough to drive the flow cannot be tolerated in the sunspace. The temperature difference between the sunspace and the outdoors in the test house was too small to create effective stack effect ventilation except when outdoor conditions were mild.

If earth cooling tubes that slope downhill toward their entrance are included in the system, the stack-effect force is further reduced. Cool air in the tubes tends to flow downhill toward the entrance to the tubes, opposite to the desired flow direction. When the outdoor air temperature and the sunspace temperature are close, the flow through the system may actually reverse and draw hot air from the roof area into the house. The test system was observed to flow in a reverse direction on several occasions, usually in the late afternoon.

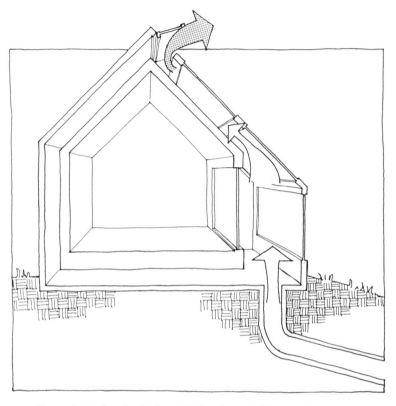

Figure 14.5. Stack effect ventilation in a double envelope house.

The exhaust vents, pointing north, were direction-sensitive; north, northeast, and northwest winds presented another problem. Even mild breezes overcame any existing stack-effect forces and caused the system to backflow. The homeowner eventually remedied the situation by installing a whole-house fan in the exhaust vent.

Radiant Heat Barriers

Infrared radiation accounts for much of the heat transfer across air gaps or voids in a building envelope. Attics are a good example. The roof deck above the attic is heated by the sun to temperatures sometimes above 160°F, and the roof then transfers heat downward by convection to the attic air and by radiation to the upper surface of the ceiling insulation (Fig. 14.6).

During sunny periods, the temperature of the ceiling insulation exceeds the attic air temperature, indicating that the radiant path from the roof to the ceiling

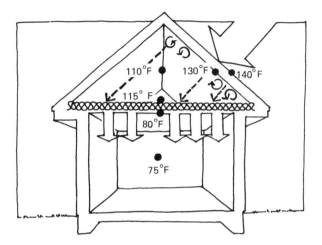

Figure 14.6. Heat transfer from roof to building interior.

is more significant than the convective path. Aluminum foil, which reflects infrared radiation, can be used to interrupt this radiation heat transfer; it may be simply stapled to the undersides of the roof rafters to form a closed air cavity. Radiant barriers are effective only if they have an adjacent air space; a layer of foil applied between the shingles and the roof deck and in contact with both would be useless.

The insulating value of the foil is difficult to describe, because the amount of radiant heat that is blocked varies greatly with the temperature of the roof deck. When solar gains are intense and attic temperatures are high, a foil barrier may provide the equivalent of an insulation value of $R25$. But when the roof deck temperature is near the outside air temperature, as it is during the night and when solar gains are small, the radiant barrier provides little or no benefit.

Tests at the Florida Solar Energy Center (Ref. 14.1) have shown that a foil radiant barrier alone on the roof rafters can reduce peak heat gains on the roof by 29%, compared with an $R19$ fiberglass batt at the ceiling. The radiant barrier was formed with ''builder's foil,'' a commercially available product made by laminating two very thin sheets of foil to either side of a Kraft paper core. The cavity above the barrier was not vented during the tests. A foil-faced batt with the foil facing upward toward the roof reduced heat flow by 44%, compared with an unfaced batt.

But keep in mind that the ceiling cooling load is only a fraction of the total cooling load and that even eliminating it completely would have a limited effect on the overall load. In the energy-conserving example house used earlier, a 44% reduction in the design cooling load for the roof/ceiling represents only a 5% reduction in overall cooling load.

Radiation heat transfer is important only when the temperature difference between the roof and the ceiling or ceiling insulation is high; this occurs during periods of high solar gains. Another fact that reduces the attractiveness of radiant barriers is that they are effective in reducing heat gains only when the roof is being heated by the sun. At other times, the $R19$ fiberglass batt performs much better than the foil barrier alone, and the faced and unfaced batts perform similarly.

Radiant heat transfer to the upper surface of the ceiling insulation is only one step in the overall heat flow from the roof to the rooms below. All the heat transferred to the building from the roof must pass through the ceiling insulation. With higher levels of ceiling insulation, the effects of radiant barriers are reduced, just as the value of attic ventilation and additional insulation is reduced when insulation levels are high. Where ceiling insulation levels of $R26$ or greater are used, the value of a radiant barrier is significantly reduced.

Two potential problems should be considered if radiant barriers are to be used: moisture and increased roof temperatures. Foil is an excellent vapor barrier and could lead to undesirable moisture accumulation in some applications. Perforated foil materials that allow water vapor to pass are available and should probably be used in most cases.

Because the roof surface cools itself partly by losing heat to the attic, a radiant barrier that reduces that heat flow will increase the temperature of the roof. Higher roof temperatures lead to reduced roof life, but information on the amount of the increase in roof temperatures caused by a radiant barrier and the effects on the roofing materials is not yet available.

At night, the roof radiates heat to the sky and often becomes cooler than the outdoor air. It is interesting to note that a radiant barrier also blocks heat flow from the ceiling and insulation to the roof and reduces this cooling effect. The increase in ceiling temperature at night with a radiant barrier can be equal to the daytime decrease, but either effect is small unless ceiling insulation levels are low.

Radiant heat barriers seem to provide a simple and relatively inexpensive method of reducing the conduction of solar heat gains through lightly insulated ceilings. However, their effects are greatly reduced by high ceiling insulation levels. In areas where high levels of ceiling insulation are used because of heating considerations, radiant barriers may provide only small benefits. They are most useful in areas where solar gains are high and cooling is the primary concern. There, the combination of a foil radiant barrier and moderate levels of ceiling insulation, $R19$ to 22, should be considered as an alternative to higher insulation levels.

Ventilated Roofs and Walls

Just as a ventilated attic can reduce heat gain through a ceiling, a ventilated wall cavity can be used to reduce heat gains through walls. But once again,

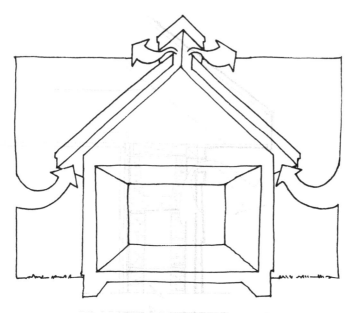

Figure 14.7. Ice house roof concept.

such measures are effective only in controlling *solar* heat gains. The best that they can do is eliminate the effect of the solar gains on the roof and walls of a building; they offer no additional protection against high outdoor air temperatures.

The ice house roof is an example of this concept that was used in the past century to reduce solar heat gains into ice houses (Fig. 14.7). Ice harvested in winter was stored through the following summer in buildings insulated with sawdust. The double-layer roof provided a cavity above the building that was vented at its lower and upper ends; solar radiation was intercepted by the outer roof layer. Air flow through the cavity, induced both by winds and by thermal forces created by the hot outer roof surface, removed heat before it could be conducted into the building below. Thick walls, floors, and ceilings with sawdust insulation completed the insulated envelope.

Information on the thermal performance of ventilated skin roofs is rather limited. The Florida Solar Energy Center has conducted an initial series of tests on roofs where the cavity is formed by a layer of foil on the undersides of the roof rafters (Ref. 14.1). The cavity is open to the attic at its lower end and to a ridge vent at the upper end to remove heated air. This configuration is certainly the simplest and least expensive method of creating a ventilated skin roof. Framing a second roof deck layer is much more costly and probably could never be justified.

Ventilated wall cavities have also been proposed and tested. The wall section

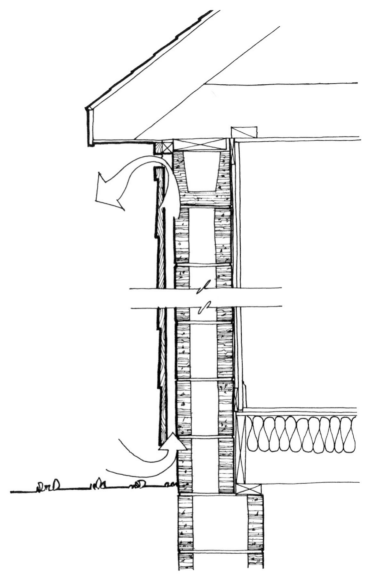

Figure 14.8. Ventilated wall cavity.

shown in Fig. 14.8 has been tested by FSEC and shown to be approximately equal to an $R11$ fiberglass batt under certain conditions. Like the radiant barrier, the ventilated wall cavity is most effective when the sun is striking the wall, causing the temperature of the outside wall surface to rise. At night and when solar gains on the wall are small, the ventilated wall has no appreciable effect.

And of course, in winter it offers no real protection against heat loss from the building. Ventilated wall sections may be useful as an alternative to insulation in the hottest regions of the country, where heating loads are quite small. They are most effective on east and west walls where morning and afternoon solar gains are high. Elsewhere, insulation is a much more effective strategy against the combination of heating and cooling loads. A ventilated wall provides protection against intense summer solar gains, but insulation provides year-round value.

AIR CONDITIONER ACCESSORIES FOR HIGH EFFICIENCY

A variety of accessories and add on devices have been marketed to improve the efficiency of air conditioners and other refrigeration systems. Some are valid alternatives, while others are little more than a sham. Generally, the more dramatic the energy and cost savings claims, the less realistic the device. There is no magic in thermodynamics and heat transfer. Be particularly wary of any gadget that is advertised as ''defying scientific principles'' or something that performs so well that ''the experts are baffled.''

Several of the more common ideas and devices are reviewed here; some are sound and some are not.

Motor Controllers

Electric motors operate most efficiently at full load conditions when the load on the motor is equal to its rated output. Under part load operation the motor is less efficient and produces less useful work for the amount of electric power it consumes. Solid-state motor controllers are available that essentially reduce the output capacity of the motor to match the load at any given time, increasing the overall efficiency of the motor. These devices are manufactured by several companies and are usually called *power factor controllers* or *Nola devices*, after their inventor, NASA researcher Frank Nola. They are sometimes suggested for use with air conditioners, fans, and home appliances; the marketing claims of some firms have been less than accurate.

Motor controllers can be very effective for energy conservation where a motor is oversized for its load or where the load varies from part load to full load conditions. Such situations are frequently found in industrial and manufacturing operations; an intermittently loaded conveyor is a good example. Electric power savings of more than 40% have been reported. But if a motor is closely matched to its load, a motor controller has no effect or provides only negligible savings. To reduce manufacturing costs and power consumption, the makers of air conditioners conscientiously avoid oversizing the motors used in the compressors and fans in air conditioners, refrigerators, laundry equipment, ventilating fans, and other package equipment. Thus, motor controllers offer almost no potential for energy savings in the home, and their use in these applications is discouraged.

Load Shedders and Duty Cyclers

The electric power rate schedules for commercial buildings usually incorporate charges both for the amount of electric power used (kilowatt hours) and the maximum rate of power use or demand (kilowatts). Most utilities do not currently bill residential customers for demand, but only for power consumption. But as the load on electric utilities and the cost of new generating plants increase, it is likely that demand charges will increase and be applied to a larger group of customers.

Load shedders or load controllers and duty cyclers provide two methods of controlling or reducing electric demand. Load shedders constantly monitor the total electric demand in a building and limit it to a set level by turning off certain pieces of equipment in a predetermined pattern. For instance, an electric hot water heater might be switched off until a large air conditioning or refrigeration unit cycles off. Duty cyclers simply switch a piece of equipment on and off in a timed pattern that may be modified for certain operating conditions, like the interior building temperature.

Load shedders can be quite effective in the right applications; three factors to look for in potential applications include; (1) demand-based electric billing rate, (2) multiple pieces of equipment or systems that can be safely and conveniently cycled on and off, and (3) controls or the cooperation of occupants to avoid overriding demand control limits. Load shedders are almost never used in residences, but they may be valuable in small commercial buildings, particularly retail buildings with numerous pieces of equipment and oversized air conditioners that can be cycled without creating severe comfort problems.

The potential for savings with a duty cycler on an air conditioner is not obvious. Although duty cyclers are sold for residential and light commercial buildings by several companies, their usefulness is seriously questioned. In essence, they simply limit the run time of the air conditioner, overriding the thermostat and turning the system off for various intervals sometimes controlled by the building temperature. Similar results at a much lower cost could be obtained by simply increasing the thermostat setting.

Some manufacturers claim that their devices keep the fan on after the compressor cycles off, thus extracting additional cooling from the evaporator. But the evaporator is usually inside the conditioned space so the "coolth" left in the evaporator at the end of a cooling cycle is not really lost. Also this practice evaporates condensed water from the evaporator coil and increases the internal humidity. Energy consumption could even increase if the fan is allowed to run for excessive periods. The Federal Trade Commission has recently taken action against three manufacturers of duty cyclers.

Compressor failures can result if the duty cycler uses too short an off or on cycle with the air conditioner. Some manufacturers of air conditioning equipment will not warrant their equipment with duty cyclers unless certain requirements are met.

Duty cyclers may appear to offer savings large enough to justify their cost, but savings are almost completely due to the occupant's acceptance of high interior temperatures. Thermostat settings may be unchanged, but temperatures will be higher, and either the increase is unnoticed or the owner tolerates it to justify his purchase. Set the thermostat higher; avoid duty cyclers.

Condenser Coil Sprays

The efficiency of any air conditioner can be improved by lowering the temperature at which the condenser operates. One obvious method of reducing condensing temperatures is to spray water over the condenser coil. Lawn sprinklers have been used for this purpose, as have a variety of low-cost gadgets. A review of the advertising in any of the do-it-yourself magazines will certainly uncover at least one such device.

Condenser coil spray can effectively reduce the power consumption of an air conditioner. In fact, many room air conditioners incorporate a "slinger ring" on the condenser fan to distribute condensed water over the condenser coils if it builds up in the unit. The cool water absorbs heat from the coils and provides more significant heat removal benefit as it evaporates. The net effect on the performance of the unit varies with the unit and the operating conditions.

Commercially available coil spray devices range from a simple, manually controlled spray nozzle mounted on a stake and connected to a garden hose to more complex systems that monitor coil temperature and turn on the water spray when needed with a solenoid valve. Although such devices can reduce the power consumed by the air conditioner, they should usually be avoided. The problem is corrosion of the condenser coil tube and heat transfer fins. Most air conditioners now use copper tubes with aluminum fins attached to the tubes; aluminum and copper are electrically reactive with one another. A phenomenon called galvanic corrosion can cause the aluminum to be sacrificed to the copper. Aluminum reacts with the copper and is gradually corroded away. As the condenser is normally dry, corrosion seldom takes place. However, if the coils are maintained in a wet condition for long periods, the aluminum fins will gradually be destroyed.

Other devices are available that provide a similar condenser heat rejection effect without wetting the condenser itself. Refrigerant from the condenser is routed through a separate heat exchanger and gives up heat to cold municipal water, which is then disposed of. Such devices will show good results only when the condenser temperature is unusually high, as would happen with a unit so installed that air circulation around the condenser was not adequate. Under normal circumstances savings of approximately 10 to 15% might be expected. The water cost of operating a device that disposed of the water after using it for a heat sink is not negligible. Typical installations use 150 to 300 gal of water per day for each ton of cooling capacity, seriously reducing the cost-effectiveness of the device. Condenser heat may also be used to heat water for use in a building, rather than simply disposing of the heat and the water. The heat exchanger is connected to the conventional water heater tank, rather than the supply water and a drain. Such systems provide air conditioning savings almost as great as the waste heat systems and also yield additional savings by displacing water heating energy consumption. When used with heat pumps, the performance improvement for the heat pump is limited to the cooling mode, for waste heat is not available in the heating mode. However, water heating is still available in the heating mode, but without an improvement in heat pump efficency. The function of these devices in improving the performance of a cooling cycle is explained in Chapter 9.

Since the installation of an add-on condenser heat reclaim device involves cutting into the refrigerant system of the air conditioner or heat pump, appropriate care must be taken to assure that the work is done properly. Also, because the device becomes part of the refrigerant system, it must be balanced to the other components. It is advisable to use a device provided or approved by the manufacturer of the air conditioner or heat pump. Many manufacturer's offer desuperheaters or similar devices on new heat pumps and air conditioners.

AIR-TO-AIR HEAT EXCHANGERS

Air-to-air heat exchangers are not cooling devices. They do, however, provide a means of reducing the latent and sensible heat gains from ventilation and infiltration. When air conditioning is in use, outdoor air that enters a building brings in heat and humidity and displaces cool, dehumidified air to the outdoors. An air-to-air heat exchanger uses conditioned air leaving the building to partially cool and dehumidify outdoor air being brought into the building; 70% or more of the cooling effect can be reclaimed.

Air-to-air heat exchangers are most often used for reclaiming heat from exhaust air in large commercial buildings or industrial facilities during the heating season. In such buildings positive ventilation is used to provide fresh air to the interior and to pressurize it slightly to reduce the discomfort and control problems from infiltration at random points. The potential for heat reclamation and favorable economic performance is best where the heating season is long and the indoor/outdoor temperature difference is great. Heat exchangers are less valuable for cooling conditions, because the temperature differential is much smaller; however latent heat recovery can be important.

Air-to-air heat exchangers are finding new applications in very tightly sealed residences where ventilation is desirable. Where significant interior sources of pollutants, such as formaldehyde, radon, or combustion products, are present, positive ventilation may be required to maintain acceptable indoor air quality. Heat exchangers can reduce the negative effect of the increased ventilation.

Most air-to-air heat exchangers used in small buildings are plate-type devices; the two air streams move through the heat exchanger in passages formed by thin parallel plates (Fig. 14.9). During the cooling season, heat flows from the entering outdoor air through the plates to the cool interior air leaving the building; a small fan moves the air.

Usually the plates are made of metal, but some units are available with plates made from paper or special plastics that allow water vapor to pass. These heat exchangers, often called *enthalpy exchangers*, may be used to recover both sensible and latent heat. The incoming air is partially dehumidified as the moisture flows to the drier air exiting the building.

The ability of a heat exchanger to recover heat or ''coolth'' is measured by its effectiveness. For cooling, heat exchanger effectiveness is defined as

$$\text{Effectiveness} = \frac{T_{\text{out}} - T_{\text{supply}}}{T_{\text{out}} - T_{\text{in}}} \times 100\%$$

where

T_{out} = outdoor air temperature, °F
T_{in} = indoor air temperature, °F
T_{supply} = temperature of air supplied by heat exchanger

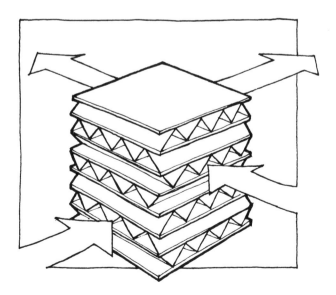

Figure 14.9. Plate type air-to-air heat exchangers.

For vapor-permeable heat exchangers, effectiveness is defined by substituting enthalpy for temperature in the equation.

The effectiveness of a heat exchanger describes the fraction of possible heat or "coolth" that is reclaimed. Some commercially available units have effectiveness ratings of 85% or more. In actual operation, the advertised effectiveness of most exchangers ranges from 60 to 80%, and one series of tests at Lawrence Berkeley Laboratories indicates performance at 45 to 75%. Residential scale, air-to-air heat exchangers provide 25 to 100 cfm of air and cost from $100 to $1000 without installation.

Although it is generally not economical to install an air-to-air heat exchanger solely for use in the cooling season, a unit installed for other reasons may be used to reduce heat gains from ventilation. If it is necessary to ventilate a building with outdoor air during the cooling season, an enthalpy exchanger should be examined as a method of reducing the cooling load associated with bringing warm, humid air into the interior.

DIRECT USE OF SURFACE AND GROUNDWATER FOR COOLING

Surface water in lakes, streams, and ponds comprises a potential heat sink for use in cooling. Stable temperatures and an essentially unlimited heat sink capacity make groundwater a particularly attractive alternative for use with heat pumps. Given low enough water temperatures, it might be possible to use water directly for cooling by circulating it through a heat exchanger in a building's forced air system. But such opportunities for the direct use of water for cooling are quite rare. The typical problem lies in the temperature of the water; although the capacity of the heat sink is immense, relatively high temperatures limit its availability for use.

Annual average groundwater temperatures are usually similar to or slightly higher than the average annual air temperature, ranging from 60 to 75°F for the majority of the country. Summer temperatures are higher. The potential temperature difference between groundwater and the 78°F interior of a building in summer is small. Piping heat gains and the heat added from the pumps required to move the water further reduce the differential. In most cases, the temperature of the water that can be delivered to the building and circulated through a cooling coil is too high to provide enough cooling to justify the pumping costs. Dehumidification is almost out of the question, because coil temperatures of 55 to 60°F are needed for effective moisture removal.

ABSORPTION AIR CONDITIONING

At first glance, absorption air conditioning might seem to be a sort of paradox— it produces cooling from heat. In an absorbtion cycle air conditioner, the compressor is replaced by a heat-operated generator that provides the pressure differential for the refrigerant. With that exception, it is similar to a vapor-compression air conditioner. The refrigerant vaporizes and absorbs heat in the evaporator and condenses and rejects heat in the condenser. Both cycles require energy to produce cooling: the vapor compression cycle uses mechanical energy, and the absorption cycle uses heat.

The fundamental theories of absorption air conditioning have been known since about 1771, and a working machine was produced in 1850. More recently, absorption air conditioning has commonly been used in commercial buildings and apartment complexes with natural gas as a heat source. The popularity of the systems has fluctuated with natural gas costs.

There have been scattered applications of absorption cooling systems with solar collectors as the heat source. But most such systems have been funded as research projects and could not be justified under normal circumstances. Absorbtion air conditioning is generally not an economical alternative for most residences and small commercial buildings. Some of the reasons, including low efficiency and high maintenance, will become apparent in the following discussion of operating principles and equipment. A simplified absorption air conditioning system is shown in Fig. 14.10.

There are two key fluid loops within the system: the refrigerant loop and the absorbant loop. The refrigerant loop provides the cooling effect by transferring heat from the building interior to the heat sink. The absorbant loop duplicates the function of the compressor in a vapor compression machine; it produces the pressure gradient in the refrigerant loop.

The major components of a vapor compression air conditioner are:

Evaporator—a chamber where the liquid refrigerant absorbs heat and evaporates into vapor.

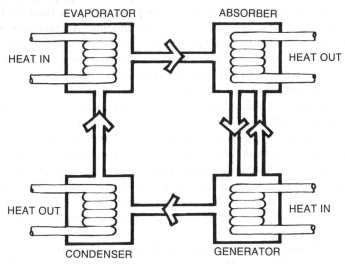

Figure 14.10. Schematic Diagram of absorption air conditioning cycle.

Condenser—a chamber where the refrigerant condenses into a liquid and rejects heat.

Refrigerant—a fluid that transfers heat by alternately evaporating and condensing in different locations; water is commonly used.

Absorbant—a substance that transports the refrigerant by alternately absorbing and releasing it; lithium bromide is used when water is the refrigerant.

Absorber—a chamber in which the refrigerant vapor is absorbed by the absorbant.

Generator, or concentrator—a chamber where the refrigerant vapor and absorbant solution is heated to release the refrigerant.

In operation the liquid refrigerant absorbs heat as it is continuously pumped over the heat exchanger in the evaporator and changes to a vapor. A separate piping loop delivers the cooling effect produced in the heat exchanger to the building. The refrigerant vapor then flows to the absorber where it condenses into a liquid and goes into a liquid solution with the absorbant.

Heat is produced when the refrigerant condenses, and also when it goes into solution with the absorber. A piping loop removes some of the heat to maintain the proper temperature. The refrigerant/absorbant solution is then pumped to the concentrator. It is then heated, causing the refrigerant to evaporate again and leaving the absorbant to return to the absorber.

The hot refrigerant vapor then flows from the absorber to the condenser where it rejects heat and changes to a liquid. Another piping loop removes heat and discharges it to the heat sink, usually a cooling tower. The liquid refrigerant flows back to the evaporator, completing the cycle.

Four additional external piping loops are required to supply and remove heat from an absorption air conditioner. One loop removes heat from the building and delivers it to the evaporator, cooling the building. Another loop provides steam or hot water to the generator to power the cycle. The last two loops remove heat from the condenser (building heat) and the absorber (heat generated by the reaction between the refrigerant and the absorbant). Viewed as a thermal system, an absorption cycle looks like Fig. 14.11.

The rated COP of lithium bromide-water absorption air conditioners used in small buildings will range from 0.5 to about 1.0 at best. Each Btu of heat provided by the gas burner results in only 0.5 to 1 Btu of cooling.

Most of the absorption air conditioning equipment now being built is designed to operate with steam providing heat to power the cycle at 200 to 220°F. As the temperature in the generator drops, the cooling capacity and efficiency of the system also drop. At temperatures below 190°F, the decrease is very severe; at 180°F, a typical unit produces less than one-third of its rated cooling capacity at 190°F.

The use of solar collectors to provide heat to an absorption air conditioner creates several difficulties. Most are centered on the temperature of the heat to

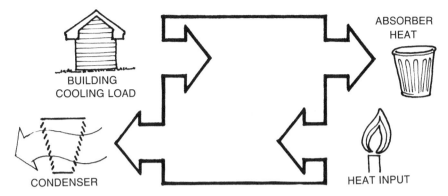

Figure 14.11. Absorption cycle as a thermal system.

be provided to the generator. Though the absorption air conditioning system requires high temperatures for best efficiency and cooling output, the efficiency and heat output of a solar collector fall as the output temperature climbs. The drop in efficiency follows through the entire solar system: higher temperatures mean higher heat losses from piping and storage tanks.

With flat plate collectors, solar-fired absorption systems must be designed to operate no higher than about 190°F to maintain reasonable collector efficiency. This means that the absorption unit will operate at partial capacity and must be significantly oversized, increasing costs. Because it is difficult to consistently produce, store, and deliver heat at 190°F with a solar system, a backup heater, usually a gas burner, must be used. Focusing, or concentrating, collectors may be used to achieve higher temperatures, but add to the expense of the system and usually still require a backup heat source.

Manufacturers of absorption air conditioning equipment are working to develop systems that will operate effectively at lower temperatures. Absorption air conditioning equipment in the 3- to 25-t range is currently manufactured by American Solar King, Yazaki, and others.

It should be obvious that an absorption air conditioner is much more complex than a vapor-compression unit. It involves many more components and processes and is more expensive to purchase and more difficult to maintain. If the unit is gas-fired, fuel costs may be high. Solar-fired systems, although they provide "free" heat, involve high capital costs and another maintenance burden. It is unlikely that absorption air conditioning will become an economically viable alternative to more conventional systems in small buildings for some years to come.

DEHUMIDIFICATION WALLS

The frustrating search for passive dehumification devices has sometimes spawned ideas that are based more on hope than on the reality of thermal sciences. One such concept is the masonry dehumidification wall proposed by several building designers and energy enthusiasts. Like perpetual motion machines, the idea is enticing, but in practice the results are disappointing. Masonry walls simply *do not* act as dehumidifiers.

A particular form of the masonry dehumidification wall has been built into passive solar double envelope homes. A portion of the west wall of the house incorporated two concrete block walls with sand-filled cores separated by a closed air space. To allow water vapor to pass through, the surfaces of the blocks were not finished. The principle of operation suggested by the designer was similar to other masonry wall dehumidification ideas. During the afternoon, the sun would heat the surface of the outer course of concrete blocks, while the inner course would remain cool. The outer surface would be dried, causing moisture to flow from the inside of the house to the outdoors (Fig. 14.12). If moisture migration were caused by temperature differences, the wall would work. However, temperature has no direct effect; the concentration of water vapor is the driving force for moisture movement. Temperature provides the driving force for heat transfer. Water vapor will flow not from hot to cold, but from high concentration to low concentration. The concentration of moisture in air is described by the vapor pressure of the water dissolved in the air, simply the pressure exerted by the water vapor.

As an example, consider 1 lb of air at 78°F and 90% relative humidity. You may wish to refer to the psychrometric chart in Chapter 3. Dissolved in the

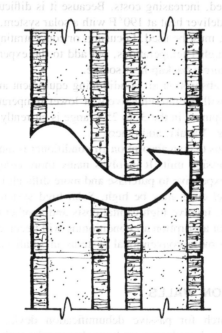

Figure 14.12. Masonry dehumidification wall.

pound of air is 0.0186 lb of water vapor. The relative humidity of 90% indicates that the air contains 90% of the maximum amount of water that can dissolve in air at 78°F. The concentration of water vapor is independent of the relative humidity; it is determined by the mass of water and the mass of air. The vapor pressure of water at the example conditions is 0.866 inches of mercury (in. Hg).

If the sample of air is heated to 100°F, the relative humidity decreases to 45% RH; air can hold more moisture at higher temperatures. After being heated, the air holds only 45% of the moisture it could potentially hold at the higher temperature. However, the mass of water and the mass of air are unchanged; the concentration of water is the same. The vapor pressure of water is still 0.866 in. Hg. Simply heating humid air does not create a driving force for moisture movement. Unfortunately, the designer had confused relative humidity with vapor pressure. The masonry wall would transfer moisture to the outdoors only when the concentration inside is higher than the concentration outside. This can occur when activities inside the house, such as bathing and cooking, lead to an interior buildup of moisture. For example, on a day when the indoor conditions are unusually humid, 75°F and 80% RH (vapor pressure = 0.697 in. Hg), and the outdoor conditions are 85°F and 50% RH (vapor pressure = 0.601 in. Hg), moisture would diffuse from the interior through the wall to the outside. Of course, it would also diffuse through other wall, ceilings, and floors. Under these conditions, it would be advantageous to have no vapor barriers in the building envelope.

However, the amount of moisture removed in this manner would be quite small, and the lack of a vapor barrier during winter and during more typical summer conditions would lead to problems. Under most summer circumstances, and particularly when air conditioning is in use, the concentration of water vapor inside a building is lower than outside it. A vapor-permeable wall would allow moisture to enter the building rather than removing it.

A masonry dehumidification wall was incorporated in a home built just north of Atlanta in 1979. After the initial results proved disappointing, the designer suggested that the homeowner cut several mature hardwood trees that shaded the west side of the house and the masonry wall. Although the removal of the trees increased the heat gain into the house, it did nothing to dehumidify the interior. The uninsulated masonry wall allows excessive heat gains in summer and heat losses in winter, noticeably reducing comfort conditions inside. Graphic evidence of the inability of such walls to dehumidify was provided by the mildew that grew behind a fabric wall hanging placed on the interior of the wall.

SHADING THE AIR CONDITIONER CONDENSER

Shading the air conditioner condenser is often mentioned in collections of cooling energy tips for homeowners. It is suggested that blocking solar heat gains to the condenser reduces the temperature of the coil and increases the cooling capacity and efficiency. Awnings, trellises, shrubs, and fences are proposed for shading devices. Extreme care must be taken to avoid interfering with the airflow around the unit.

It is more important to locate the condenser or the outdoor unit in an area with general shade than simply providing shade on the unit itself. Because the condenser moves very large amounts of air through the coil, the temperature of the air is very important. The air temperature in shaded areas is usually several degrees cooler than in nearby sunny areas. For a typical 3-t unit, the efficiency increases about 1% for each 1°F decrease in outdoor air temperature. An awning shading only the condenser does almost nothing to reduce the temperature of the air drawn in by the fan.

Generally the best location for the condenser is on the north side of the building in a shaded location. Sunny areas on any side of the building, and particularly the west, should be avoided. Well-shaded areas anywhere around the building are good.

A condenser shade should probably not be considered until all west-, east-, and south-facing glazing has been shaded. An east or west window exposed to direct summer sun can add more than 1000 Btu/day per ft^2 directly to the building. Effective window shading is certainly a higher priority.

Maintaining good airflow through the condenser is much more important than shading it. Any shading device, including plants, should be kept well away from the condenser, at least 3 ft. Enclosures around the unit, such as fences or groups of plants, should be avoided.

HEAT PUMP WATER HEATERS

Heat pump water heaters are small unitary heat pumps designed to heat water using the air as a heat source. A typical residential unit is about the same size as the smallest room air conditioners. The units are designed to be installed in a mild climate or in a space where the temperature does not fall below 45°F. Because they extract heat from the air, heat pump water heaters produce a cooling effect that may also be useful in cooling a building.

The heat pump water heater manufactured by E-Tech in Atlanta (Ref. 14.3) is representative of several currently sold in the United States. It is an independent unit that is coupled to the conventional water heater by two hoses; other manufacturers offer a heat pump/tank combination in a single package. The refrigerant circuit in the heater is controlled by a thermostat in the water heater tank and cycles on whenever the water temperature drops below the setpoint. The E-Tech unit has a water heating capacity of 12,000 Btuh with an air temperature of 80°F. It consumes about 1200 W of electric power when operating and produces a net cooling effect of 8000 Btuh at normal conditions. The total amount of cooling produced varies with the hot water load and the air temper-

Figure 14.13. E-tech heat pump water heater. (Courtesy of E-Tech, Inc.)

ature and humidity. In a typical household, a total cooling effect of 40,000 Btu/ day would be available, with a dehumidification effect of 6 to 7 pt of water per day. The unit sells for about $600.

Two limitations keep the heat pump water heater from being an ideal part of a low-energy cooling solution. First, the units are somewhat noisy, similar to a small room air conditioner. Second, unless cooling is needed year-round, some provision must be made for rerouting the cooling effect to another appropriate space that meets the temperature limitations of the unit. The units now being sold do not incorporate a duct system or other provision for such switching. A number of alternatives are possible, from moving the unit twice each year with the seasons to building a custom duct and damper system. Care must be taken not to impede the normal airflow through the heat pump. Again, another good project for tinkerers.

Heat pump water heater/air conditioner combinations are now available for commercial buildings. Good applications include restaurants and laundries, both require cooling and large amounts of hot water.

REFERENCES

1.1. Bruce T. Sherwood, Director, Hay House, The Georgia Trust for Historic Preservation, 934 Georgia Avenue, Macon, Georgia 31201 (912) 742-8155.

2.1. Lau, Andrew and Hyatt, Ted, "Residential Heating and Cooling Loads and Costs for the South," *Proceedings of the Sixth National Passive Solar Conference, September 8–12, 1981, Portland, Oregon*, American Section of the International Solar Energy Society, Inc. 2030 17th Street, Boulder, Colorado 80302.

2.2. *ASHRAE Handbook, 1985 Fundamentals*, American Society of Heating, Refrigerating, and Air-Conditioning Engineers, Inc. 1791 Tullie Circle, N.E., Atlanta, Georgia 30329.

2.3. *Climatic Atlas of the United States*, National Climatic Center, Federal Building, Asheville, North Carolina 28801, June, 1968. (704) 258-2850, ext. 682. $15.00. Weather data in this chapter is extracted from this publication.

2.4. *Climatic Database*, Tennessee Valley Authority Solar Outreach and Technology Group, Architectural Design Branch.

2.5. *Facility Design and Planning Engineering Weather Data* AFM 88-29; TM 5-785; NAVFAC P-89; Departments of the Air Force, Army, and Navy; July 1, 1978. Available from government book stores and the Superintendant of Documents, Government Printing Office, Washington, D.C. 26402. $12.00.

2.6. *Insulation Manual, Homes and Apartments*, National Association of Home Builders Research Foundation, 627 Southlawn Lane, P.O. Box 1627, Rockville, Maryland 20850.

2.7. Also available from the National Climatic Center. See Ref. 2.3.

3.1. Carrier Corporation, Syracuse, New York 13221.

4.1. "ANSI/ASHRAE Standard 55, Thermal Environmental Standards for Human Occupancy," American Society of Heating, Refrigerating, and Air-Conditioning Engineers, Inc. 1791 Tullie Circle, N.E., Atlanta, Georgia 30329.

4.2. Olgyay, Victor, *Design With Climate*, Princeton University Press, Princeton, New Jersey, 1963.

5.1. *ASHRAE Handbook, 1985 Fundamentals*, American Society of Heating, Refrigerating, and Air-Conditioning Engineers, Inc. 1791 Tullie Circle, N.E., Atlanta, Georgia 30329.

5.2. *Cooling and Heating Load Calculation Manual*, GRP 158; ASHRAE. Makes the load calculation procedures from the *Fundamentals Handbook* available at a much lower cost.

5.3. *Manual J, Load Calculation for Residential Winter and Summer Air Conditioning*, Air Conditioning Contractors of America, 1228 17th Street N.W., Washington, D.C. 20036.

5.4. Drake, George R., *Weatherizing Your Home*, Reston Publishing Company, Reston, Virginia, 1978.

5.5. Lau, Andrew S., "How to Design Fixed Overhangs," Solar Age Magazine, Church Hill, Harrisville, New Hampshire 03450, February, 1983.

6.1. Arens, E., cited in *World Literature Review and Annotated Bibliography, Passive Cooling by Natural Ventilation*, FSEC-CR-81-21 (TT), Florida Solar Energy Center, 300 State Road 401, Cape Canaveral, Florida 32920, 1981.

6.2. Chandra, S. et al., *A Handbook for Designing Naturally Ventilated Buildings*, FSEC-CR-60-82 (EA), Florida Solar Energy Center, 300 State Road 401, Cape Canaveral, Florida 32920, 1982.

6.3. *Passive Solar and Low Energy Building Design Residential Conservation Demonstration Project, Final Report*, University of Central Florida College of Engineering and Florida Solar Energy Center for the Florida Public Service Commission, October, 1982.

6.4. *Residential Conservation Demonstration Program, Final Report*, Florida Public Service Commission, January, 1983.

6.5. *Summer Attic and Whole-House Ventilation*, NBS Special Publication 548, National Bureau of Standards, available from Superintendent of Documents, U.S. Government Printing Office, Washington, D.C. 20402, July, 1979.

6.6. Grot, Richard A. and Siu, Chock I., "Effect of Powered Attic Ventilation on Ceiling Heat Transfer and Cooling Load in Two Townhouses," Center for Building Technology, National Bureau of Standards, published in Reference 6.5.

6.7. Burch, D. M. and Treado, S. J., "Ventilating Residences and Their Attics for Energy Conservation," Center for Building Technology, National Bureau of Standards, published in Reference 6.5.

6.8. Brewster, Darrell and Arkfield, Tom, "Analysis of Attic Ventilation Test," Lincoln Electric System, Suite 300, 1200 N. Street, Lincoln, Nebraska 68508, published in Reference 6.5.

6.9. Heating, Piping, and Air Conditioning Magazine, May, 1944.

6.10. Kusuda, T. and Bean, J. W., "Savings in Electric Cooling Energy by the use of a Whole-House Fan," NBS Technical Note 1138, Center for Building Technology, National Bureau of Standards.

6.11. Akridge, J. M. and Benton, C. C., "Performance Study of a Thermal Envelope House, Phase II, Cooling Performance," College of Architecture, Georgia Institute of Technology, January, 1981.

7.1. Clark, E. and Berdahl, P., "Radiative Cooling: Resource and Application," *Passive Cooling Handbook*, Prepared for the U.S. Department of Energy under contract W-7405-ENG-48, 1980.

10.1. McGuigan, Dermott, *Heat Pumps, An Efficient Heating and Cooling Alternative*, Garden Way Publishing, Charlotte, Vermont, 1981.

10.2. National Water Well Association, 500 W. Wilson Bridge Road, Worthington, Ohio 43085, (614) 846-9355.

10.3. Dexheimer, R. Donald, *Water Source Heat Pump Handbook*, National Water Well Association, 500 W. Wilson Bridge Road, Worthington, Ohio 43085, 1985.

10.4. Mammoth, A Nortech Company. "Sol-A-Terra Water Source Heat Pump, Ground Water Applications Manual," 13120-B County Road 6, Minneapolis, Minnesota 55441.

10.5. Bose, James E., *Water Source HVAC Design Manual*, Oklahoma State University, Technology Extension, 313 Crutchfield, Stillwater, Oklahoma 74078, (405) 624-5714.

13.1. Labs, Kenneth, "Underground Building Climate," Solar Age Magazine, Church Hill, Harrisville, New Hampshire 03450, October, 1979.

13.2. Ingersoll, Zobel, and Ingersoll, *Heat Conduction with Engineering, Geological and Other Applications*, Maple Press, 1954.

13.3. Abrams, D. W., Benton, C. C., and Akridge, J. M., "Simulated and Measured Performance of Earth Cooling Tubes, *Proceedings of the Sixth National Passive Solar Conference*, October 19–26, 1980, American Section International Solar Energy Society.

13.4. Akridge, J. M. and Benton, C. C., "Performance Study of a Thermal Envelope House, Final Report Phase I," College of Architecture, Georgia Institute of Technology, 1980.

14.1. Fairey, P. W., "Effects of Infrared Radiation Barriers on the Effective Thermal Resistance of Building Envelopes," ASHRAE/USDOE Conference on Thermal Performance of the Exterior Envelopes of Buildings II, Las Vegas, Nevada, December 5–9, 1982.

14.2. Florida Solar Energy Center, "Principles of Low Energy Building Design in Warm, Humid Climates," workshop manual, April 4–5, 1983.

14.3. E-Tech, Inc., 3570 American Drive, Chamblee, Georgia 30341.

Index

Absorbant, 296
ACH, air changes per hour, 75–76
Absorber, 296
Absorption air conditioning, 294–297
Adiabatic process, 49
Air conditioning, 185–211
  approximate power input, 199
  control and operation, 203–210
  dehumidification capacity, 241–243
  guidelines for efficient operation, 210–211
  high efficiency, 241–242
  oversizing, 194–195
  operating cost, 198–199
  operation with dehumidifier, 246–247
  performance as a function of air flow, 202
  selection and sizing, 193–196
  specification sheets, 199–203
  system shutdown, 208–210
  theory of operation, 185–192
  with ventilation, 203–210
Air mixtures, 53–54
Air motion, effect on comfort, 57, 59, 61, 62, 63–65, 120, 127, 131, 140, 279, 110
Air-to-air heat exchanger, 80, 292–293
Akridge, J. Max, 276
ARI, Air-Conditioning and Refrigeration Institute, 196, 216–218, 200–202, 222
ASHRAE (American Society of Heating, Refrigerating, and Air Conditioning Engineers), 60, 63, 65, 69, 72, 76, 81, 86, 198, 204
  ASHRAE Standards
    Standard 55-1981, 60, 63
    Standard 90, 90
    Fundamentals Handbook, 11, 31, 43, 83
Attic fan, 135–139, 140. *See also* Whole-house fan
Attic heat gain control, 284–286
Attic ventilation, 135–139

Baer, Steve, 152
Balance point
  building, 68, 100
  heat pump system, 217–218
Benton, C. C., 276
Bin temperature data, 30
Bioclimatic chart, 31, 60–63
Black body, 178
Btu, definition, 36

Carrier, Dr. Willis, 38
CLF, cooling load factor, 81
Climate
  developing information for site, 29–35
  effects of cooling loads, 25–26
Clo, 60, 61
Clothing, effects on comfort, 9, 60–61, 65
Comfort, 58–66
Comfort conditions or comfort zone
  Olgyay, 60–63
  ASHRAE, 64
  ASHRAE extended, 63–65
Compressor, 185
Condenser, 24, 185–187, 189–192, 200, 222–223, 232, 233, 243–244, 296
Condenser coil spray, 291–292
Condenser shading, 299–300
Conservation factor, 73
Conversion factors, 22
Cooling
  combined sensible and latent, 51–53
  evaporative, 23, 27
  human scale, 5
  latent cooling
    definition, 46–47
  mechanical, 24, 25
  methods, 23
  problem, 8–35